PEARSON

ALWAYS LEARNING

Beginning Algebra

Second Custom Edition for California State University – Los Angeles

Taken from:
Beginning and Intermediate Algebra, Fifth Edition
by Elayn Martin-Gay

Geometry: Fundamental Concepts and Applications
by Alan Bass

Taken from:

Beginning and Intermediate Algebra, Fifth Edition
by Elayn Martin-Gay
Copyright © 2013, 2009, 2005, 2001, 1996 by Pearson Education, Inc.
Upper Saddle River, New Jersey 07458

Geometry: Fundamental Concepts and Applications
by Alan Bass
Copyright © 2008 by Pearson Education, Inc.
Published by Addison Wesley
Upper Saddle River, New Jersey 07458

This special edition published in cooperation with Pearson Learning Solutions.

All trademarks, service marks, registered trademarks, and registered service marks are the property of their respective owners and are used herein for identification purposes only.

Pearson Learning Solutions, 501 Boylston Street, Suite 900, Boston, MA 02116
A Pearson Education Company
www.pearsoned.com

Printed in the United States of America

1 2 3 4 5 6 7 8 9 10 V0ZN 14 13 12

000200010271308625

BW

ISBN 10: 1-256-67969-0
ISBN 13: 978-1-256-67969-1

Contents

The following chapters were taken from *Beginning and Intermediate Algebra*, Fifth Edition

The following chapters were taken from *Geometry: Fundamental Concepts and Applications.*

Student Resources

These resources, located in the back of the text, give you a variety of tools conveniently located in one place to help you succeed in math.

Study Skills Builders

Attitude and Study Tips:

1. Have You Decided to Complete This Course Successfully?
2. Tips for Studying for an Exam
3. What to Do the Day of an Exam
4. Are You Satisfied with Your Performance on a Particular Quiz or Exam?
5. How Are You Doing?
6. Are You Preparing for Your Final Exam?

Organizing Your Work:

7. Learning New Terms
8. Are You Organized?
9. Organizing a Notebook
10. How Are Your Homework Assignments Going?

MyMathLab and MathXL:

11. Tips for Turning in Your Homework on Time
12. Tips for Doing Your Homework Online
13. Organizing Your Work
14. Getting Help with Your Homework Assignments
15. Tips for Preparing for an Exam
16. How Well Do You Know the Resources Available to You in MyMathLab?

Additional Help Inside and Outside Your Textbook:

17. How Well Do You Know Your Textbook?
18. Are You Familiar with Your Textbook Supplements?
19. Are You Getting All the Mathematics Help That You Need?

The Bigger Picture–Study Guide Outline

Practice Final Exam

Answers to Selected Exercises

A New Tool to Help You Succeed

Introducing Martin-Gay's New Student Organizer

The new **Student Organizer** guides you through three important parts of studying effectively—note-taking, practice, and homework.

It is designed to help you organize your learning materials and develop the study habits you need to be successful. The Student Organizer includes:

- How to prepare for class
- Space to take class notes
- Step-by-step worked examples
- Your Turn exercises (modeled after the examples)
- Answers to the Your Turn exercises as well as worked-out solutions via references to the Martin-Gay text and videos
- Helpful hints and directions for completing homework assignments

A flexible design allows instructors to assign any or all parts of the Student Organizer.

The Student Organizer is available in a loose-leaf, notebook-ready format. It is also available for download in MyMathLab.

For more information, please go to

www.pearsonhighered.com/martingay

www.mypearsonstore.com
    (search Martin-Gay, Beginning & Intermediate Algebra, Fifth Edition)
your Martin-Gay MyMathLab° course

Martin-Gay Video Resources to Help You Succeed

Interactive DVD Lecture Series

Active Learning at Your Pace

Designed for use on your computer or DVD player, these interactive videos include a 15–20 minute lecture for every section in the text as well as Concept Checks, Study Skills Builders, and a Practice Final Exam.

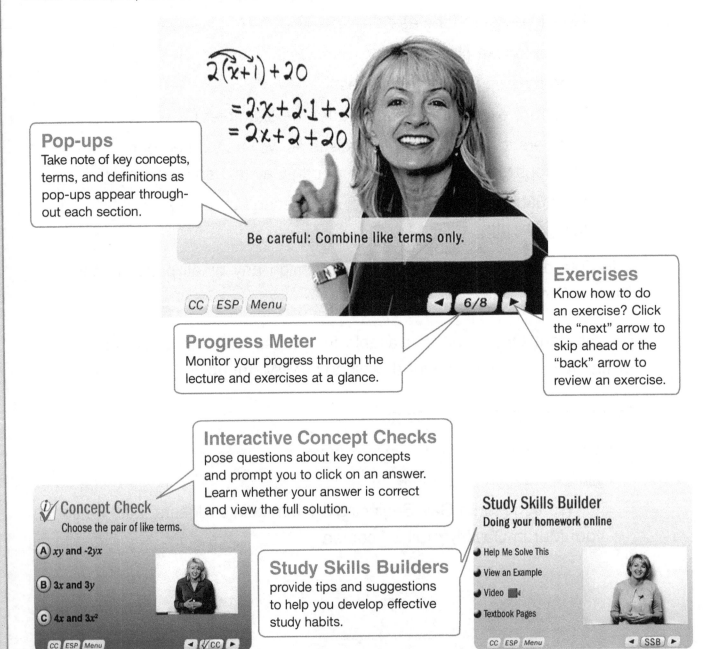

Pop-ups
Take note of key concepts, terms, and definitions as pop-ups appear throughout each section.

$$2\widehat{(x+1)}+20$$
$$=2 \cdot x+2 \cdot 1+2$$
$$=2x+2+20$$

Be careful: Combine like terms only.

CC   ESP   Menu   ◄ 6/8 ►

Exercises
Know how to do an exercise? Click the "next" arrow to skip ahead or the "back" arrow to review an exercise.

Progress Meter
Monitor your progress through the lecture and exercises at a glance.

Interactive Concept Checks
pose questions about key concepts and prompt you to click on an answer. Learn whether your answer is correct and view the full solution.

Ⓘ Concept Check
Choose the pair of like terms.

(A) xy and $-2yx$

(B) $3x$ and $3y$

(C) $4x$ and $3x^2$

CC ESP Menu   ◄ ✓CC ►

Study Skills Builders
provide tips and suggestions to help you develop effective study habits.

Study Skills Builder
Doing your homework online

● Help Me Solve This
● View an Example
● Video
● Textbook Pages

CC ESP Menu   ◄ SSB ►

Chapter Test Prep Videos

Step-by-step solutions on video for all chapter test exercises from the text. Available via:

- Interactive DVD Lecture Series
- MyMathLab®
- You Tube™

English and Spanish Subtitles Available

AlgebraPrep Apps for the iPhone™ and iPod Touch®

Your 24/7 Algebra Tutor–Anytime, Anywhere!

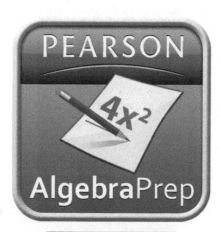

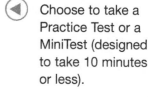

Choose to take a Practice Test or a MiniTest (designed to take 10 minutes or less).

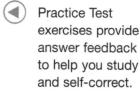

Practice Test exercises provide answer feedback to help you study and self-correct.

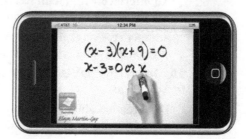

Step-by-step video solutions give you the guidance of an expert tutor whenever you need help.

Preface

***Beginning & Intermediate Algebra,* Fifth Edition,** was written to provide a solid foundation in algebra for students who might not have previous experience in algebra. Specific care was taken to make sure students have the most up-to-date, relevant text preparation for their next mathematics course or for nonmathematical courses that require an understanding of algebraic fundamentals. I have tried to achieve this by writing a user-friendly text that is keyed to objectives and contains many worked-out examples. As suggested by AMATYC and the NCTM Standards (plus Addenda), real-life and real-data applications, data interpretation, conceptual understanding, problem solving, writing, cooperative learning, appropriate use of technology, mental mathematics, number sense, estimation, critical thinking, and geometric concepts are emphasized and integrated throughout the book.

The many factors that contributed to the success of the previous editions have been retained. In preparing the Fifth Edition, I considered comments and suggestions of colleagues, students, and many users of the prior edition throughout the country.

What's New in the Fifth Edition?

- **The Martin-Gay Program** has been revised and enhanced with a new design in the text and MyMathLab to actively encourage students to use the text, video program, and Student Organizer as an integrated learning system.

- **The Student Organizer** is designed by me to help students develop the study habits they need to be successful. This Organizer guides students through the three main components of studying effectively—note-taking, practice, and homework—and helps them develop the habits that will enable them to succeed in future courses. The Student Organizer can be packaged with the text in loose-leaf, notebook-ready format and is also available for download in MyMathLab.

- **New Vocabulary, Readiness & Video Check** questions have been added prior to every section exercise set. These exercises quickly check a student's understanding of new vocabulary words. The **readiness** exercises center on a student's understanding of a concept that is necessary in order to continue to the exercise set. **New video check questions for the Martin-Gay Interactive Lecture videos** are now included in every section for each learning objective. **These exercises are all available for assignment in MyMathLab** and are a great way to assess whether students have viewed and understood the key concepts presented in the videos.

- **The Interactive DVD Lecture Series,** featuring your text author (Elayn Martin-Gay), provides students with active learning at their own pace. The videos offer the following resources and more:

  A complete lecture for each section of the text highlights key examples and exercises from the text. New "pop-ups" reinforce key terms, definitions, and concepts.

  An interface with menu navigation features allows students to quickly find and focus on the examples and exercises they need to review.

  Interactive Concept Check exercises measure students' understanding of key concepts and common trouble spots.

  The Interactive DVD Lecture Series also includes the following resources for test prep:

  The Practice Final Exam helps students prepare for an end-of-course final. Students can watch full video solutions to each exercise.

The Chapter Test Prep Videos help students during their most teachable moment–when they are preparing for a test. This innovation provides step-by-step solutions for the Chapter Test exercises found at the end of each chapter in the text. The videos are captioned in English and Spanish. For the Fifth Edition, the chapter test prep videos are also available on YouTube™.

- **The Martin-Gay MyMathLab course** has been updated and revised to provide more exercise coverage, including assignable video check questions, and an expanded video program. There are section lecture videos for every section, students can also access at the specific objective level, and there are an increased number of watch clips at the exercise level to help students while doing homework in MathXL. Suggested homework assignments have been premade for assignment at the instructor's discretion.

- **New MyMathLab Ready to Go courses** (access code required) provide students with all the same great MyMathLab features that you're used to, but make it easier for instructors to get started. Each course includes preassigned homework and quizzes to make creating your course even simpler. Ask your Pearson representative about the details for this particular course or to see a copy of this course.

- **A new section** (12.4) devoted specifically to exponential growth and decay and applications has been added. This section includes the definition and examples of half-life.

- **The new Student Resources** section, located in the back of the text, gives students a variety of tools that are conveniently located in one place to help them achieve success in mathematics.

  - **Study Skills Builders** give students tips and suggestions on successful study habits and help them take responsibility for their learning. Assignable exercises check students' progress in improving their skills.

  - The **Bigger Picture—Study Guide Outline** covers key concepts of the course—simplifying expressions and solving equations and inequalities—to help students transition from thinking section-by-section to thinking about how the material they are learning fits into mathematics as a whole. This outline provides a model for students on how to organize and develop their own study guide.

  - The **Practice Final Exam** helps students prepare for the end-of-the-course exam. Students can also watch the step-by-step solutions to all the Practice Final Exam exercises on the new Interactive DVD Lecture Series and in MyMathLab.

  - The **Answers to Selected Exercises** section allows students to check their answers for all Practice exercises; odd-numbered Vocabulary, Readiness & Video Check exercises; odd-numbered section exercises; odd-numbered Chapter Review and Cumulative Review exercises; and all Integrated Review and Chapter Test exercises.

- **New guided application exercises** appear in many sections throughout the text, beginning with Section 2.4. These applications prompt students on how to set up the application and get started with the solution process. These guided exercises will help students prepare to solve application exercises on their own.

- **Enhanced emphasis on Study Skills** helps students develop good study habits and makes it more convenient for instructors to incorporate or assign study skills in their courses. The following changes have been made in the Fifth Edition:

  Section 1.1, Tips for Success in Mathematics, has been updated to include helpful hints for doing homework online in MyMathLab. Exercises pertaining to doing homework online in MyMathLab are now included in the exercise set for 1.1.

The Study Skills Builders, formerly located at the end of select exercise sets, are now included in the new **Student Resources** section at the back of the book and are organized by topic for ease of assignment. This section now also includes new Study Skills Builders on doing homework online in MyMathLab.

- All exercise sets have been reviewed and updated to ensure that even- and odd-numbered exercises are paired.

Key Pedagogical Features

The following key features have been retained and/or updated for the Fifth Edition of the text:

Problem-Solving Process   This is formally introduced in Chapter 2 with a four-step process that is integrated throughout the text. The four steps are **Understand, Translate, Solve,** and **Interpret.** The repeated use of these steps in a variety of examples shows their wide applicability. Reinforcing the steps can increase students' comfort level and confidence in tackling problems.

Exercise Sets Revised and Updated   The exercise sets have been carefully examined and extensively revised. Special focus was placed on making sure that even- and odd-numbered exercises are paired.

Examples   Detailed, step-by-step examples were added, deleted, replaced, or updated as needed. Many of these reflect real life. Additional instructional support is provided in the annotated examples.

Practice Exercises   Throughout the text, each worked-out example has a parallel Practice Exercise. These invite students to be actively involved in the learning process. Students should try each Practice Exercise after finishing the corresponding example. Learning by doing will help students grasp ideas before moving on to other concepts. Answers to the Practice Exercises are provided in the back of the text.

Helpful Hints   Helpful Hints contain practical advice on applying mathematical concepts. Strategically placed where students are most likely to need immediate reinforcement, Helpful Hints help students avoid common trouble areas and mistakes.

Concept Checks   This feature allows students to gauge their grasp of an idea as it is being presented in the text. Concept Checks stress conceptual understanding at the point-of-use and help suppress misconceived notions before they start. Answers appear at the bottom of the page. Exercises related to Concept Checks are included in the exercise sets.

Mixed Practice Exercises   Found in the section exercise sets, each requires students to determine the problem type and strategy needed to solve it just as they would need to do on a test.

Integrated Reviews   A unique, mid-chapter exercise set that helps students assimilate new skills and concepts that they have learned separately over several sections. These reviews provide yet another opportunity for students to work with "mixed" exercises as they master the topics.

Vocabulary Check   Provides an opportunity for students to become more familiar with the use of mathematical terms as they strengthen their verbal skills. These appear at the end of each chapter before the Chapter Highlights. Vocabulary, Readiness & Video Check exercises also provide vocabulary practice at the section level.

Chapter Highlights   Found at the end of every chapter, these contain key definitions and concepts with examples to help students understand and retain what they have learned and help them organize their notes and study for tests.

Chapter Review   The end of every chapter contains a comprehensive review of topics introduced in the chapter. The Chapter Review offers exercises keyed to every section in the chapter, as well as Mixed Review exercises that are not keyed to sections.

Chapter Test and Chapter Test Prep Video   The Chapter Test is structured to include those problems that involve common student errors. The **Chapter Test Prep Videos** give students instant access to a step-by-step video solution of each exercise in the Chapter Test.

Cumulative Review   Follows every chapter in the text (except Chapter 1). Each odd-numbered exercise contained in the Cumulative Review is an earlier worked example in the text that is referenced in the back of the book along with the answer.

Writing Exercises   ＼These exercises occur in almost every exercise set and require students to provide a written response to explain concepts or justify their thinking.

Applications   Real-world and real-data applications have been thoroughly updated and many new applications are included. These exercises occur in almost every exercise set and show the relevance of mathematics and help students gradually, and continuously, develop their problem-solving skills.

Review and Preview Exercises   These exercises occur in each exercise set (except in Chapter 1) and are keyed to earlier sections. They review concepts learned earlier in the text that will be needed in the next section or chapter.

Exercise Set Resource Icons   Located at the opening of each exercise set, these icons remind students of the resources available for extra practice and support:

MyMathLab®

See Student Resources descriptions on page xviii for details on the individual resources available.

Exercise Icons   These icons facilitate the assignment of specialized exercises and let students know what resources can support them.

- ▶ Video icon: exercise worked on the Interactive DVD Lecture Series and in MyMathLab.
- △ Triangle icon: identifies exercises involving geometric concepts.
- ＼ Pencil icon: indicates a written response is needed.
- ▦ Calculator icon: optional exercises intended to be solved using a scientific or graphing calculator.

Optional: Graphing Calculator Exploration Boxes and Calculator Exercises   The optional Graphing Calculator Explorations provide keystrokes and exercises at appropriate points to give an opportunity for students to become familiar with these tools. Section exercises that are best completed by using a calculator are identified by ▦ for ease of assignment.

Student and Instructor Resources

STUDENT RESOURCES

Student Organizer

Guides students through the 3 main components of studying effectively–note-taking, practice, and homework.

The organizer includes before-class preparation exercises, note-taking pages in a 2-column format for use in class, and examples paired with exercises for practice for each section. It is 3-hole-punched. Also available in MyMathLab.

Student Solutions Manual

Provides complete worked-out solutions to

- the odd-numbered section exercises; all Practice Exercises; all exercises in the Integrated Reviews, Chapter Reviews, Chapter Tests, and Cumulative Reviews

Interactive DVD Lecture Series

Provides students with active learning at their pace. The videos offer:

- A complete lecture for each text section. The interface allows easy navigation to examples and exercises students need to review.
- Interactive Concept Check exercises
- Study Skills Builders
- Practice Final Exam
- Chapter Test Prep Videos

Chapter Test Prep Videos

- Step-by-step solutions to every exercise in each Chapter Practice Test.
- Available in MyMathLab® and on YouTube, and in the Interactive DVD Lecture Series.

INSTRUCTOR RESOURCES

Annotated Instructor's Edition

Contains all the content found in the student edition, plus the following:

- Answers to exercises on the same text page
- Answers to graphing exercises and all video exercises
- Teaching Tips throughout the text placed at key points.
- Classroom Examples in the margin paired to each example in the text.

Instructor's Resource Manual with Tests and Mini-Lectures

- Mini-lectures for each text section
- Additional Practice worksheets for each section
- Several forms of test per chapter–free response and multiple choice
- Group activities
- Video key to the example number in the video questions and section exercises worked in the videos
- Answers to all items

Instructor's Solutions Manual
TestGen® (Available for download from the IRC)

Online Resources
MyMathLab® (access code required)

MathXL® (access code required)

Acknowledgments

There are many people who helped me develop this text, and I will attempt to thank some of them here. Cindy Trimble and Carrie Green were *invaluable* for contributing to the overall accuracy of the text. Dawn Nuttall, Courtney Slade, and JoAnne Thomasson were *invaluable* for their many suggestions and contributions during the development and writing of this Fifth Edition. Debbie Meyer and Amanda Zagnoli of Integra-Chicago provided guidance throughout the production process.

A very special thank you goes to my editor, Mary Beckwith, for being there 24/7/365, as my students say. Last, my thanks to the staff at Pearson for all their support: Patty Bergin, Heather Scott, Michelle Renda, Chris Hoag, and Greg Tobin.

I would like to thank the following reviewers for their input and suggestions:

Sandi Athanassiou, *University of Missouri–Columbia*
Michelle Beerman, *Pasco-Hernandez Community College*
Monika Bender, *Central Texas College*
Bob Hervey, *Hillsborough Community College*
Michael Maltenfort, *Truman College*
Jorge Romero, *Hillsborough Community College*
Joseph Wakim, *Brevard Community College*
Flo Wilson, *Central Texas College*
Marie Caruso and students, *Middlesex Community College*

I would also like to thank the following dedicated group of instructors who participated in our focus groups, Martin-Gay Summits, and our design review for the series. Their feedback and insights have helped to strengthen this edition of the text. These instructors include:

Billie Anderson, *Tyler Junior College*
Joey Anderson, *Central Piedmont Community College*
Cedric Atkins, *Mott Community College*
Teri Barnes, *McLennan Community College*
Andrea Barnett, *Tri-County Technical College*
Lois Beardon, *Schoolcraft College*
Michelle Beerman, *Pasco-Hernandez Community College*
Laurel Berry, *Bryant & Stratton College*
John Beyers, *University of Maryland*
Jennifer Brahier, *Pensacola Junior College*
Bob Brown, *Community College of Baltimore County–Essex*
Lisa Brown, *Community College of Baltimore County–Essex*
NeKeith Brown, *Richland College*
Sue Brown, *Guilford Technical Community College*
Gail Burkett, *Palm Beach State College*
Cheryl Cantwell, *Seminole Community College*
Janie Chapman, *Spartanburg Community College*
Jackie Cohen, *Augusta State College*
Julie Dewan, *Mohawk Valley Community College*
Janice Ervin, *Central Piedmont Community College*
Karen Estes, *St. Petersburg College*
Richard Fielding, *Southwestern College*
Sonia Ford, *Midland College*
Julie Francavilla, *State College of Florida*
Cindy Gaddis, *Tyler Junior College*
Nita Graham, *St. Louis Community College*
Pauline Hall, *Iowa State College*
Elizabeth Hamman, *Cypress College*
Kathy Hoffmaster, *Thomas Nelson Community College*
Pat Hussey, *Triton College*
Dorothy Johnson, *Lorain County Community College*
Sonya Johnson, *Central Piedmont Community College*

Irene Jones, *Fullerton College*
Paul Jones, *University of Cincinnati*
Mike Kirby, *Tidewater Community College*
Kathy Kopelousos, *Lewis and Clark Community College*
Nancy Lange, *Inver Hills Community College*
Judy Langer, *Westchester Community College*
Lisa Lindloff, *McLennan Community College*
Sandy Lofstock, *St. Petersburg College*
Kathy Lovelle, *Westchester Community College*
Jamie Malek, *Florida State College*
Jean McArthur, *Joliet Junior College*
Kevin McCandless, *Evergreen Valley College*
Daniel Miller, *Niagara County Community College*
Marcia Molle, *Metropolitan Community College*
Carol Murphy, *San Diego Miramar College*
Charlotte Newsom, *Tidewater Community College*
Greg Nguyen, *Fullerton College*
Eric Ollila, *Jackson Community College*
Linda Padilla, *Joliet Junior College*
Rena Petrello, *Moorpark College*
Davidson Pierre, *State College of Florida*
Marilyn Platt, *Gaston College*
Susan Poss, *Spartanburg Community College*
Natalie Rivera, *Estrella Mountain Community College*
Judy Roane, *Pearl River Community College*
Claudinna Rowley, *Montgomery Community College, Rockville*
Ena Salter, *State College of Florida*
Carole Shapero, *Oakton Community College*
Janet Sibol, *Hillsborough Community College*
Anne Smallen, *Mohawk Valley Community College*
Mike Stack, *South Suburban College*
Barbara Stoner, *Reading Area Community College*
Jennifer Strehler, *Oakton Community College*
Ellen Stutes, *Louisiana State University Eunice*
Tanomo Taguchi, *Fullerton College*
Sam Tinsley, *Richland College*
Linda Tucker, *Rose State College*
MaryAnn Tuerk, *Elgin Community College*
Gwen Turbeville, *J. Sargeant Reynolds Community College*
Walter Wang, *Baruch College*
Leigh Ann Wheeler, *Greenville Technical Community College*
Jenny Wilson, *Tyler Junior College*
Valerie Wright, *Central Piedmont Community College*

A special thank you to those students who participated in our design review: Katherine Browne, Mike Bulfin, Nancy Canipe, Ashley Carpenter, Jeff Chojnachi, Roxanne Davis, Mike Dieter, Amy Dombrowski, Kay Herring, Todd Jaycox, Kaleena Levan, Matt Montgomery, Tony Plese, Abigail Polkinghorn, Harley Price, Eli Robinson, Avery Rosen, Robyn Schott, Cynthia Thomas, and Sherry Ward.

Elayn Martin-Gay

About the Author

Elayn Martin-Gay has taught mathematics at the University of New Orleans for more than 25 years. Her numerous teaching awards include the local University Alumni Association's Award for Excellence in Teaching, and Outstanding Developmental Educator at University of New Orleans, presented by the Louisiana Association of Developmental Educators.

Prior to writing textbooks, Elayn Martin-Gay developed an acclaimed series of lecture videos to support developmental mathematics students in their quest for success. These highly successful videos originally served as the foundation material for her texts. Today, the videos are specific to each book in the Martin-Gay series. The author has also created Chapter Test Prep Videos to help students during their most "teachable moment"—as they prepare for a test—along with Instructor-to-Instructor videos that provide teaching tips, hints, and suggestions for each developmental mathematics course, including basic mathematics, prealgebra, beginning algebra, and intermediate algebra. Her most recent innovations are the AlgebraPrep Apps for the iPhone and iPod Touch. These Apps embrace the different learning styles, schedules, and paces of students and provide them with quality math tutoring.

Elayn is the author of 12 published textbooks as well as interactive multimedia mathematics, all specializing in developmental mathematics courses. She has participated as an author across the broadest range of educational materials: textbooks, videos, tutorial software, and courseware. This provides the opportunity of various combinations for an integrated teaching and learning package that offers great consistency for the student.

Applications Index

The following chapters were taken from
Beginning and Intermediate Algebra, Fifth Edition.

Review of Real Numbers

National Park Service Regions

The National Park Service (NPS) is a federal agency that manages all national parks and many other historic monuments and properties. The NPS has 21,989 employees and had a total of 281 million recreational visitors in 2010 alone. The map above shows the different geographic regions of the NPS, and the bar graph below shows the number of recreational visits per year shown.

In Section 1.2, Exercises 71 through 76, we shall study this bar graph further.

In this chapter, we review the basic symbols and words—the language—of arithmetic and introduce using variables in place of numbers. This is our starting place in the study of algebra.

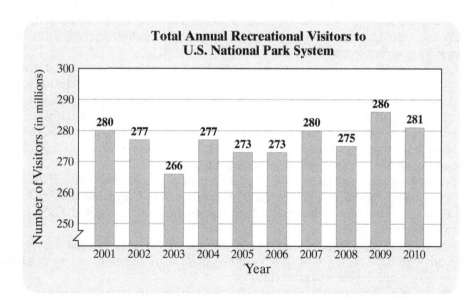

Total Annual Recreational Visitors to U.S. National Park System

1.1 Tips for Success in Mathematics

OBJECTIVES

1 Get Ready for This Course.

2 Understand Some General Tips for Success.

3 Understand How to Use This Text.

4 Get Help as Soon as You Need It.

5 Learn How to Prepare for and Take an Exam.

6 Develop Good Time Management.

Before reading this section, remember that your instructor is your best source of information. Please see your instructor for any additional help or information.

OBJECTIVE
1 Getting Ready for This Course

Now that you have decided to take this course, remember that a *positive attitude* will make all the difference in the world. Your belief that you can succeed is just as important as your commitment to this course. Make sure you are ready for this course by having the time and positive attitude that it takes to succeed.

Next, make sure that you have scheduled your math course at a time that will give you the best chance for success. For example, if you are also working, you may want to check with your employer to make sure that your work hours will not conflict with your course schedule.

On the day of your first class period, double-check your schedule and allow yourself extra time to arrive on time in case of traffic problems or difficulty locating your classroom. Make sure that you bring at least your textbook, paper, and a writing instrument. Are you required to have a lab manual, graph paper, calculator, or some other supplies besides this text? If so, also bring this material with you.

OBJECTIVE
2 General Tips for Success

Following are some general tips that will increase your chance for success in a mathematics class. Many of these tips will also help you in other courses you may be taking.

Exchange names and phone numbers or email addresses with at least one other person in class. This contact person can be a great help if you miss an assignment or want to discuss math concepts or exercises that you find difficult.

Choose to attend all class periods. If possible, sit near the front of the classroom. This way, you will see and hear the presentation better. It may also be easier for you to participate in classroom activities.

Do your homework. You've probably heard the phrase "practice makes perfect" in relation to music and sports. It also applies to mathematics. You will find that the more time you spend solving mathematics exercises, the easier the process becomes. Be sure to schedule enough time to complete your assignments before the next due date assigned by your instructor.

Check your work. Review the steps you made while working a problem. Learn to check your answers in the original problems. You may also compare your answers with the "Answers to Selected Exercises" section in the back of the book. If you have made a mistake, try to figure out what went wrong. Then correct your mistake. If you can't find what went wrong, don't erase your work or throw it away. Bring your work to your instructor, a tutor in a math lab, or a classmate. It is easier for someone to find where you had trouble if he or she looks at your original work.

Learn from your mistakes and be patient with yourself. Everyone, even your instructor, makes mistakes. (That definitely includes me—Elayn Martin-Gay.) Use your errors to learn and to become a better math student. The key is finding and understanding your errors.

Was your mistake a careless one, or did you make it because you can't read your own math writing? If so, try to work more slowly or write more neatly and make a conscious effort to check your work carefully.

Did you make a mistake because you don't understand a concept? Take the time to review the concept or ask questions to understand it better.

Did you skip too many steps? Skipping steps or trying to do too many steps mentally may lead to preventable mistakes.

Know how to get help if you need it. It's all right to ask for help. In fact, it's a good idea to ask for help whenever there is something that you don't understand. Make sure you know when your instructor has office hours and how to find his or her office. Find

---

▶ Helpful Hint

MyMathLab® and **MathXL®** If you are doing your homework online, you can work and rework those exercises that you struggle with until you master them. Try working through all the assigned exercises twice before the due date.

▶ Helpful Hint

MyMathLab® and **MathXL®** If you are completing your homework online, it's important to work each exercise on paper before submitting the answer. That way, you can check your work and follow your steps to find and correct any mistakes.

out whether math tutoring services are available on your campus. Check on the hours, location, and requirements of the tutoring service.

Organize your class materials, including homework assignments, graded quizzes and tests, and notes from your class or lab. All of these items will make valuable references throughout your course and when studying for upcoming tests and the final exam. Make sure that you can locate these materials when you need them.

Read your textbook before class. Reading a mathematics textbook is unlike reading a novel or a newspaper. Your pace will be much slower. It is helpful to have paper and a pencil with you when you read. Try to work out examples on your own as you encounter them in your text. You should also write down any questions that you want to ask in class. When you read a mathematics textbook, sometimes some of the information in a section will be unclear. But after you hear a lecture or watch a lecture video on that section, you will understand it much more easily than if you had not read your text beforehand.

Don't be afraid to ask questions. You are not the only person in class with questions. Other students are normally grateful that someone has spoken up.

Turn in assignments on time. This way, you can be sure that you will not lose points for being late. Show every step of a problem and be neat and organized. Also be sure that you understand which problems are assigned for homework. If allowed, you can always double-check the assignment with another student in your class.

OBJECTIVE
3 Using This Text

Many helpful resources are available to you. It is important to become familiar with and use these resources. They should increase your chances for success in this course.

- *Practice Exercises*. Each example in every section has a parallel Practice exercise. As you read a section, try each Practice exercise after you've finished the corresponding example. This learn-by-doing approach will help you grasp ideas before you move on to other concepts. Answers are at the back of the text.

- *Chapter Test Prep Videos*. These videos provide solutions to all of the Chapter Test exercises worked out by the author. This supplement is very helpful before a test or exam.

- *Interactive DVD Lecture Series*. Exercises marked with a ⊙ are fully worked out by the author on the DVDs. The lecture series provides approximately 20 minutes of instruction per section.

- *Symbols at the Beginning of an Exercise Set*. If you need help with a particular section, the symbols listed at the beginning of each exercise set will remind you of the numerous supplements available.

- *Objectives*. The main section of exercises in each exercise set is referenced by an objective, such as 1 or 2, and by an example(s). There is also often a section of exercises entitled "Mixed Practice," which is referenced by two or more objectives or sections. These are mixed exercises written to prepare you for your next exam. Use all of this referencing if you have trouble completing an assignment from the exercise set.

- *Icons (Symbols)*. Make sure that you understand the meaning of the icons that are beside many exercises. ⊙ tells you that the corresponding exercise may be viewed on the video segment that corresponds to that section. ⬉ tells you that this exercise is a writing exercise in which you should answer in complete sentences. △ tells you that the exercise involves geometry.

- *Integrated Reviews*. Found in the middle of each chapter, these reviews offer you a chance to practice—in one place—the many concepts that you have learned separately over several sections.

- *End-of-Chapter Opportunities*. There are many opportunities at the end of each chapter to help you understand the concepts of the chapter.

  Vocabulary Checks contain key vocabulary terms introduced in the chapter.

  Chapter Highlights contain chapter summaries and examples.

  Chapter Reviews contain review problems. The first part is organized section by section and the second part contains a set of mixed exercises.

Chapter Tests are sample tests to help you prepare for an exam. The Chapter Test Prep Videos, found in this text, contain all the Chapter Test exercises worked by the author.

Cumulative Reviews consist of material from the beginning of the book to the end of that particular chapter.

- *Student Resources in Your Textbook*. You will find a **Student Resources** section at the back of this textbook. It contains the following to help you study and prepare for tests:

  Study Skill Builders contain study skills advice. To increase your chance for success in the course, read these study tips and answer the questions.

  Bigger Picture—Study Guide Outline provides you with a study guide outline of the course, with examples.

  Practice Final provides you with a Practice Final Exam to help you prepare for a final. The video solutions to each question are provided in the Interactive DVD Lecture Series and within MyMathLab®.

- *Resources to Check Your Work*. The **Answers to Selected Exercises** section provides answers to all odd-numbered section exercises and all integrated review and chapter test exercises.

▶ Helpful Hint

MyMathLab® and **MathXL®**
- Use the **Help Me Solve This** button to get step-by-step help for the exercise you are working. You will need to work an additional exercise of the same type before you can get credit for having worked it correctly.
- Use the **Video** button to view a video clip of the author working a similar exercise.

OBJECTIVE
4   Getting Help

If you have trouble completing assignments or understanding the mathematics, get help as soon as you need it! This tip is presented as an objective on its own because it is so important. In mathematics, usually the material presented in one section builds on your understanding of the previous section. This means that if you don't understand the concepts covered during a class period, there is a good chance that you will not understand the concepts covered during the next class period. If this happens to you, get help as soon as you can.

Where can you get help? Many suggestions have been made in this section on where to get help, and now it is up to you to get it. Try your instructor, a tutoring center, or a math lab, or you may want to form a study group with fellow classmates. If you do decide to see your instructor or go to a tutoring center, make sure that you have a neat notebook and are ready with your questions.

OBJECTIVE
5   Preparing for and Taking an Exam

Make sure that you allow yourself plenty of time to prepare for a test. If you think that you are a little "math anxious," it may be that you are not preparing for a test in a way that will ensure success. The way that you prepare for a test in mathematics is important. To prepare for a test:

▶ Helpful Hint

MyMathLab® and **MathXL®**
Review your written work for previous assignments. Then, go back and rework previous assignments. Open a previous assignment and click **Similar Exercise** to generate new exercises. Rework the exercises until you fully understand them and can work them without help features.

1. Review your previous homework assignments.

2. Review any notes from class and section-level quizzes you have taken. (If this is a final exam, also review chapter tests you have taken.)

3. Review concepts and definitions by reading the Chapter Highlights at the end of each chapter.

4. Practice working out exercises by completing the Chapter Review found at the end of each chapter. (If this is a final exam, go through a Cumulative Review. There is one at the end of each chapter except Chapter 1. Choose the review found at the end of the latest chapter that you have covered in your course.) *Don't stop here!*

5. It is important to place yourself in conditions similar to test conditions to find out how you will perform. In other words, as soon as you feel that you know the material, get a few blank sheets of paper and take a sample test. A Chapter Test is available at the end of each chapter, or you can work selected problems from the Chapter

Review. Your instructor may also provide you with a review sheet. During this sample test, do not use your notes or your textbook. Then check your sample test. If you are not satisfied with the results, study the areas that you are weak in and try again.

6. On the day of the test, allow yourself plenty of time to arrive where you will be taking your exam.

When taking your test:

1. Read the directions on the test carefully.

2. Read each problem carefully as you take the test. Make sure that you answer the question asked.

3. Watch your time and pace yourself so that you can attempt each problem on your test.

4. If you have time, check your work and answers.

5. Do not turn your test in early. If you have extra time, spend it double-checking your work.

OBJECTIVE
6   Managing Your Time

As a college student, you know the demands that classes, homework, work, and family place on your time. Some days, you probably wonder how you'll ever get everything done. One key to managing your time is developing a schedule. Here are some hints for making a schedule:

1. Make a list of all your weekly commitments for the term. Include classes, work, regular meetings, extracurricular activities, etc. You may also find it helpful to list such things as laundry, regular workouts, grocery shopping, etc.

2. Next, estimate the time needed for each item on the list. Also make a note of how often you will need to do each item. Don't forget to include time estimates for the reading, studying, and homework you do outside of your classes. You may want to ask your instructor for help estimating the time needed.

3. In the exercise set that follows, you are asked to block out a typical week on the schedule grid given. Start with items with fixed time slots like classes and work.

4. Next, include the items on your list with flexible time slots. Think carefully about how best to schedule items such as study time.

5. Don't fill up every time slot on the schedule. Remember that you need to allow time for eating, sleeping, and relaxing! You should also allow a little extra time in case some items take longer than planned.

6. If you find that your weekly schedule is too full for you to handle, you may need to make some changes in your workload, classload, or other areas of your life. You may want to talk to your advisor, manager or supervisor at work, or someone in your college's academic counseling center for help with such decisions.

1.1   Exercise Set   MyMathLab®

1. What is your instructor's name?

2. What are your instructor's office location and office hours?

3. What is the best way to contact your instructor?

4. Do you have the name and contact information of at least one other student in class?

5. Will your instructor allow you to use a calculator in this class?

6. Why is it important that you write step-by-step solutions to homework exercises and keep a hard copy of all work submitted?

7. Is a tutoring service available on campus? If so, what are its hours? What services are available?

8. Have you attempted this course before? If so, write down ways that you might improve your chances of success during this second attempt.

9. List some steps that you can take if you begin having trouble understanding the material or completing an assignment. If you are completing your homework in MyMathLab® and MathXL®, list the resources you can use for help.

10. How many hours of studying does your instructor advise for each hour of instruction?

11. What does the ＼ icon in this text mean?

12. What does the ◗ icon in this text mean?

13. What does the △ icon in this text mean?

14. What are Practice exercises?

15. When might be the best time to work a Practice exercise?

16. Where are the answers to Practice exercises?

17. What answers are contained in this text and where are they?

18. What and where are the study skills builders?

19. What and where are Integrated Reviews?

20. How many times is it suggested that you work through the homework exercises in MathXL® before the submission deadline?

21. How far in advance of the assigned due date is it suggested that homework be submitted online? Why?

22. Chapter Highlights are found at the end of each chapter. Find the Chapter 1 Highlights and explain how you might use it and how it might be helpful.

23. Chapter Reviews are found at the end of each chapter. Find the Chapter 1 Review and explain how you might use it and how it might be useful.

24. Chapter Tests are at the end of each chapter. Find the Chapter 1 Test and explain how you might use it and how it might be helpful when preparing for an exam on Chapter 1. Include how the Chapter Test Prep Videos may help. If you are working in MyMathLab® and MathXL®, how can you use previous homework assignments to study?

25. Read or reread objective 6 and fill out the schedule grid below.

	Monday	*Tuesday*	*Wednesday*	*Thursday*	*Friday*	*Saturday*	*Sunday*
1:00 a.m.							
2:00 a.m.							
3:00 a.m.							
4:00 a.m.							
5:00 a.m.							
6:00 a.m.							
7:00 a.m.							
8:00 a.m.							
9:00 a.m.							
10:00 a.m.							
11:00 a.m.							
Noon							
1:00 p.m.							
2:00 p.m.							
3:00 p.m.							
4:00 p.m.							
5:00 p.m.							
6:00 p.m.							
7:00 p.m.							
8:00 p.m.							
9:00 p.m.							
10:00 p.m.							
11:00 p.m.							
Midnight							

1.2 | Symbols and Sets of Numbers

1 Use a Number Line to Order Numbers.
2 Translate Sentences into Mathematical Statements.
3 Identify Natural Numbers, Whole Numbers, Integers, Rational Numbers, Irrational Numbers, and Real Numbers.
4 Find the Absolute Value of a Real Number.

OBJECTIVE
1   Using a Number Line to Order Numbers

We begin with a review of the set of natural numbers and the set of whole numbers and how we use symbols to compare these numbers. A **set** is a collection of objects, each of which is called a **member** or **element** of the set. A pair of brace symbols $\{\ \}$ encloses the list of elements and is translated as "the set of" or "the set containing."

Natural Numbers

The set of **natural numbers** is $\{1, 2, 3, 4, 5, 6, \ldots\}$.

Whole Numbers

The set of **whole numbers** is $\{0, 1, 2, 3, 4, \ldots\}$.

> The three dots (an ellipsis) means that the list continues in the same manner indefinitely.

These numbers can be pictured on a **number line.** We will use number lines often to help us visualize distance and relationships between numbers.

To draw a number line, first draw a line. Choose a point on the line and label it 0. To the right of 0, label any other point 1. Being careful to use the same distance as from 0 to 1, mark off equally spaced distances. Label these points 2, 3, 4, 5, and so on. Since the whole numbers continue indefinitely, it is not possible to show every whole number on this number line. The arrow at the right end of the line indicates that the pattern continues indefinitely.

A number line

Picturing whole numbers on a number line helps us see the order of the numbers. Symbols can be used to describe concisely in writing the order that we see.

The **equal symbol** $=$ means "is equal to."

The symbol $\neq$ means "is not equal to."

These symbols may be used to form a **mathematical statement.** The statement might be true or it might be false. The two statements below are both true.

$2 = 2$ states that "two is equal to two."

$2 \neq 6$ states that "two is not equal to six."

If two numbers are not equal, one number is larger than the other.
The symbol $>$ means "is greater than."
The symbol $<$ means "is less than." For example,

$3 < 5$ states that "three is less than five."

$2 > 0$ states that "two is greater than zero."

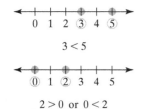

$3 < 5$

$2 > 0$ or $0 < 2$

On a number line, we see that a number **to the right of** another number is **larger.** Similarly, a number **to the left of** another number is smaller. For example, 3 is to the left of 5 on a number line, which means that 3 is less than 5, or $3 < 5$. Similarly, 2 is to the right of 0 on a number line, which means 2 is greater than 0, or $2 > 0$. Since 0 is to the left of 2, we can also say that 0 is less than 2, or $0 < 2$.

The symbols $\neq$, $<$, and $>$ are called **inequality symbols.**

> ▶ Helpful Hint
>
> Notice that $2 > 0$ has exactly the same meaning as $0 < 2$. Switching the order of the numbers and reversing the direction of the inequality symbol does not change the meaning of the statement.
>
> $3 < 5$ has the same meaning as $5 > 3$.
>
> Also notice that, when the statement is true, the inequality arrow points to the smaller number.

EXAMPLE 1 Insert $<$, $>$, or $=$ in the space between each pair of numbers to make each statement true

a. 2   3   **b.** 7   4   **c.** 72   27

Solution

a. $2 < 3$ since 2 is to the left of 3 on the number line.

b. $7 > 4$ since 7 is to the right of 4 on the number line.

c. $72 > 27$ since 72 is to the right of 27 on the number line.   ☐

PRACTICE

1   Insert $<$, $>$, or $=$ in the space between each pair of numbers to make each statement true.

a. 5   8   **b.** 6   4   **c.** 16   82

Two other symbols are used to compare numbers.
The symbol $\leq$ means "is less than or equal to."
The symbol $\geq$ means "is greater than or equal to." For example,

$$7 \leq 10 \text{ states that "seven is less than or equal to ten."}$$

This statement is true since $7 < 10$ is true. If either $7 < 10$ or $7 = 10$ is true, then $7 \leq 10$ is true.

$$3 \geq 3 \text{ states that "three is greater than or equal to three."}$$

This statement is true since $3 = 3$ is true. If either $3 > 3$ or $3 = 3$ is true, then $3 \geq 3$ is true.

The statement $6 \geq 10$ is false since neither $6 > 10$ nor $6 = 10$ is true. The symbols $\leq$ and $\geq$ are also called **inequality symbols.**

EXAMPLE 2 Tell whether each statement is true or false.

a. $8 \geq 8$ **b.** $8 \leq 8$ **c.** $23 \leq 0$ **d.** $23 \geq 0$

Solution

a. True. Since $8 = 8$ is true, then $8 \geq 8$ is true.

b. True. Since $8 = 8$ is true, then $8 \leq 8$ is true.

c. False. Since neither $23 < 0$ nor $23 = 0$ is true, then $23 \leq 0$ is false.

d. True. Since $23 > 0$ is true, then $23 \geq 0$ is true.   ☐

PRACTICE

2   Tell whether each statement is true or false.

a. $9 \geq 3$ **b.** $3 \geq 8$ **c.** $25 \leq 25$ **d.** $4 \leq 14$

OBJECTIVE

2   **Translating Sentences**

Now, let's use the symbols discussed to translate sentences into mathematical statements.

EXAMPLE 3 Translate each sentence into a mathematical statement.

a. Nine is less than or equal to eleven.

b. Eight is greater than one.

c. Three is not equal to four.

Solution

a.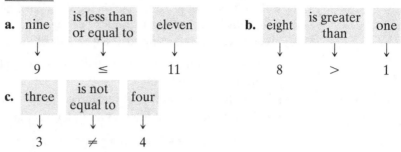

nine	is less than or equal to	eleven
↓	↓	↓
9	≤	11

b.

eight	is greater than	one
↓	↓	↓
8	>	1

c.

three	is not equal to	four
↓	↓	↓
3	≠	4

PRACTICE
3 Translate each sentence into a mathematical statement.

a. Three is less than eight.

b. Fifteen is greater than or equal to nine.

c. Six is not equal to seven.

OBJECTIVE
3 **Identifying Common Sets of Numbers**

Whole numbers are not sufficient to describe many situations in the real world. For example, quantities less than zero must sometimes be represented, such as temperatures less than 0 degrees.

Numbers Less Than Zero on a Number Line

Zero

$$\xleftarrow{\hspace{1cm}} \overbrace{}$$
$$\xleftarrow[\ -5\ \ -4\ \ -3\ \ -2\ \ -1\ \ \ 0\ \ \ 1\ \ \ 2\ \ \ 3\ \ \ 4\ \ \ 5\ ]{}\xrightarrow{}$$

Numbers less than 0 are to the left of 0 and are labeled −1, −2, −3, and so on. A − sign, such as the one in −1, tells us that the number is to the left of 0 on a number line. In words, −1 is read "negative one." A + sign or no sign tells us that a number lies to the right of 0 on the number line. For example, 3 and +3 both mean positive three.

The numbers we have pictured are called the set of **integers**. Integers to the left of 0 are called **negative integers;** integers to the right of 0 are called **positive integers**. The integer **0 is neither positive nor negative.**

negative integers ┆ positive integers
$$\xleftarrow[\ -5\ \ -4\ \ -3\ \ -2\ \ -1\ \ \ 0\ \ \ 1\ \ \ 2\ \ \ 3\ \ \ 4\ \ \ 5\ ]{}\xrightarrow{}$$

Integers

The set of **integers** is $\{ \dots, -3, -2, -1, 0, 1, 2, 3, \dots \}$.

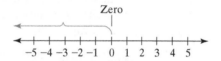

The ellipses (three dots) to the left and to the right indicate that the positive integers and the negative integers continue indefinitely.

EXAMPLE 4 Use an integer to express the number in the following. "Pole of Inaccessibility, Antarctica, is the coldest location in the world, with an average annual temperature of 72 degrees below zero." (*Source: The Guinness Book of Records*)

Solution The integer −72 represents 72 degrees below zero.

PRACTICE
4 Use an integer to express the number in the following. The elevation of Laguna Salada in Mexico is 10 meters below sea level. (*Source: The World Almanac*)

A problem with integers in real-life settings arises when quantities are smaller than some integer but greater than the next smallest integer. On a number line, these quantities may be visualized by points between integers. Some of these quantities between integers can be represented as a quotient of integers. For example,

The point on a number line halfway between 0 and 1 can be represented by $\frac{1}{2}$, a quotient of integers.

The point on a number line halfway between 0 and −1 can be represented by $-\frac{1}{2}$. Other quotients of integers and their graphs are shown to the left.

These numbers, each of which can be represented as a quotient of integers, are examples of **rational numbers.** It's not possible to list the set of rational numbers using the notation that we have been using. For this reason, we will use a different notation.

Rational Numbers

$$\left\{ \frac{a}{b} \,\middle|\, a \text{ and } b \text{ are integers and } b \neq 0 \right\}$$

We read this set as "the set of all numbers $\frac{a}{b}$ such that a and b are integers and b **is not equal to 0.**" Notice that every integer is also a rational number since each integer can be expressed as a quotient of integers. For example, the integer 5 is also a rational number since $5 = \frac{5}{1}$.

The number line also contains points that cannot be expressed as quotients of integers. These numbers are called **irrational numbers** because they cannot be represented by rational numbers. For example, $\sqrt{2}$ and π are irrational numbers.

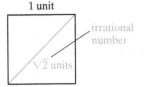

1 unit

irrational number

$\sqrt{2}$ units

Irrational Numbers

The set of **irrational numbers** is

{Nonrational numbers that correspond to points on the number line}.

That is, an irrational number is a number that cannot be expressed as a quotient of integers.

Both rational numbers and irrational numbers can be written as decimal numbers. The decimal equivalent of a rational number will either terminate or repeat in a pattern. For example, upon dividing we find that

Rational Numbers
$$\begin{cases} \frac{3}{4} = 0.75 \text{ (decimal number terminates or ends)} \\ \frac{2}{3} = 0.66666\ldots \text{ (decimal number repeats in a pattern)} \end{cases}$$

The decimal representation of an irrational number will neither terminate nor repeat. For example, the decimal representations of irrational numbers $\sqrt{2}$ and π are

Irrational Numbers
$$\begin{cases} \sqrt{2} = 1.414213562\ldots \text{ (decimal number does not terminate or repeat in a pattern)} \\ \pi = 3.141592653\ldots \text{ (decimal number does not terminate or repeat in a pattern)} \end{cases}$$

(For further review of decimals, see the Appendix.)

Combining the rational numbers with the irrational numbers gives the set of **real numbers.** One and only one point on a number line corresponds to each real number.

Real Numbers

The set of **real numbers** is

{All numbers that correspond to points on the number line}

▶ Helpful Hint

From our previous definitions, we have that

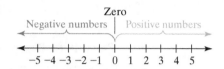

On the following number line, we see that real numbers can be positive, negative, or 0. Numbers to the left of 0 are called **negative numbers;** numbers to the right of 0 are called **positive numbers.** Positive and negative numbers are also called **signed numbers.**

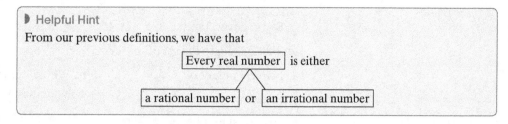

Several different sets of numbers have been discussed in this section. The following diagram shows the relationships among these sets of real numbers.

Common Sets of Numbers

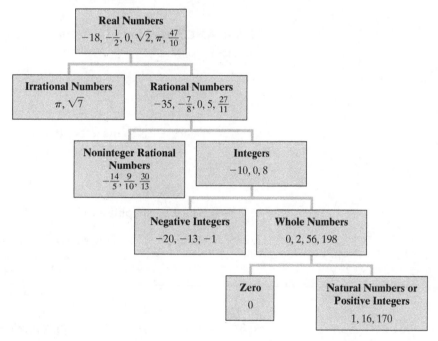

EXAMPLE 5   Given the set $\left\{-2, 0, \frac{1}{4}, -1.5, 112, -3, 11, \sqrt{2}\right\}$, list the numbers in this set that belong to the set of:

a. Natural numbers   **b.** Whole numbers

c. Integers   **d.** Rational numbers

e. Irrational numbers   **f.** Real numbers

Solution

a. The natural numbers are 11 and 112.

b. The whole numbers are 0, 11, and 112.

c. The integers are $-3, -2, 0, 11$, and 112.

d. Recall that integers are rational numbers also. The rational numbers are $-3, -2,$ $-1.5, 0, \frac{1}{4}, 11$, and 112.

e. The irrational number is $\sqrt{2}$.

f. The real numbers are all numbers in the given set.

PRACTICE

5   Given the set $\left\{25, \dfrac{7}{3}, -15, \dfrac{-3}{4}, \sqrt{5}, -3.7, 8.8, -99\right\}$, list the numbers in this set that belong to the set of:

a. Natural numbers

b. Whole numbers

c. Integers

d. Rational numbers

e. Irrational numbers

f. Real numbers

We now extend the meaning and use of inequality symbols such as $<$ and $>$ to all real numbers.

Order Property for Real Numbers

For any two real numbers a and b, a is less than b if a is to the left of b on a number line.

$a < b$ or also $b > a$

EXAMPLE 6   Insert $<, >$, or $=$ in the appropriate space to make each statement true.

a. $-1 \quad 0$ b. $7 \quad \dfrac{14}{2}$ c. $-5 \quad -6$

Solution

a. $-1 < 0$ since -1 is to the left of 0 on a number line.

$-1 < 0$

b. $7 = \dfrac{14}{2}$ since $\dfrac{14}{2}$ simplifies to 7.

c. $-5 > -6$ since -5 is to the right of -6 on the number line.

$-5 > -6$

PRACTICE

6   Insert $<, >$, or $=$ in the appropriate space to make each statement true.

a. $0 \quad 3$ b. $15 \quad -5$ c. $3 \quad \dfrac{12}{4}$

OBJECTIVE

4   Finding the Absolute Value of a Real Number

A number line also helps us visualize the distance between numbers. The distance between a real number a and 0 is given a special name called the **absolute value** of a. "The absolute value of a" is written in symbols as $|a|$.

Absolute Value

The absolute value of a real number a, denoted by $|a|$, is the distance between a and 0 on a number line.

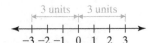

For example, $|3| = 3$ and $|-3| = 3$ since both 3 and -3 are a distance of 3 units from 0 on a number line.

> ▶ Helpful Hint
>
> Since $|a|$ is a distance, $|a|$ is always either positive or 0, never negative. That is, **for any real number a, $|a| \geq 0$.**

EXAMPLE 7   Find the absolute value of each number.

a. $|4|$ **b.** $|-5|$ **c.** $|0|$ **d.** $\left|-\dfrac{1}{2}\right|$ **e.** $|5.6|$

Solution

a. $|4| = 4$ since 4 is 4 units from 0 on a number line.

b. $|-5| = 5$ since -5 is 5 units from 0 on a number line.

c. $|0| = 0$ since 0 is 0 units from 0 on a number line.

d. $\left|-\dfrac{1}{2}\right| = \dfrac{1}{2}$ since $-\dfrac{1}{2}$ is $\dfrac{1}{2}$ unit from 0 on a number line.

e. $|5.6| = 5.6$ since 5.6 is 5.6 units from 0 on a number line.   □

PRACTICE
7   Find the absolute value of each number.

a. $|-8|$ **b.** $|9|$ **c.** $|-2.5|$ **d.** $\left|\dfrac{5}{11}\right|$ **e.** $|\sqrt{3}|$

....

EXAMPLE 8   Insert $<$, $>$, or $=$ in the appropriate space to make each statement true.

a. $|0|$ 2   **b.** $|-5|$ 5   **c.** $|-3|$ $|-2|$ **d.** $|5|$ $|6|$ **e.** $|-7|$ $|6|$

Solution

a. $|0| < 2$ since $|0| = 0$ and $0 < 2$.   **b.** $|-5| = 5$ since $5 = 5$.

c. $|-3| > |-2|$ since $3 > 2$.   **d.** $|5| < |6|$ since $5 < 6$.

e. $|-7| > |6|$ since $7 > 6$.   □

PRACTICE
8   Insert $<$, $>$, or $=$ in the appropriate space to make each statement true.

a. $|8|$ $|-8|$ **b.** $|-3|$ 0   **c.** $|-7|$ $|-11|$ **d.** $|3|$ $|2|$ **e.** $|0|$ $|-4|$

....

Vocabulary, Readiness & Video Check

Use the choices below to fill in each blank.

real   natural   whole   irrational

$|b|$ inequality   integers   rational

1. The _____ numbers are $\{0, 1, 2, 3, 4, \dots\}$.

2. The _____ numbers are $\{1, 2, 3, 4, 5, \dots\}$.

3. The symbols $\neq$, $\leq$, and $>$ are called _____ symbols.

4. The _____ are $\{\dots, -3, -2, -1, 0, 1, 2, 3, \dots\}$.

5. The _____ numbers are {all numbers that correspond to points on the number line}.

6. The _____ numbers are $\left\{\dfrac{a}{b} \,\middle|\, a \text{ and } b \text{ are integers}, b \neq 0\right\}$.

7. The _____ numbers are {nonrational numbers that correspond to points on the number line}.

8. The distance between a number b and 0 on a number line is _____.

Martin-Gay Interactive Videos

See Video 1.2

Watch the section lecture video and answer the following questions.

OBJECTIVE 1

9. In Example 2, why is the symbol < inserted between the two numbers?

OBJECTIVE 2

10. Write the sentence given in Example 4 and translate it to a mathematical statement, using symbols.

OBJECTIVE 3

11. Which sets of numbers does the number in Example 6 belong to? Why is this number not an irrational number?

OBJECTIVE 4

12. Complete this statement based on the lecture given before Example 8. The _____ of a real number a, denoted by $|a|$, is the distance between a and 0 on a number line.

1.2 Exercise Set   MyMathLab®

Insert <, >, or = in the appropriate space to make the statement true. See Example 1.

1. 7   3

2. 9   15

3. 6.26   6.26

4. 2.13   1.13

5. 0   7

6. 20   0

7. −2   2

8. −4   −6

9. The freezing point of water is 32° Fahrenheit. The boiling point of water is 212° Fahrenheit. Write an inequality statement using < or > comparing the numbers 32 and 212.

10. The freezing point of water is 0° Celsius. The boiling point of water is 100° Celsius. Write an inequality statement using < or > comparing the numbers 0 and 100.

△ **11.** An angle measuring 30° is shown and an angle measuring 45° is shown. Use the inequality symbol ≤ or ≥ to write a statement comparing the numbers 30 and 45.

△ **12.** The sum of the measures of the angles of a triangle is 180°. The sum of the measures of the angles of a parallelogram is 360°. Use the inequality symbol ≤ or ≥ to write a statement comparing the numbers 360 and 180.

Are the following statements true or false? See Examples 2 and 6.

13. 11 ≤ 11

14. 4 ≥ 7

15. 10 > 11

16. 17 > 16

17. 3 + 8 ≥ 3(8)

18. 8·8 ≤ 8·7

19. 9 > 0

20. 4 < 7

21. −6 > −2

22. 0 < −15

TRANSLATING

Write each sentence as a mathematical statement. See Example 3.

23. Eight is less than twelve.

24. Fifteen is greater than five.

25. Five is greater than or equal to four.

26. Negative ten is less than or equal to thirty-seven.

27. Fifteen is not equal to negative two.

28. Negative seven is not equal to seven.

Use integers to represent the values in each statement. See Example 4.

29. The highest elevation in California is Mt. Whitney, with an altitude of 14,494 feet. The lowest elevation in California is Death Valley, with an altitude of 282 feet below sea level. (*Source:* U.S. Geological Survey)

30. Driskill Mountain, in Louisiana, has an altitude of 535 feet. New Orleans, Louisiana, lies 8 feet below sea level. (*Source:* U.S. Geological Survey)

31. The number of graduate students at the University of Texas at Austin is 28,000 fewer than the number of undergraduate students. (*Source:* University of Texas at Austin)

32. The number of students admitted to the class of 2011 at UCLA was 38,792 fewer students than the number that had applied. (*Source:* UCLA)

33. Aaron Miller deposited $350 in his savings account. He later withdrew $126.

34. Aris Peña was deep-sea diving. During her dive, she ascended 30 feet and later descended 50 feet.

Tell which set or sets each number belongs to: natural numbers, whole numbers, integers, rational numbers, irrational numbers, and real numbers. See Example 5.

35. 0

36. $\frac{1}{4}$

37. −2

38. $-\frac{1}{2}$

39. 6

40. 5

41. $\dfrac{2}{3}$

42. $\sqrt{3}$

43. $-\sqrt{5}$

44. $-1\dfrac{5}{9}$

Tell whether each statement is true or false.

45. Every rational number is also an integer.

46. Every negative number is also a rational number.

47. Every natural number is positive.

48. Every rational number is also a real number.

49. 0 is a real number.

50. Every real number is also a rational number.

51. Every whole number is an integer.

52. $\dfrac{1}{2}$ is an integer.

53. A number can be both rational and irrational.

54. Every whole number is positive.

Insert $<, >,$ *or* $=$ *in the appropriate space to make a true statement. See Examples 6 through 8.*

55. $-10 \quad -100$

56. $-200 \quad -20$

57. $32 \quad 5.2$

58. $7.1 \quad -7$

59. $\dfrac{18}{3} \quad \dfrac{24}{3}$

60. $\dfrac{8}{2} \quad \dfrac{12}{3}$

61. $-51 \quad -50$

62. $|-20| \quad -200$

63. $|-5| \quad -4$

64. $0 \quad |0|$

65. $|-1| \quad |1|$

66. $\left|\dfrac{2}{5}\right| \quad \left|-\dfrac{2}{5}\right|$

67. $|-2| \quad |-3|$

68. $-500 \quad |-50|$

69. $|0| \quad |-8|$

70. $|-12| \quad \dfrac{24}{2}$

CONCEPT EXTENSIONS

The graph below is called a bar graph. This particular graph shows the annual numbers of recreational visitors to U.S. National Parks. Each bar represents a different year, and the height of the bar represents the number of visitors (in millions) in that year.

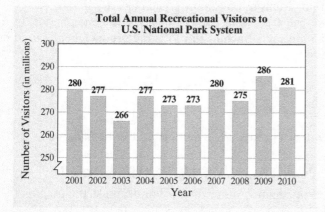

Total Annual Recreational Visitors to U.S. National Park System

(*Note:* The ⌇ symbol means that some numbers are missing. Along the vertical data line, notice the numbers between 0 and 250 are missing or not shown.)

71. In which year(s) was the number of visitors the greatest?

72. What was the greatest number of visitors shown?

73. In what year(s) was the number of visitors greater than 280 million?

74. In what year(s) was the number of visitors less than 270 million?

75. Write an inequality statement comparing the number of annual visitors in 2001 and 2010.

76. Do you notice any trends shown by this bar graph?

The bar graph shows cranberry production from the top five cranberry-producing states.

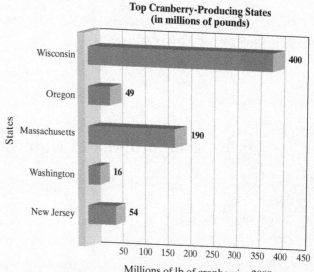

Top Cranberry-Producing States (in millions of pounds)

Data from National Agricultural Statistics Service

77. Write an inequality comparing the 2009 cranberry production in Oregon with the 2009 cranberry production in Washington.

78. Write an inequality comparing the 2009 cranberry production in Massachusetts with the 2009 cranberry production in Wisconsin.

79. Determine the difference between the 2009 cranberry production in Washington and the 2009 cranberry production in New Jersey.

80. According to the bar graph, which two states had almost equal 2009 cranberry crops?

The apparent magnitude of a star is the measure of its brightness as seen by someone on Earth. The smaller the apparent magnitude, the brighter the star. Use the apparent magnitudes in the table on page 16 to answer Exercises 81 through 86.

81. The apparent magnitude of the sun is -26.7. The apparent magnitude of the star Arcturus is -0.04. Write an inequality statement comparing the numbers -0.04 and -26.7.

Star	Apparent Magnitude	Star	Apparent Magnitude
Arcturus	−0.04	Spica	0.98
Sirius	−1.46	Rigel	0.12
Vega	0.03	Regulus	1.35
Antares	0.96	Canopus	−0.72
Sun	−26.7	Hadar	0.61

(Data from *Norton's Star Atlas and Reference Handbook*, 20th Edition, edited by Ian Ridpath. © 2004 Pearson Education, Inc.)

82. The apparent magnitude of Antares is 0.96. The apparent magnitude of Spica is 0.98. Write an inequality statement comparing the numbers 0.96 and 0.98.

83. Which is brighter, the sun or Arcturus?

84. Which is dimmer, Antares or Spica?

85. Which star listed is the brightest?

86. Which star listed is the dimmest?

Rewrite the following inequalities so that the inequality symbol points in the opposite direction and the resulting statement has the same meaning as the given one.

87. $25 \geq 20$

88. $-13 \leq 13$

89. $0 < 6$

90. $5 > 3$

91. $-10 > -12$

92. $-4 < -2$

93. In your own words, explain how to find the absolute value of a number.

94. Give an example of a real-life situation that can be described with integers but not with whole numbers.

1.3 Fractions and Mixed Numbers

OBJECTIVES

1 Write Fractions in Simplest Form.

2 Multiply and Divide Fractions.

3 Add and Subtract Fractions.

4 Perform Operations on Mixed Numbers.

OBJECTIVE

1 Writing Fractions in Simplest Form

A quotient of two numbers such as $\frac{2}{9}$ is called a **fraction.** The parts of a fraction are:

Fraction bar $\rightarrow \dfrac{2}{9} \begin{array}{l}\leftarrow \text{Numerator} \\ \leftarrow \text{Denominator}\end{array}$

$\frac{2}{9}$ of the circle is shaded.

A fraction may be used to refer to part of a whole. For example, $\frac{2}{9}$ of the circle above is shaded. The denominator 9 tells us how many equal parts the whole circle is divided into, and the numerator 2 tells us how many equal parts are shaded.

To simplify fractions, we can factor the numerator and the denominator. In the statement $3 \cdot 5 = 15$, 3 and 5 are called **factors** and 15 is the **product.** (The raised dot symbol indicates multiplication.)

$$\underset{\underset{\text{factor}}{\uparrow}}{3} \quad \cdot \quad \underset{\underset{\text{factor}}{\uparrow}}{5} \quad = \quad \underset{\underset{\text{product}}{\uparrow}}{15}$$

To **factor** 15 means to write it as a product. The number 15 can be factored as $3 \cdot 5$ or as $1 \cdot 15$.

A fraction is said to be **simplified** or in **lowest terms** when the numerator and the denominator have no factors in common other than 1. For example, the fraction $\frac{5}{11}$ is in lowest terms since 5 and 11 have no common factors other than 1.

To help us simplify fractions, we write the numerator and the denominator as a product of **prime numbers.**

> **Prime Number and Composite Number**
>
> A **prime number** is a natural number, other than 1, whose only factors are 1 and itself. The first few prime numbers are
>
> $$2, 3, 5, 7, 11, 13, 17, 19, 23, 29, \text{ and so on.}$$
>
> A natural number, other than 1, that is not a prime number is called a **composite number.**

> ▶ Helpful Hint
> The natural number 1 is neither prime nor composite.

Every composite number can be written as a product of prime numbers. We call this product of prime numbers the **prime factorization** of the composite number.

EXAMPLE 1 Write each of the following numbers as a product of primes.

a. 40   **b.** 63

Solution

a. First, write 40 as the product of any two whole numbers other than 1.

$$40 = 4 \cdot 10$$

Next, factor each of these numbers. Continue this process until all of the factors are prime numbers.

$$40 = 4 \cdot 10$$
$$= 2 \cdot 2 \cdot 2 \cdot 5$$

All the factors are now prime numbers. Then 40 written as a product of primes is

$$40 = 2 \cdot 2 \cdot 2 \cdot 5$$

b. $63 = 9 \cdot 7$
$$= 3 \cdot 3 \cdot 7$$

PRACTICE
1 Write each of the following numbers as a product of primes.

a. 36   **b.** 200

To use prime factors to write a fraction in lowest terms (or simplified form), apply the fundamental principle of fractions.

> **Fundamental Principle of Fractions**
>
> If $\dfrac{a}{b}$ is a fraction and c is a nonzero real number, then
>
> $$\frac{a \cdot c}{b \cdot c} = \frac{a}{b}$$

To understand why this is true, we use the fact that since c is not zero, $\dfrac{c}{c} = 1$.

$$\frac{a \cdot c}{b \cdot c} = \frac{a}{b} \cdot \frac{c}{c} = \frac{a}{b} \cdot 1 = \frac{a}{b}$$

We will call this process dividing out the common factor of c.

EXAMPLE 2 Simplify each fraction (write it in lowest terms).

a. $\dfrac{42}{49}$ **b.** $\dfrac{11}{27}$ **c.** $\dfrac{88}{20}$

Solution

a. Write the numerator and the denominator as products of primes; then apply the fundamental principle to the common factor 7.

$$\frac{42}{49} = \frac{2 \cdot 3 \cdot 7}{7 \cdot 7} = \frac{2 \cdot 3}{7} \cdot \frac{7}{7} = \frac{2 \cdot 3}{7} = \frac{6}{7}$$

b. $\dfrac{11}{27} = \dfrac{11}{3 \cdot 3 \cdot 3}$

There are no common factors other than 1, so $\dfrac{11}{27}$ is already in simplest form.

c. $\dfrac{88}{20} = \dfrac{2 \cdot 2 \cdot 2 \cdot 11}{2 \cdot 2 \cdot 5} = \dfrac{2}{2} \cdot \dfrac{2}{2} \cdot \dfrac{2 \cdot 11}{5} = \dfrac{22}{5}$

PRACTICE
2 Write each fraction in lowest terms.

a. $\dfrac{63}{72}$ **b.** $\dfrac{64}{12}$ **c.** $\dfrac{7}{25}$

✓**CONCEPT CHECK**
Explain the error in the following steps.

a. $\dfrac{15}{55} = \dfrac{1\cancel{5}}{5\cancel{5}} = \dfrac{1}{5}$ **b.** $\dfrac{6}{7} = \dfrac{\cancel{5} + 1}{\cancel{5} + 2} = \dfrac{1}{2}$

OBJECTIVE
2 **Multiplying and Dividing Fractions**

To multiply two fractions, multiply numerator times numerator to obtain the numerator of the product; multiply denominator times denominator to obtain the denominator of the product.

> **Multiplying Fractions**
>
> $$\frac{a}{b} \cdot \frac{c}{d} = \frac{a \cdot c}{b \cdot d} \quad \text{if } b \ne 0 \text{ and } d \ne 0$$

EXAMPLE 3 Multiply $\dfrac{2}{15}$ and $\dfrac{5}{13}$. Simplify the product if possible.

Solution $\dfrac{2}{15} \cdot \dfrac{5}{13} = \dfrac{2 \cdot 5}{15 \cdot 13}$ Multiply numerators.
                                       Multiply denominators.

Next, simplify the product by dividing the numerator and the denominator by any common factors.

$$= \frac{2 \cdot \overset{1}{\cancel{5}}}{3 \cdot \underset{1}{\cancel{5}} \cdot 13}$$

$$= \frac{2}{39}$$

PRACTICE
3 Multiply $\dfrac{3}{8}$ and $\dfrac{7}{9}$. Simplify the product if possible.

Answers to Concept Check:
answers may vary

Before dividing fractions, we first define **reciprocals.** Two fractions are reciprocals of each other if their product is 1.

For example:

The reciprocal of $\dfrac{2}{3}$ is $\dfrac{3}{2}$ because $\dfrac{2}{3} \cdot \dfrac{3}{2} = \dfrac{6}{6} = 1$.

The reciprocal of 5 is $\dfrac{1}{5}$ because $5 \cdot \dfrac{1}{5} = \dfrac{5}{1} \cdot \dfrac{1}{5} = \dfrac{5}{5} = 1$.

To divide fractions, multiply the first fraction by the reciprocal of the second fraction.

Dividing Fractions

$$\frac{a}{b} \div \frac{c}{d} = \frac{a}{b} \cdot \frac{d}{c}, \qquad \text{if } b \neq 0, d \neq 0, \text{ and } c \neq 0$$

EXAMPLE 4   Divide. Simplify all quotients if possible.

a. $\dfrac{4}{5} \div \dfrac{5}{16}$ 　　　　 **b.** $\dfrac{7}{10} \div 14$ 　　　　 **c.** $\dfrac{3}{8} \div \dfrac{3}{10}$

Solution

a. $\dfrac{4}{5} \div \dfrac{5}{16} = \dfrac{4}{5} \cdot \dfrac{16}{5} = \dfrac{4 \cdot 16}{5 \cdot 5} = \dfrac{64}{25}$ 　　 The numerator and denominator have no common factors.

b. $\dfrac{7}{10} \div 14 = \dfrac{7}{10} \div \dfrac{14}{1} = \dfrac{7}{10} \cdot \dfrac{1}{14} = \dfrac{\overset{1}{\cancel{7}} \cdot 1}{2 \cdot 5 \cdot 2 \cdot \underset{1}{\cancel{7}}} = \dfrac{1}{20}$

c. $\dfrac{3}{8} \div \dfrac{3}{10} = \dfrac{3}{8} \cdot \dfrac{10}{3} = \dfrac{\overset{1}{\cancel{3}} \cdot \overset{1}{\cancel{2}} \cdot 5}{2 \cdot 2 \cdot 2 \cdot \underset{1}{\cancel{3}}} = \dfrac{5}{4}$

PRACTICE
4　Divide. Simplify all quotients if possible.

a. $\dfrac{3}{4} \div \dfrac{4}{9}$ 　　　　 **b.** $\dfrac{5}{12} \div 15$ 　　　　 **c.** $\dfrac{7}{6} \div \dfrac{7}{15}$

OBJECTIVE
3　**Adding and Subtracting Fractions** ▶

To add or subtract fractions with the same denominator, combine numerators and place the sum or difference over the common denominator.

Adding and Subtracting Fractions with the Same Denominator

$$\frac{a}{b} + \frac{c}{b} = \frac{a+c}{b}, \qquad \text{if } b \neq 0$$

$$\frac{a}{b} - \frac{c}{b} = \frac{a-c}{b}, \qquad \text{if } b \neq 0$$

EXAMPLE 5　Add or subtract as indicated. Simplify each result if possible.

a. $\dfrac{2}{7} + \dfrac{4}{7}$ 　 **b.** $\dfrac{3}{10} + \dfrac{2}{10}$ 　 **c.** $\dfrac{9}{7} - \dfrac{2}{7}$ 　 **d.** $\dfrac{5}{3} - \dfrac{1}{3}$

Solution

a. $\dfrac{2}{7} + \dfrac{4}{7} = \dfrac{2+4}{7} = \dfrac{6}{7}$ 　　　　 **b.** $\dfrac{3}{10} + \dfrac{2}{10} = \dfrac{3+2}{10} = \dfrac{5}{10} = \dfrac{\overset{1}{\cancel{5}}}{2 \cdot \underset{1}{\cancel{5}}} = \dfrac{1}{2}$

c. $\dfrac{9}{7} - \dfrac{2}{7} = \dfrac{9-2}{7} = \dfrac{7}{7} = 1$ 　　　　 **d.** $\dfrac{5}{3} - \dfrac{1}{3} = \dfrac{5-1}{3} = \dfrac{4}{3}$

5 Add or subtract as indicated. Simplify each result if possible.

a. $\dfrac{8}{5} - \dfrac{3}{5}$ **b.** $\dfrac{8}{5} - \dfrac{2}{5}$ **c.** $\dfrac{3}{5} + \dfrac{1}{5}$ **d.** $\dfrac{5}{12} + \dfrac{1}{12}$

Whole

$$\dfrac{3}{4} = \dfrac{12}{16}$$

To add or subtract fractions without the same denominator, first write the fractions as equivalent fractions with a common denominator. **Equivalent fractions** are fractions that represent the same quantity. For example,

$$\dfrac{3}{4} \text{ and } \dfrac{12}{16} \text{ are equivalent fractions}$$

since they represent the same portion of a whole, as the diagram shows. Count the larger squares, and the shaded portion is $\dfrac{3}{4}$. Count the smaller squares, and the shaded portion is $\dfrac{12}{16}$. Thus, $\dfrac{3}{4} = \dfrac{12}{16}$.

We can write equivalent fractions by multiplying a given fraction by 1, as shown in the next example. Multiplying a fraction by 1 does not change the value of the fraction.

EXAMPLE 6 Write $\dfrac{2}{5}$ as an equivalent fraction with a denominator of 20.

Solution Since $5 \cdot 4 = 20$, multiply the fraction by $\dfrac{4}{4}$. Multiplying by $\dfrac{4}{4} = 1$ does not change the value of the fraction.

Multiply by $\dfrac{4}{4}$ or 1.

$$\dfrac{2}{5} = \dfrac{2}{5} \cdot \dfrac{4}{4} = \dfrac{2 \cdot 4}{5 \cdot 4} = \dfrac{8}{20}$$

Thus, $\dfrac{2}{5} = \dfrac{8}{20}$.

6 Write $\dfrac{2}{3}$ as an equivalent fraction with a denominator of 21.

To add or subtract with different denominators, we first write the fractions as **equivalent fractions** with the same denominator. We use the smallest or **least common denominator**, or **LCD**. (The LCD is the same as the least common multiple of the denominators.)

EXAMPLE 7 Add or subtract as indicated. Write each answer in simplest form.

a. $\dfrac{2}{5} + \dfrac{1}{4}$ **b.** $\dfrac{19}{6} - \dfrac{23}{12}$ **c.** $\dfrac{1}{2} + \dfrac{17}{22} - \dfrac{2}{11}$

Solution

a. Fractions must have a common denominator before they can be added or subtracted. Since 20 is the smallest number that both 5 and 4 divide into evenly, 20 is the **least common denominator** (LCD). Write both fractions as equivalent fractions with denominators of 20. Since

$$\dfrac{2}{5} \cdot \dfrac{4}{4} = \dfrac{2 \cdot 4}{5 \cdot 4} = \dfrac{8}{20} \quad \text{and} \quad \dfrac{1}{4} \cdot \dfrac{5}{5} = \dfrac{1 \cdot 5}{4 \cdot 5} = \dfrac{5}{20}$$

then

$$\dfrac{2}{5} + \dfrac{1}{4} = \dfrac{8}{20} + \dfrac{5}{20} = \dfrac{13}{20}$$

b. The LCD is 12. We write both fractions as equivalent fractions with denominators of 12.

$$\frac{19}{6} - \frac{23}{12} = \frac{38}{12} - \frac{23}{12}$$

$$= \frac{15}{12} = \frac{\overset{1}{\cancel{3}} \cdot 5}{2 \cdot 2 \cdot \underset{1}{\cancel{3}}} = \frac{5}{4}$$

c. The LCD for denominators 2, 22, and 11 is 22. First, write each fraction as an equivalent fraction with a denominator of 22. Then add or subtract from left to right.

$$\frac{1}{2} = \frac{1}{2} \cdot \frac{11}{11} = \frac{11}{22}, \qquad \frac{17}{22} = \frac{17}{22}, \qquad \text{and} \qquad \frac{2}{11} = \frac{2}{11} \cdot \frac{2}{2} = \frac{4}{22}$$

Then

$$\frac{1}{2} + \frac{17}{22} - \frac{2}{11} = \frac{11}{22} + \frac{17}{22} - \frac{4}{22} = \frac{24}{22} = \frac{12}{11}$$

PRACTICE
7   Add or subtract as indicated. Write answers in simplest form.

a. $\dfrac{5}{11} + \dfrac{1}{7}$ **b.** $\dfrac{5}{21} - \dfrac{1}{6}$ **c.** $\dfrac{1}{3} + \dfrac{29}{30} - \dfrac{4}{5}$

OBJECTIVE
4   Performing Operations on Mixed Numbers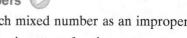

To multiply or divide mixed numbers, first write each mixed number as an improper fraction. To recall how this is done, let's write $3\dfrac{1}{5}$ as an improper fraction.

$$3\frac{1}{5} = 3 + \frac{1}{5} = \frac{15}{5} + \frac{1}{5} = \frac{16}{5}$$

Because of the steps above, notice that we can use a shortcut process for writing a mixed number as an improper fraction.

$$3\frac{1}{5} = \frac{5 \cdot 3 + 1}{5} = \frac{16}{5}$$

EXAMPLE 8   Divide: $2\dfrac{1}{8} \div 1\dfrac{2}{3}$

Solution   First write each mixed number as an improper fraction.

$$2\frac{1}{8} = \frac{8 \cdot 2 + 1}{8} = \frac{17}{8}; \qquad 1\frac{2}{3} = \frac{3 \cdot 1 + 2}{3} = \frac{5}{3}$$

Now divide as usual.

$$2\frac{1}{8} \div 1\frac{2}{3} = \frac{17}{8} \div \frac{5}{3} = \frac{17}{8} \cdot \frac{3}{5} = \frac{51}{40}$$

The fraction $\dfrac{51}{40}$ is improper. To write it as an equivalent mixed number, remember that the fraction bar means division and divide.

$$\begin{array}{r} 1\frac{11}{40} \\ 40\overline{)51} \\ -40 \\ \hline 11 \end{array}$$

Thus, the quotient is $\dfrac{51}{40}$ or $1\dfrac{11}{40}$.

PRACTICE
8   Multiply: $5\dfrac{1}{6} \cdot 4\dfrac{2}{5}$

As a general rule, if the original exercise contains mixed numbers, write the result as a mixed number if possible.

When adding or subtracting mixed numbers, you might want to use the following method.

EXAMPLE 9   Subtract: $50\frac{1}{6} - 38\frac{1}{3}$

Solution

$$50\frac{1}{6} = \quad 50\frac{1}{6} = \quad 49\frac{7}{6} \qquad 50\frac{1}{6} = 49 + 1 + \frac{1}{6} = 49\frac{7}{6}$$

$$-38\frac{1}{3} = -38\frac{2}{6} = -38\frac{2}{6}$$

$$\overline{\qquad\qquad 11\frac{5}{6}}$$

PRACTICE 9   Subtract: $76\frac{1}{12} - 35\frac{1}{4}$

Vocabulary, Readiness & Video Check

Use the choices below to fill in each blank. Some choices may be used more than once.

simplified   reciprocals   equivalent   denominator

product   factors   fraction   numerator

1. A quotient of two numbers, such as $\frac{5}{8}$, is called a(n) _____.

2. In the fraction $\frac{3}{11}$, the number 3 is called the _____ and the number 11 is called the _____.

3. To factor a number means to write it as a(n) _____.

4. A fraction is said to be _____ when the numerator and the denominator have no common factors other than 1.

5. In $7 \cdot 3 = 21$, the numbers 7 and 3 are called _____ and the number 21 is called the _____.

6. The fractions $\frac{2}{9}$ and $\frac{9}{2}$ are called _____.

7. Fractions that represent the same quantity are called _____ fractions.

Martin-Gay Interactive Videos

See Video 1.3

Watch the section lecture video and answer the following questions.

OBJECTIVE 1
8. What is the common factor in the numerator and denominator of Example 1? What principle is used to simplify this fraction?

OBJECTIVE 2
9. During the solving of Example 3, what two things change in the first step?

OBJECTIVE 3
10. What is the first step needed in order to subtract the fractions in Example 6 and why?

OBJECTIVE 4
11. For Example 7, why is the sum not left as $4\frac{7}{6}$?

1.3 Exercise Set   MyMathLab®

Represent the shaded part of each geometric figure by a fraction.

1.

2.

3.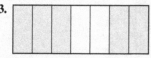

4.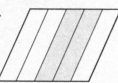

Write each number as a product of primes. See Example 1.

5. 33

6. 60

7. 98

8. 27

9. 20

10. 56

11. 75

12. 32

13. 45

14. 24

Write the fraction in lowest terms. See Example 2.

15. $\dfrac{2}{4}$

16. $\dfrac{3}{6}$

17. $\dfrac{10}{15}$

18. $\dfrac{15}{20}$

19. $\dfrac{3}{7}$

20. $\dfrac{5}{9}$

21. $\dfrac{18}{30}$

22. $\dfrac{42}{45}$

23. $\dfrac{120}{244}$

24. $\dfrac{360}{700}$

Multiply or divide as indicated. Simplify the answer if possible. See Examples 3 and 4.

25. $\dfrac{1}{2} \cdot \dfrac{3}{4}$

26. $\dfrac{7}{11} \cdot \dfrac{3}{5}$

27. $\dfrac{2}{3} \cdot \dfrac{3}{4}$

28. $\dfrac{7}{8} \cdot \dfrac{3}{21}$

29. $\dfrac{1}{2} \div \dfrac{7}{12}$

30. $\dfrac{7}{12} \div \dfrac{1}{2}$

31. $\dfrac{3}{4} \div \dfrac{1}{20}$

32. $\dfrac{3}{5} \div \dfrac{9}{10}$

33. $\dfrac{7}{10} \cdot \dfrac{5}{21}$

34. $\dfrac{3}{35} \cdot \dfrac{10}{63}$

35. $\dfrac{25}{9} \cdot \dfrac{1}{3}$

36. $\dfrac{1}{4} \cdot \dfrac{19}{6}$

The area of a plane figure is a measure of the amount of surface of the figure. Find the area of each figure below. (The area of a rectangle is the product of its length and width. The area of a triangle is $\dfrac{1}{2}$ the product of its base and height.)

37.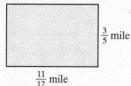

$\dfrac{3}{5}$ mile

$\dfrac{11}{12}$ mile

38.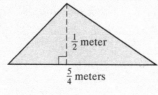

$\dfrac{1}{2}$ meter

$\dfrac{5}{4}$ meters

39.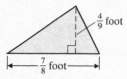

$\dfrac{4}{9}$ foot

$\dfrac{7}{8}$ foot

40.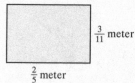

$\dfrac{3}{11}$ meter

$\dfrac{2}{5}$ meter

Add or subtract as indicated. Write the answer in lowest terms. See Example 5.

41. $\dfrac{4}{5} - \dfrac{1}{5}$

42. $\dfrac{6}{7} - \dfrac{1}{7}$

43. $\dfrac{4}{5} + \dfrac{1}{5}$

44. $\dfrac{6}{7} + \dfrac{1}{7}$

45. $\dfrac{17}{21} - \dfrac{10}{21}$

46. $\dfrac{18}{35} - \dfrac{11}{35}$

47. $\dfrac{23}{105} + \dfrac{4}{105}$

48. $\dfrac{13}{132} + \dfrac{35}{132}$

Write each fraction as an equivalent fraction with the given denominator. See Example 6.

49. $\dfrac{7}{10}$ with a denominator of 30

50. $\dfrac{2}{3}$ with a denominator of 9

51. $\dfrac{2}{9}$ with a denominator of 18

52. $\dfrac{8}{7}$ with a denominator of 56

53. $\dfrac{4}{5}$ with a denominator of 20

54. $\dfrac{4}{5}$ with a denominator of 25

Add or subtract as indicated. Write the answer in simplest form. See Example 7.

55. $\dfrac{2}{3} + \dfrac{3}{7}$

56. $\dfrac{3}{4} + \dfrac{1}{6}$

57. $\dfrac{4}{15} - \dfrac{1}{12}$

58. $\dfrac{11}{12} - \dfrac{1}{16}$

59. $\dfrac{5}{22} - \dfrac{5}{33}$

60. $\dfrac{7}{10} - \dfrac{8}{15}$

61. $\dfrac{12}{5} - 1$

62. $2 - \dfrac{3}{8}$

Each circle in Exercises 63–68 represents a whole, or 1. Use subtraction to determine the unknown part of the circle.

63.

$\dfrac{3}{10}$ $\dfrac{5}{10}$?

64.

$\dfrac{3}{11}$ $\dfrac{2}{11}$?

65.

66.

67.

68.

Perform the indicated operations. See Examples 8 and 9.

69. $5\frac{1}{9} \cdot 3\frac{2}{3}$

70. $2\frac{3}{4} \cdot 1\frac{7}{8}$

71. $8\frac{3}{5} \div 2\frac{9}{10}$

72. $1\frac{7}{8} \div 3\frac{8}{9}$

73. $17\frac{2}{5} + 30\frac{2}{3}$

74. $26\frac{11}{20} + 40\frac{7}{10}$

75. $8\frac{11}{12} - 1\frac{5}{6}$

76. $4\frac{7}{8} - 2\frac{3}{16}$

MIXED PRACTICE

Perform the following operations. Write answers in simplest form.

77. $\frac{10}{21} + \frac{5}{21}$

78. $\frac{11}{35} + \frac{3}{35}$

79. $\frac{10}{3} - \frac{5}{21}$

80. $\frac{11}{7} - \frac{3}{35}$

81. $\frac{2}{3} \cdot \frac{3}{5}$

82. $\frac{3}{4} \cdot \frac{7}{12}$

83. $\frac{2}{3} \div \frac{3}{5}$

84. $\frac{3}{4} \div \frac{7}{12}$

85. $5 + \frac{2}{3}$

86. $7 + \frac{1}{10}$

87. $7\frac{2}{5} \div \frac{1}{5}$

88. $9\frac{5}{6} \div \frac{1}{6}$

89. $\frac{1}{2} - \frac{14}{33}$

90. $\frac{7}{15} - \frac{7}{25}$

91. $\frac{23}{105} - \frac{2}{105}$

92. $\frac{57}{132} - \frac{13}{132}$

93. $1\frac{1}{2} + 3\frac{2}{3}$

94. $2\frac{3}{5} + 4\frac{7}{10}$

95. $\frac{2}{3} - \frac{5}{9} + \frac{5}{6}$

96. $\frac{8}{11} - \frac{1}{4} + \frac{1}{2}$

The perimeter of a plane figure is the total distance around the figure. Find the perimeter of each figure in Exercises 97 and 98.

△ **97.**

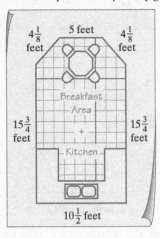

△ **98.**

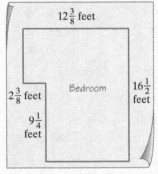

99. In your own words, explain how to add two fractions with different denominators.

100. In your own words, explain how to multiply two fractions.

The following trail chart is given to visitors at the Lakeview Forest Preserve.

Trail Name	Distance (miles)
Robin Path	$3\frac{1}{2}$
Red Falls	$5\frac{1}{2}$
Green Way	$2\frac{1}{8}$
Autumn Walk	$1\frac{3}{4}$

101. How much longer is Red Falls Trail than Green Way Trail?

102. Find the total distance traveled by someone who hiked along all four trails.

CONCEPT EXTENSIONS

The graph shown is called a circle graph or a pie chart. Use the graph to answer Exercises 103 through 106.

Fraction of U.S. Screens by Theater Type

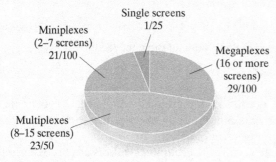

Data from Motion Picture Association of America

103. What fraction of U.S. movie screens are in miniplexes?

104. What fraction of U.S. movie screens are in single-screen theaters or multiplexes?

105. What theater type has the greatest fraction of screens?

106. What fraction of U.S. movie screens are in megaplexes or miniplexes?

For Exercises 107 through 110, determine whether the work is correct or incorrect. If incorrect, find the error and correct. See the Concept Check in this section.

107. $\dfrac{12}{24} = \dfrac{2 + 4 + 6}{2 + 4 + 6 + 12} = \dfrac{1}{12}$

108. $\dfrac{30}{60} = \dfrac{2 \cdot 3 \cdot 5}{2 \cdot 2 \cdot 3 \cdot 5} = \dfrac{1}{2}$

109. $\dfrac{2}{7} + \dfrac{9}{7} = \dfrac{11}{14}$

110. $\dfrac{16}{28} = \dfrac{2 \cdot 5 + 6 \cdot 1}{2 \cdot 5 + 6 \cdot 3} = \dfrac{1}{3}$

1.4 # Exponents, Order of Operations, Variable Expressions, and Equations

OBJECTIVES

1 Define and Use Exponents and the Order of Operations.

2 Evaluate Algebraic Expressions, Given Replacement Values for Variables.

3 Determine Whether a Number Is a Solution of a Given Equation.

4 Translate Phrases into Expressions and Sentences into Statements.

OBJECTIVE

1   Using Exponents and the Order of Operations

Frequently in algebra, products occur that contain repeated multiplication of the same factor. For example, the volume of a cube whose sides each measure 2 centimeters is $(2 \cdot 2 \cdot 2)$ cubic centimeters. We may use **exponential notation** to write such products in a more compact form. For example,

$$2 \cdot 2 \cdot 2 \quad \textit{may be written as} \quad 2^3.$$

The 2 in 2^3 is called the **base;** it is the repeated factor. The 3 in 2^3 is called the **exponent** and is the number of times the base is used as a factor. The expression 2^3 is called an **exponential expression.**

$$\underset{\text{base}}{} 2^{\overset{\text{exponent}}{3}} = 2 \cdot 2 \cdot 2 = 8$$

2 is a factor 3 times

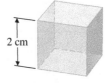

Volume is $(2 \cdot 2 \cdot 2)$ cubic centimeters.

EXAMPLE 1   Evaluate the following:

a. 3^2 [read as "3 squared" or as "3 to the second power"]

b. 5^3 [read as "5 cubed" or as "5 to the third power"]

c. 2^4 [read as "2 to the fourth power"]

d. 7^1 **e.** $\left(\dfrac{3}{7}\right)^2$

Solution

a. $3^2 = 3 \cdot 3 = 9$ **b.** $5^3 = 5 \cdot 5 \cdot 5 = 125$

c. $2^4 = 2 \cdot 2 \cdot 2 \cdot 2 = 16$ **d.** $7^1 = 7$

e. $\left(\dfrac{3}{7}\right)^2 = \left(\dfrac{3}{7}\right)\left(\dfrac{3}{7}\right) = \dfrac{9}{49}$

PRACTICE
1 Evaluate:

a. 1^3 **b.** 5^2 **c.** $\left(\dfrac{1}{10}\right)^2$ **d.** 9^1 **e.** $\left(\dfrac{2}{5}\right)^3$

> **Helpful Hint**
> $2^3 \neq 2 \cdot 3$ since 2^3 indicates repeated **multiplication** of the same factor.
> $$2^3 = 2 \cdot 2 \cdot 2 = 8, \text{ whereas } 2 \cdot 3 = 6.$$

Using symbols for mathematical operations is a great convenience. However, the more operation symbols present in an expression, the more careful we must be when performing the indicated operation. For example, in the expression $2 + 3 \cdot 7$, do we add first or multiply first? To eliminate confusion, **grouping symbols** are used. Examples of grouping symbols are parentheses ( ), brackets [ ], braces { }, and the fraction bar. If we wish $2 + 3 \cdot 7$ to be simplified by adding first, we enclose $2 + 3$ in parentheses.

$$(2 + 3) \cdot 7 = 5 \cdot 7 = 35$$

If we wish to multiply first, $3 \cdot 7$ may be enclosed in parentheses.

$$2 + (3 \cdot 7) = 2 + 21 = 23$$

To eliminate confusion when no grouping symbols are present, use the following agreed-upon order of operations.

Order of Operations

Simplify expressions using the order below. If grouping symbols such as parentheses are present, simplify expressions within those first, starting with the innermost set. If fraction bars are present, simplify the numerator and the denominator separately.

1. Evaluate exponential expressions.

2. Perform multiplications or divisions in order from left to right.

3. Perform additions or subtractions in order from left to right.

Now simplify $2 + 3 \cdot 7$. There are no grouping symbols and no exponents, so we multiply and then add.

$$2 + 3 \cdot 7 = 2 + 21 \quad \text{Multiply.}$$
$$= 23 \quad\quad\quad \text{Add.}$$

EXAMPLE 2 Simplify each expression.

a. $6 \div 3 + 5^2$ **b.** $20 \div 5 \cdot 4$ **c.** $\dfrac{2(12 + 3)}{|-15|}$ **d.** $3 \cdot 4^2$ **e.** $\dfrac{3}{2} \cdot \dfrac{1}{2} - \dfrac{1}{2}$

Solution

a. Evaluate 5^2 first.

$$6 \div 3 + 5^2 = 6 \div 3 + 25$$

Next divide, then add.

$$= 2 + 25 \quad \text{Divide.}$$
$$= 27 \quad\quad \text{Add.}$$

b. $20 \div 5 \cdot 4 = 4 \cdot 4$
$$= 16$$

> **Helpful Hint**
> Remember to multiply or divide in order from left to right.

c. First, simplify the numerator and the denominator separately.

$$\frac{2(12 + 3)}{|-15|} = \frac{2(15)}{15} \quad \text{Simplify numerator and denominator separately.}$$

$$= \frac{30}{15}$$

$$= 2 \quad \text{Simplify.}$$

d. In this example, only the 4 is squared. The factor of 3 is not part of the base because no grouping symbol includes it as part of the base.

$$3 \cdot 4^2 = 3 \cdot 16 \quad \text{Evaluate the exponential expression.}$$
$$= 48 \quad \text{Multiply.}$$

e. The order of operations applies to operations with fractions in exactly the same way as it applies to operations with whole numbers.

$$\frac{3}{2} \cdot \frac{1}{2} - \frac{1}{2} = \frac{3}{4} - \frac{1}{2} \quad \text{Multiply.}$$

$$= \frac{3}{4} - \frac{2}{4} \quad \text{The least common denominator is 4.}$$

$$= \frac{1}{4} \quad \text{Subtract.}$$

PRACTICE
2   Simplify each expression

a. $6 + 3 \cdot 9$ **b.** $4^3 \div 8 + 3$ **c.** $\left(\frac{2}{3}\right)^2 \cdot |-8|$

d. $\dfrac{9(14 - 6)}{|-2|}$ **e.** $\dfrac{7}{4} \cdot \dfrac{1}{4} - \dfrac{1}{4}$

> ▶ **Helpful Hint**
>
> Be careful when evaluating an exponential expression. In $3 \cdot 4^2$, the exponent 2 applies only to the base 4. In $(3 \cdot 4)^2$, we multiply first because of parentheses, so the exponent 2 applies to the product $3 \cdot 4$.
>
> $$3 \cdot 4^2 = 3 \cdot 16 = 48 \qquad (3 \cdot 4)^2 = (12)^2 = 144$$

Expressions that include many grouping symbols can be confusing. When simplifying these expressions, keep in mind that grouping symbols separate the expression into distinct parts. Each is then simplified separately.

EXAMPLE 3   Simplify $\dfrac{3 + |4 - 3| + 2^2}{6 - 3}$.

Solution   The fraction bar serves as a grouping symbol and separates the numerator and denominator. Simplify each separately. Also, the absolute value bars here serve as a grouping symbol. We begin in the numerator by simplifying within the absolute value bars.

$$\frac{3 + |4 - 3| + 2^2}{6 - 3} = \frac{3 + |1| + 2^2}{6 - 3} \quad \text{Simplify the expression inside the absolute value bars.}$$

$$= \frac{3 + 1 + 2^2}{3} \quad \text{Find the absolute value and simplify the denominator.}$$

$$= \frac{3 + 1 + 4}{3} \quad \text{Evaluate the exponential expression.}$$

$$= \frac{8}{3} \quad \text{Simplify the numerator.}$$

PRACTICE
3   Simplify $\dfrac{6^2 - 5}{3 + |6 - 5| \cdot 8}$.

EXAMPLE 4   Simplify $3[4 + 2(10 - 1)]$.

Solution   Notice that both parentheses and brackets are used as grouping symbols. Start with the innermost set of grouping symbols.

$$
\begin{aligned}
3[4 + 2(10 - 1)] &= 3[4 + 2(9)] \quad \text{Simplify the expression in parentheses.} \\
&= 3[4 + 18] \quad \text{Multiply.} \\
&= 3[22] \quad \text{Add.} \\
&= 66 \quad \text{Multiply.}
\end{aligned}
$$

> **▶ Helpful Hint**
> Be sure to follow order of operations and resist the temptation to incorrectly add 4 and 2 first.

PRACTICE
4   Simplify $4[25 - 3(5 + 3)]$.

EXAMPLE 5   Simplify $\dfrac{8 + 2 \cdot 3}{2^2 - 1}$.

Solution

$$
\frac{8 + 2 \cdot 3}{2^2 - 1} = \frac{8 + 6}{4 - 1} = \frac{14}{3}
$$

PRACTICE
5   Simplify $\dfrac{36 \div 9 + 5}{5^2 - 3}$.

OBJECTIVE
2   Evaluating Algebraic Expressions

In algebra, we use symbols, usually letters such as *x, y,* or *z,* to represent unknown numbers. A symbol that is used to represent a number is called a **variable.** An **algebraic expression** is a collection of numbers, variables, operation symbols, and grouping symbols. For example,

$$
2x, \qquad -3, \qquad 2x + 10, \qquad 5(p^2 + 1), \qquad \text{and} \qquad \frac{3y^2 - 6y + 1}{5}
$$

are algebraic expressions.

Expression	Meaning
$2x$	$2 \cdot x$
$5(p^2 + 1)$	$5 \cdot (p^2 + 1)$
$3y^2$	$3 \cdot y^2$
xy	$x \cdot y$

If we give a specific value to a variable, we can **evaluate an algebraic expression.** To evaluate an algebraic expression means to find its numerical value once we know the values of the variables.

Algebraic expressions are often used in problem solving. For example, the expression

$$16t^2$$

gives the distance in feet (neglecting air resistance) that an object will fall in *t* seconds.

EXAMPLE 6 Evaluate each expression if $x = 3$ and $y = 2$.

a. $2x - y$ **b.** $\dfrac{3x}{2y}$ **c.** $\dfrac{x}{y} + \dfrac{y}{2}$ **d.** $x^2 - y^2$

Solution

a. Replace x with 3 and y with 2.

$$2x - y = 2(3) - 2 \quad \text{Let } x = 3 \text{ and } y = 2.$$
$$= 6 - 2 \qquad \text{Multiply.}$$
$$= 4 \qquad \text{Subtract.}$$

b. $\dfrac{3x}{2y} = \dfrac{3 \cdot 3}{2 \cdot 2} = \dfrac{9}{4} \quad \text{Let } x = 3 \text{ and } y = 2.$

c. Replace x with 3 and y with 2. Then simplify.

$$\frac{x}{y} + \frac{y}{2} = \frac{3}{2} + \frac{2}{2} = \frac{5}{2}$$

d. Replace x with 3 and y with 2.

$$x^2 - y^2 = 3^2 - 2^2 = 9 - 4 = 5$$

PRACTICE

6 Evaluate each expression if $x = 2$ and $y = 5$.

a. $2x + y$ **b.** $\dfrac{4x}{3y}$ **c.** $\dfrac{3}{x} + \dfrac{x}{y}$ **d.** $x^3 + y^2$

OBJECTIVE

3   Determining Whether a Number Is a Solution of an Equation

Many times, a problem-solving situation is modeled by an equation. An **equation** is a mathematical statement that two expressions have equal value. The equal symbol "=" is used to equate the two expressions. For example,

$$3 + 2 = 5, \quad 7x = 35, \quad \frac{2(x-1)}{3} = 0, \text{ and } I = PRT \text{ are all equations.}$$

> ▶ Helpful Hint
> An equation contains the equal symbol "=". An algebraic expression does not.

✓CONCEPT CHECK
Which of the following are equations? Which are expressions?
a. $5x = 8$ **b.** $5x - 8$ **c.** $12y + 3x$ **d.** $12y = 3x$

When an equation contains a variable, deciding which values of the variable make an equation a true statement is called **solving** an equation for the variable. A **solution** of an equation is a value for the variable that makes the equation true. For example, 3 is a solution of the equation $x + 4 = 7$ because if x is replaced with 3, the statement is true.

$$x + 4 = 7$$
$$\downarrow$$
$$3 + 4 = 7 \quad \text{Replace } x \text{ with 3.}$$
$$7 = 7 \quad \text{True}$$

Similarly, 1 is not a solution of the equation $x + 4 = 7$ because $1 + 4 = 7$ is **not** a true statement.

EXAMPLE 7 Decide whether 2 is a solution of $3x + 10 = 8x$.

Solution Replace x with 2 and see if a true statement results.

$$3x + 10 = 8x \qquad \text{Original equation}$$
$$3(2) + 10 \stackrel{?}{=} 8(2) \qquad \text{Replace } x \text{ with 2.}$$
$$6 + 10 \stackrel{?}{=} 16 \qquad \text{Simplify each side.}$$
$$16 = 16 \qquad \text{True}$$

Since we arrived at a true statement after replacing x with 2 and simplifying both sides of the equation, 2 is a solution of the equation. ☐

PRACTICE
7 Decide whether 4 is a solution of $9x - 6 = 7x$.

OBJECTIVE
4 **Translating Phrases to Expressions and Sentences to Statements** ▶

Now that we know how to represent an unknown number by a variable, let's practice translating phrases into algebraic expressions and sentences into statements. Oftentimes, solving problems requires the ability to translate word phrases and sentences into symbols. Below is a list of some key words and phrases to help us translate.

> ▶ Helpful Hint
> Order matters when subtracting and dividing, so be especially careful with these translations.

Addition ($+$)	*Subtraction* ($-$)	*Multiplication* ($\cdot$)	*Division* ($\div$)	*Equality* ($=$)
Sum	Difference of	Product	Quotient	Equals
Plus	Minus	Times	Divide	Gives
Added to	Subtracted from	Multiply	Into	Is/was/should be
More than	Less than	Twice	Ratio	Yields
Increased by	Decreased by	Of	Divided by	Amounts to
Total	Less			Represents/ Is the same as

EXAMPLE 8 Write an algebraic expression that represents each phrase. Let the variable x represent the unknown number.

a. The sum of a number and 3   **b.** The product of 3 and a number

c. Twice a number   **d.** 10 decreased by a number

e. 5 times a number, increased by 7

Solution

a. $x + 3$ since "sum" means to add

b. $3 \cdot x$ and $3x$ are both ways to denote the product of 3 and x

c. $2 \cdot x$ or $2x$

d. $10 - x$ because "decreased by" means to subtract

e. $\underbrace{5x}_{\text{5 times a number}} + 7$ ☐

PRACTICE
8 Write an algebraic expression that represents each phase. Let the variable x represent the unknown number.

a. Six times a number   **b.** A number decreased by 8

c. The product of a number and 9   **d.** Two times a number, plus 3

e. The sum of 7 and a number

> ▶ Helpful Hint
> Make sure you understand the difference when translating phrases containing "decreased by," "subtracted from," and "less than."
>
> | *Phrase* | *Translation* |
> |---|---|
> | A number decreased by 10 | $x - 10$ |
> | A number subtracted from 10 | $10 - x$ |
> | 10 less than a number | $x - 10$ |
> | A number less 10 | $x - 10$ |
>
> $\left.\vphantom{\begin{array}{c}1\\2\\3\\4\end{array}}\right\}$ Notice the order.

Now let's practice translating sentences into equations.

EXAMPLE 9   Write each sentence as an equation or inequality. Let x represent the unknown number.

a. The quotient of 15 and a number is 4.

b. Three subtracted from 12 is a number.

c. Four times a number, added to 17, is not equal to 21.

d. Triple a number is less than 48.

Solution

a. In words: the quotient of 15 and a number   is   4

Translate: $\dfrac{15}{x}$ $=$ 4

b. In words: three subtracted **from** 12   is   a number

Translate: $12 - 3$ $=$ x

Care must be taken when the operation is subtraction. The expression $3 - 12$ would be incorrect. Notice that $3 - 12 \neq 12 - 3$.

c. In words: four times a number   added to   17   is not equal to   21

Translate: $4x$ $+$ 17 $\neq$ 21

d. In words: triple a number   is less than   48

Translate: $3x$ $<$ 48

PRACTICE

9   Write each sentence as an equation or inequality. Let x represent the unknown number.

a. A number increased by 7 is equal to 13.

b. Two less than a number is 11.

c. Double a number, added to 9, is not equal to 25.

d. Five times 11 is greater than or equal to an unknown number.

Graphing Calculator Explorations

Exponents

To evaluate exponential expressions on a scientific calculator, find the key marked y^x or $\wedge$. To evaluate, for example, 3^5, press the following keys: $\boxed{3}$ $\boxed{y^x}$ $\boxed{5}$ $\boxed{=}$ or $\boxed{3}$ $\boxed{\wedge}$ $\boxed{5}$ $\boxed{=}$.

$\updownarrow$ or

$\boxed{\text{ENTER}}$

The display should read $\boxed{243}$ or $\boxed{\begin{array}{l}3\wedge5 \\ \qquad 243\end{array}}$

Order of Operations

Some calculators follow the order of operations, and others do not. To see whether your calculator has the order of operations built in, use your calculator to find $2 + 3 \cdot 4$. To do this, press the following sequence of keys:

$\boxed{2}$ $\boxed{+}$ $\boxed{3}$ $\boxed{\times}$ $\boxed{4}$ $\boxed{=}$.

$\updownarrow$ or

$\boxed{\text{ENTER}}$

The correct answer is 14 because the order of operations is to multiply before we add. If the calculator displays $\boxed{14}$, then it has the order of operations built in.

Even if the order of operations is built in, parentheses must sometimes be inserted. For example, to simplify $\dfrac{5}{12 - 7}$, press the keys

$\boxed{5}$ $\boxed{\div}$ $\boxed{(}$ $\boxed{1}$ $\boxed{2}$ $\boxed{-}$ $\boxed{7}$ $\boxed{)}$ $\boxed{=}$.

$\updownarrow$ or

$\boxed{\text{ENTER}}$

The display should read $\boxed{1}$ or $\boxed{\begin{array}{l}5/(12 - 7) \\ \qquad\qquad 1\end{array}}$

Use a calculator to evaluate each expression.

1. 5^4

2. 7^4

3. 9^5

4. 8^6

5. $2(20 - 5)$

6. $3(14 - 7) + 21$

7. $24(862 - 455) + 89$

8. $99 + (401 + 962)$

9. $\dfrac{4623 + 129}{36 - 34}$

10. $\dfrac{956 - 452}{89 - 86}$

Vocabulary, Readiness & Video Check

Use the choices below to fill in each blank.

equation   variable   base   grouping

expression   solution   solving   exponent

1. In the expression 5^2, the 5 is called the _____ and the 2 is called the _____.

2. The symbols ( ), [ ], and { } are examples of _____ symbols.

3. A symbol that is used to represent a number is called a(n) _____.

4. A collection of numbers, variables, operation symbols, and grouping symbols is called a(n) _____.

5. A mathematical statement that two expressions are equal is called a(n) _____.

6. A value for the variable that makes an equation a true statement is called a(n) _____.

7. Deciding what values of a variable make an equation a true statement is called _____ the equation.

Martin-Gay Interactive Videos

See Video 1.4 🍊

Watch the section lecture video and answer the following questions.

OBJECTIVE 1

8. In Example 3 and the lecture before, what is the main point made about the order of operations?

OBJECTIVE 2

9. What happens with the replacement value for z in Example 6 and why?

OBJECTIVE 3

10. Is the value 0 a solution of the equation given in ▱ Example 9? How is this determined?

OBJECTIVE 4

11. Earlier in this video the point was made that equations have =, while expressions do not. In the lecture before ▱ Example 10, translating from English to math is discussed and another difference between expressions and equations is explained. What is it?

1.4 Exercise Set

MyMathLab®

Evaluate. See Example 1.

1. 3^5

2. 2^5

3. 3^3

4. 4^4

5. 1^5

6. 1^8

7. 5^1

8. 8^1

9. 7^2

10. 9^2

11. $\left(\dfrac{2}{3}\right)^4$

12. $\left(\dfrac{6}{11}\right)^2$

13. $\left(\dfrac{1}{5}\right)^3$

14. $\left(\dfrac{1}{2}\right)^5$

15. $(1.2)^2$

16. $(1.5)^2$

17. $(0.04)^3$

18. $(0.03)^3$

MIXED PRACTICE

Simplify each expression. See Examples 2 through 5.

19. $5 + 6 \cdot 2$

20. $8 + 5 \cdot 3$

21. $4 \cdot 8 - 6 \cdot 2$

22. $12 \cdot 5 - 3 \cdot 6$

23. $2(8 - 3)$

24. $5(6 - 2)$

25. $2 + (5 - 2) + 4^2$

26. $6 - 2 \cdot 2 + 2^5$

27. $5 \cdot 3^2$

28. $2 \cdot 5^2$

29. $\dfrac{1}{4} \cdot \dfrac{2}{3} - \dfrac{1}{6}$

30. $\dfrac{3}{4} \cdot \dfrac{1}{2} + \dfrac{2}{3}$

31. $2[5 + 2(8 - 3)]$

32. $3[4 + 3(6 - 4)]$

33. $\dfrac{19 - 3 \cdot 5}{6 - 4}$

34. $\dfrac{4 \cdot 3 + 2}{4 + 3 \cdot 2}$

35. $\dfrac{|6 - 2| + 3}{8 + 2 \cdot 5}$

36. $\dfrac{15 - |3 - 1|}{12 - 3 \cdot 2}$

37. $\dfrac{3 + 3(5 + 3)}{3^2 + 1}$

38. $\dfrac{3 + 6(8 - 5)}{4^2 + 2}$

39. $\dfrac{6 + |8 - 2| + 3^2}{18 - 3}$

40. $\dfrac{16 + |13 - 5| + 4^2}{17 - 5}$

41. $2 + 3[10(4 \cdot 5 - 16) - 30]$

42. $3 + 4[8(5 \cdot 5 - 20) - 41]$

43. $\left(\dfrac{2}{3}\right)^3 + \dfrac{1}{9} + \dfrac{1}{3} \cdot \dfrac{4}{3}$

44. $\left(\dfrac{3}{8}\right)^2 + \dfrac{1}{4} + \dfrac{1}{8} \cdot \dfrac{3}{2}$

For Exercises 45 and 46, match each expression in the first column with its value in the second column.

45.
a. $(6 + 2) \cdot (5 + 3)$	19
b. $(6 + 2) \cdot 5 + 3$	22
c. $6 + 2 \cdot 5 + 3$	64
d. $6 + 2 \cdot (5 + 3)$	43

46.
a. $(1 + 4) \cdot 6 - 3$	15
b. $1 + 4 \cdot (6 - 3)$	13
c. $1 + 4 \cdot 6 - 3$	27
d. $(1 + 4) \cdot (6 - 3)$	22

Evaluate each expression when $x = 1$, $y = 3$, and $z = 5$.
See Example 6.

47. $3y$ **48.** $4x$

49. $\dfrac{z}{5x}$ **50.** $\dfrac{y}{2z}$

51. $3x - 2$ **52.** $6y - 8$

53. $|2x + 3y|$ **54.** $|5z - 2y|$

55. $xy + z$ **56.** $yz - x$

57. $5y^2$ **58.** $2z^2$

Evaluate each expression if $x = 12$, $y = 8$, and $z = 4$.
See Example 6.

59. $\dfrac{x}{z} + 3y$ **60.** $\dfrac{y}{z} + 8x$

61. $x^2 - 3y + x$ **62.** $y^2 - 3x + y$

63. $\dfrac{x^2 + z}{y^2 + 2z}$ **64.** $\dfrac{y^2 + x}{x^2 + 3y}$

Neglecting air resistance, the expression $16t^2$ gives the distance in feet an object will fall in t seconds.

65. Complete the chart below. To evaluate $16t^2$, remember to first find t^2, then multiply by 16.

Time t (in seconds)	Distance $16t^2$ (in feet)
1	
2	
3	
4	

66. Does an object fall the same distance *during* each second? Why or why not? (See Exercise 65.)

Decide whether the given number is a solution of the given equation. See Example 7.

67. Is 5 a solution of $3x + 30 = 9x$?

68. Is 6 a solution of $2x + 7 = 3x$?

69. Is 0 a solution of $2x + 6 = 5x - 1$?

70. Is 2 a solution of $4x + 2 = x + 8$?

71. Is 8 a solution of $2x - 5 = 5$?

72. Is 6 a solution of $3x - 10 = 8$?

73. Is 2 a solution of $x + 6 = x + 6$?

74. Is 10 a solution of $x + 6 = x + 6$?

75. Is 0 a solution of $x = 5x + 15$?

76. Is 1 a solution of $4 = 1 - x$?

TRANSLATING

Write each phrase as an algebraic expression. Let x represent the unknown number. See Example 8.

77. Fifteen more than a number

78. A number increased by 9

79. Five subtracted from a number

80. Five decreased by a number

81. The ratio of a number and 4

82. The quotient of a number and 9

83. Three times a number, increased by 22

84. Twice a number, decreased by 72

TRANSLATING

Write each sentence as an equation or inequality. Use x to represent any unknown number. See Example 9.

85. One increased by two equals the quotient of nine and three.

86. Four subtracted from eight is equal to two squared.

87. Three is not equal to four divided by two.

88. The difference of sixteen and four is greater than ten.

89. The sum of 5 and a number is 20.

90. Seven subtracted from a number is 0.

91. The product of 7.6 and a number is 17.

92. 9.1 times a number equals 4.

93. Thirteen minus three times a number is 13.

94. Eight added to twice a number is 42.

CONCEPT EXTENSIONS

Fill in each blank with one of the following:
add   subtract   multiply   divide

95. To simplify the expression $1 + 3 \cdot 6$, first _____.

96. To simplify the expression $(1 + 3) \cdot 6$, first _____.

97. To simplify the expression $(20 - 4) \cdot 2$, first _____.

98. To simplify the expression $20 - 4 \div 2$, first _____.

99. Are parentheses necessary in the expression $2 + (3 \cdot 5)$? Explain your answer.

100. Are parentheses necessary in the expression $(2 + 3) \cdot 5$? Explain your answer.

△ *Recall that perimeter measures the distance around a plane figure and area measures the amount of surface of a plane figure. The expression $2l + 2w$ gives the perimeter of the rectangle below (measured in units), and the expression lw gives its area (measured in square units). Complete the chart below for the given lengths and widths. Be sure to include units.*

	Length: l	Width: w	Perimeter of Rectangle: $2l + 2w$	Area of Rectangle: lw
101.	4 in.	3 in.		
102.	6 in.	1 in.		
103.	5.3 in.	1.7 in.		
104.	4.6 in.	2.4 in.		

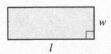

105. Study the perimeters and areas found in the chart on the previous page. Do you notice any trends?

106. In your own words, explain the difference between an expression and an equation.

107. Insert one set of parentheses so that the following expression simplifies to 32.

$$20 - 4 \cdot 4 \div 2$$

108. Insert one set of parentheses so that the following expression simplifies to 28.

$$2 \cdot 5 + 3^2$$

Determine whether each is an expression or an equation. See the Concept Check in this section.

109. a. $5x + 6$
   b. $2a = 7$
   c. $3a + 2 = 9$
   d. $4x + 3y - 8z$
   e. $5^2 - 2(6 - 2)$

110. a. $3x^2 - 26$
   b. $3x^2 - 26 = 1$
   c. $2x - 5 = 7x - 5$
   d. $9y + x - 8$
   e. $3^2 - 4(5 - 3)$

111. Why is 4^3 usually read as "four cubed"? (*Hint:* What is the volume of the **cube** below?)

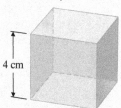

4 cm

112. Why is 8^2 usually read as "eight squared"? (*Hint:* What is the area of the **square** below?)

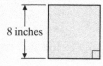

8 inches

113. Write any expression, using 3 or more numbers, that simplifies to -11.

114. Write any expression, using 4 or more numbers, that simplifies to 7.

115. The area of a figure is the total enclosed surface of the figure. Area is measured in square units. The expression lw represents the area of a rectangle when l is its length and w is its width. Find the area of the following rectangular-shaped lot.

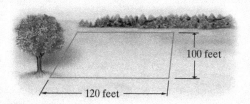

100 feet

— 120 feet —

116. A trapezoid is a four-sided figure with exactly one pair of parallel sides. The expression $\frac{1}{2}h(B + b)$ represents its area, when B and b are the lengths of the two parallel sides and h is the height between these sides. Find the area if $B = 15$ inches, $b = 7$ inches, and $h = 5$ inches.

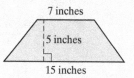

7 inches

5 inches

15 inches

117. The expression $\frac{d}{t}$ represents the average speed in miles per hour if a distance of d miles is traveled in t hours. Find the speed to the nearest whole number if the distance between Dallas, Texas, and Kaw City, Oklahoma, is 432 miles, and it takes Peter Callac 8.5 hours to drive the distance.

118. The expression $\frac{I}{PT}$ represents the rate of interest being charged if a loan of P dollars for T years required I dollars in interest to be paid. Find the interest rate if a $650 loan for 3 years to buy a used IBM personal computer requires $126.75 in interest to be paid.

1.5   Adding Real Numbers

OBJECTIVES

1 Add Real Numbers.

2 Solve Applications That Involve Addition of Real Numbers.

3 Find the Opposite of a Number.

OBJECTIVE

1   Adding Real Numbers

Real numbers can be added, subtracted, multiplied, divided, and raised to powers, just as whole numbers can. We use a number line to help picture the addition of real numbers. We begin by adding numbers with the same sign.

EXAMPLE 1   Add: $3 + 2$

Solution   Recall that 3 and 2 are called **addends.** We start at 0 on a number line and draw an arrow representing the addend 3. This arrow is three units long and points to the right since 3 is positive. From the tip of this arrow, we draw another arrow, representing the addend 2. The number below the tip of this arrow is the sum, 5.

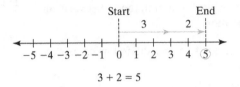

$$3 + 2 = 5$$

PRACTICE
1 Add using a number line: $2 + 4$.

EXAMPLE 2 Add: $-1 + (-2)$

Solution Here, -1 and -2 are addends. We start at 0 on a number line and draw an arrow representing -1. This arrow is one unit long and points to the left since -1 is negative. From the tip of this arrow, we draw another arrow, representing -2. The number below the tip of this arrow is the sum, -3.

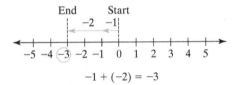

$$-1 + (-2) = -3$$

PRACTICE
2 Add using a number line: $-2 + (-3)$.

Thinking of signed numbers as money earned or lost might help make addition more meaningful. Earnings can be thought of as positive numbers. If $1 is earned and later another $3 is earned, the total amount earned is $4. In other words, $1 + 3 = 4$.

On the other hand, losses can be thought of as negative numbers. If $1 is lost and later another $3 is lost, a total of $4 is lost. In other words,

$$(-1) + (-3) = -4.$$

Using a number line each time we add two numbers can be time consuming. Instead, we can notice patterns in the previous examples and write rules for adding signed numbers. When adding two numbers with the same sign, notice that the sign of the sum is the same as the sign of the addends.

> **Adding Two Numbers with the Same Sign**
> Add their absolute values. Use their common sign as the sign of the sum.

EXAMPLE 3 Add.

a. $-3 + (-7)$ **b.** $-1 + (-20)$ **c.** $-2 + (-10)$

Solution Notice that each time, we are adding numbers with the same sign.

a. $-3 + (-7) = -10$ ←— Add their absolute values: $3 + 7 = 10$.
                    ⌐——— Use their common sign.

b. $-1 + (-20) = -21$ ←— Add their absolute values: $1 + 20 = 21$.
                     ⌐——— Common sign.

c. $-2 + (-10) = -12$ ←— Add their absolute values.
                     ⌐——— Common sign.

PRACTICE
3 Add. **a.** $-5 + (-8)$ **b.** $-31 + (-1)$

Adding numbers whose signs are not the same can also be pictured on a number line.

EXAMPLE 4   Add: $-4 + 6$

Solution

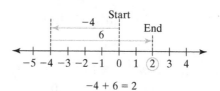

$$-4 + 6 = 2$$

PRACTICE
4   Add using a number line: $-3 + 8$.

Using temperature as an example, if the thermometer registers 4 degrees below 0 degrees and then rises 6 degrees, the new temperature is 2 degrees above 0 degrees. Thus, it is reasonable that $-4 + 6 = 2$.

Once again, we can observe a pattern: when adding two numbers with different signs, the sign of the sum is the same as the sign of the addend whose absolute value is larger.

Adding Two Numbers with Different Signs

Subtract the smaller absolute value from the larger absolute value. Use the sign of the number whose absolute value is larger as the sign of the sum.

EXAMPLE 5   Add.

a. $3 + (-7)$ **b.** $-2 + 10$ **c.** $0.2 + (-0.5)$

Solution   Notice that each time, we are adding numbers with different signs.

a. $3 + (-7) = -4$ ← Subtract their absolute values: $7 - 3 = 4$.
       └──────── The negative number, -7, has the larger absolute value so
                 the sum is negative.

b. $-2 + 10 = 8$ ← Subtract their absolute values: $10 - 2 = 8$.
       └──────── The positive number, 10, has the larger absolute value so
                 the sum is positive.

c. $0.2 + (-0.5) = -0.3$ ← Subtract their absolute values: $0.5 - 0.2 = 0.3$.
       └──────── The negative number, -0.5, has the larger absolute
                 value so the sum is negative.

PRACTICE
5   Add.

a. $15 + (-18)$ **b.** $-19 + 20$ **c.** $-0.6 + 0.4$

In general, we have the following:

Adding Real Numbers

To add two real numbers

1. with the *same sign,* add their absolute values. Use their common sign as the sign of the answer.

2. with *different signs,* subtract their absolute values. Give the answer the same sign as the number with the larger absolute value.

EXAMPLE 6 Add.

a. $-8 + (-11)$ **b.** $-5 + 35$ **c.** $0.6 + (-1.1)$

d. $-\dfrac{7}{10} + \left(-\dfrac{1}{10}\right)$ **e.** $11.4 + (-4.7)$ **f.** $-\dfrac{3}{8} + \dfrac{2}{5}$

Solution

a. $-8 + (-11) = -19$ Same sign. Add absolute values and use the common sign.

b. $-5 + 35 = 30$ Different signs. Subtract absolute values and use the sign of the number with the larger absolute value.

c. $0.6 + (-1.1) = -0.5$ Different signs.

d. $-\dfrac{7}{10} + \left(-\dfrac{1}{10}\right) = -\dfrac{8}{10} = -\dfrac{4}{5}$ Same sign.

> **▶ Helpful Hint**
> Don't forget that a common denominator is needed when adding or subtracting fractions. The common denominator here is 40.

e. $11.4 + (-4.7) = 6.7$

f. $-\dfrac{3}{8} + \dfrac{2}{5} = -\dfrac{15}{40} + \dfrac{16}{40} = \dfrac{1}{40}$

PRACTICE
6 Add.

a. $-\dfrac{3}{5} + \left(-\dfrac{2}{5}\right)$ **b.** $3 + (-9)$

c. $2.2 + (-1.7)$ **d.** $-\dfrac{2}{7} + \dfrac{3}{10}$

EXAMPLE 7 Add.

a. $3 + (-7) + (-8)$ **b.** $[7 + (-10)] + [-2 + |-4|]$

Solution

a. Perform the additions from left to right.

$$3 + (-7) + (-8) = -4 + (-8) \quad \text{Adding numbers with different signs.}$$
$$= -12 \quad \text{Adding numbers with like signs.}$$

> **▶ Helpful Hint**
> Don't forget that brackets are grouping symbols. We simplify within them first.

b. Simplify inside brackets first.

$$[7 + (-10)] + [-2 + |-4|] = [-3] + [-2 + 4]$$
$$= [-3] + [2]$$
$$= -1 \quad \text{Add.}$$

PRACTICE
7 Add.

a. $8 + (-5) + (-9)$ **b.** $[-8 + 5] + [-5 + |-2|]$

✓CONCEPT CHECK
What is wrong with the following calculation?
$5 + (-22) = 17$

OBJECTIVE
2 Solving Applications by Adding Real Numbers

Positive and negative numbers are often used in everyday life. Stock market returns show gains and losses as positive and negative numbers. Temperatures in cold climates often dip into the negative range, commonly referred to as "below zero" temperatures. Bank statements report deposits and withdrawals as positive and negative numbers.

EXAMPLE 8   Calculating Temperature

In Philadelphia, Pennsylvania, the record extreme high temperature is 104°F. Decrease this temperature by 111 degrees, and the result is the record extreme low temperature. Find this temperature. (*Source:* National Climatic Data Center)

Solution:

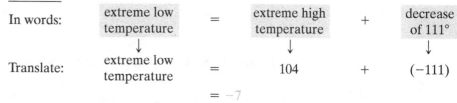

In words:

extreme low temperature	=	extreme high temperature	+	decrease of 111°

Translate:

extreme low temperature	=	104	+	(−111)

$$= -7$$

The record extreme low temperature in Philadelphia, Pennsylvania, is −7°F.

PRACTICE

8   If the temperature was −7° Fahrenheit at 6 a.m., and it rose 4 degrees by 7 a.m. and then rose another 7 degrees in the hour from 7 a.m. to 8 a.m., what was the temperature at 8 a.m.?

OBJECTIVE

3   Finding the Opposite of a Number

To help us subtract real numbers in the next section, we first review the concept of opposites. The graphs of 4 and −4 are shown on a number line below.

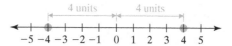

Notice that 4 and −4 lie on opposite sides of 0, and each is 4 units away from 0.

 This relationship between −4 and +4 is an important one. Such numbers are known as **opposites** or **additive inverses** of each other.

> **Opposites or Additive Inverses**
>
> Two numbers that are the same distance from 0 but lie on opposite sides of 0 are called **opposites** or **additive inverses** of each other.

EXAMPLE 9   Find the opposite or additive inverse of each number.

a. 5   **b.** −6   **c.** $\frac{1}{2}$ **d.** −4.5

Solution

a. The opposite of 5 is −5. Notice that 5 and −5 are on opposite sides of 0 when plotted on a number line and are equal distances away.

b. The opposite of −6 is 6.

c. The opposite of $\frac{1}{2}$ is $-\frac{1}{2}$.

d. The opposite of −4.5 is 4.5.

PRACTICE

9   Find the opposite or additive inverse of each number.

a. $-\frac{5}{9}$ **b.** 8   **c.** 6.2   **d.** −3

We use the symbol "−" to represent the phrase "the opposite of" or "the additive inverse of." In general, if a is a number, we write the opposite or additive inverse of a as $-a$. We know that the opposite of -3 is 3. Notice that this translates as

the opposite of $\quad$ − 3 $\quad$ is $\quad$ 3

$-\quad\quad(-3)\quad=\quad 3$

This is true in general.

If a is a number, then $-(-a) = a$.

EXAMPLE 10 Simplify each expression.

a. $-(-10)$ $\quad$ **b.** $-\left(-\dfrac{1}{2}\right)$ $\quad$ **c.** $-(-2x)$ $\quad$ **d.** $-|-6|$

Solution

a. $-(-10) = 10$ $\quad$ **b.** $-\left(-\dfrac{1}{2}\right) = \dfrac{1}{2}$ $\quad$ **c.** $-(-2x) = 2x$

d. Since $|-6| = 6$, then $-|-6| = -6$.

PRACTICE
10 Simplify each expression.

a. $-|-15|$ $\quad$ **b.** $-\left(-\dfrac{3}{5}\right)$ $\quad$ **c.** $-(-5y)$ $\quad$ **d.** $-(-8)$

Let's discover another characteristic about opposites. Notice that the sum of a number and its opposite is 0.

$$10 + (-10) = 0$$
$$-3 + 3 = 0$$
$$\frac{1}{2} + \left(-\frac{1}{2}\right) = 0$$

In general, we can write the following:

The sum of a number a and its opposite $-a$ is 0.

$$a + (-a) = 0$$

This is why opposites are also called additive inverses. Notice that this also means that the opposite of 0 is then 0 since $0 + 0 = 0$.

Vocabulary, Readiness & Video Check

Use the choices below to fill in each blank.

a positive number $\quad\quad$ n $\quad\quad$ opposites
a negative number $\quad\quad$ 0 $\quad\quad$ $-n$

1. Two numbers that are the same distance from 0 but lie on opposite sides of 0 are called _____.

2. If n is a number, then $n + (-n) = $ _____.

3. If n is a number, then $-(-n) = $ _____.

4. The sum of two negative numbers is always _____.

Martin-Gay Interactive Videos

See Video 1.5

Watch the section lecture video and answer the following questions.

OBJECTIVE
1

5. Complete this statement based on the lecture given before
Example 1. To add two numbers with the same sign, add their
_____ and use their common sign as the sign of the sum.

OBJECTIVE
1

6. What is the sign of the sum in Example 6 and why?

OBJECTIVE
2

7. What is the real life application of negative numbers used in
Example 9? The answer to Example 9 is −6. What does this
number mean in the context of the problem?

OBJECTIVE
3

8. Example 12 illustrates the idea that if *a* is a real number, the
opposite of −*a* is *a*. Example 13 looks similar to Example 12,
but it's actually quite different. Explain the difference.

1.5   Exercise Set

MyMathLab®

MIXED PRACTICE

Add. See Examples 1 through 7.

1. $6 + 3$

2. $9 + (-12)$

3. $-6 + (-8)$

4. $-6 + (-14)$

5. $8 + (-7)$

6. $6 + (-4)$

7. $-14 + 2$

8. $-10 + 5$

9. $-2 + (-3)$

10. $-7 + (-4)$

11. $-9 + (-3)$

12. $7 + (-5)$

13. $-7 + 3$

14. $-5 + 9$

15. $10 + (-3)$

16. $8 + (-6)$

17. $5 + (-7)$

18. $3 + (-6)$

19. $-16 + 16$

20. $23 + (-23)$

21. $27 + (-46)$

22. $53 + (-37)$

23. $-18 + 49$

24. $-26 + 14$

25. $-33 + (-14)$

26. $-18 + (-26)$

27. $6.3 + (-8.4)$

28. $9.2 + (-11.4)$

29. $|-8| + (-16)$

30. $|-6| + (-61)$

31. $117 + (-79)$

32. $144 + (-88)$

33. $-9.6 + (-3.5)$

34. $-6.7 + (-7.6)$

35. $-\dfrac{3}{8} + \dfrac{5}{8}$

36. $-\dfrac{5}{12} + \dfrac{7}{12}$

37. $-\dfrac{7}{16} + \dfrac{1}{4}$

38. $-\dfrac{5}{9} + \dfrac{1}{3}$

39. $-\dfrac{7}{10} + \left(-\dfrac{3}{5}\right)$

40. $-\dfrac{5}{6} + \left(-\dfrac{2}{3}\right)$

41. $-15 + 9 + (-2)$

42. $-9 + 15 + (-5)$

43. $-21 + (-16) + (-22)$

44. $-18 + (-6) + (-40)$

45. $-23 + 16 + (-2)$

46. $-14 + (-3) + 11$

47. $|5 + (-10)|$

48. $|7 + (-17)|$

49. $6 + (-4) + 9$

50. $8 + (-2) + 7$

51. $[-17 + (-4)] + [-12 + 15]$

52. $[-2 + (-7)] + [-11 + 22]$

53. $|9 + (-12)| + |-16|$

54. $|43 + (-73)| + |-20|$

55. $-1.3 + [0.5 + (-0.3) + 0.4]$

56. $-3.7 + [0.1 + (-0.6) + 8.1]$

Solve. See Example 8.

57. The low temperature in Anoka, Minnesota, was −15° last
night. During the day, it rose only 9°. Find the high temperature for the day.

58. On January 2, 1943, the temperature was −4° at 7:30 a.m. in
Spearfish, South Dakota. Incredibly, it got 49° warmer in the
next 2 minutes. To what temperature did it rise by 7:32?

59. The lowest point in Africa is −512 feet at Lake Assal in
Djibouti. If you are standing at a point 658 feet above Lake Assal, what is your elevation? (*Source:* Microsoft Encarta)

60. The lowest elevation in Australia is −52 feet at Lake Eyre. If
you are standing at a point 439 feet above Lake Eyre, what is
your elevation? (*Source:* National Geographic Society)

A negative net income results when a company spends more money than it brings in.

61. Johnson Outdoors Inc. had the following quarterly net incomes during its 2009 fiscal year. (Data from Yahoo Finance)

Quarter of Fiscal 2009	Net Income (in millions)
First	2.5
Second	9
Third	−14.2
Fourth	−4.2

What was the total net income for fiscal year 2009?

62. LeapFrog Enterprises Inc. had the following quarterly net incomes during its 2009 fiscal year. (Data from Yahoo Finance)

Quarter of Fiscal 2009	Net Income (in millions)
First	−27.1
Second	−12.2
Third	7.2
Fourth	29.4

What was the total net income for fiscal year 2009?

In golf, scores that are under par for the entire round are shown as negative scores; positive scores are shown for scores that are over par, and 0 is par.

63. Sandra Gal was the winner of the 2011 LPGA Kia Classic in California. Her scores were −6, −5, −3, and −2. What was her overall score? (*Source:* Ladies Professional Golf Association)

64. During the 2011 PGA Waste Management Phoenix Open, Mark Wilson won with scores of −6, −7, −3, and −2. What was his overall score? (*Source:* Professional Golf Association)

Find each additive inverse or opposite. See Example 9.

65. 6   **66.** 4   **67.** −2

68. −8   **69.** 0   **70.** $-\dfrac{1}{4}$

71. $|-6|$ **72.** $|-11|$

Simplify each of the following. See Example 10.

73. $-|-2|$ **74.** $-(-3)$ **75.** $-|0|$

76. $\left|-\dfrac{2}{3}\right|$ **77.** $-\left|-\dfrac{2}{3}\right|$ **78.** $-(-7)$

Decide whether the given number is a solution of the given equation.

79. Is −4 a solution of $x + 9 = 5$?

80. Is 10 a solution of $7 = -x + 3$?

81. Is −1 a solution of $y + (-3) = -7$?

82. Is −6 a solution of $1 = y + 7$?

CONCEPT EXTENSIONS

The following bar graph shows each month's average daily low temperature in degrees Fahrenheit for Barrow, Alaska. Use this graph to answer Exercises 83 through 88.

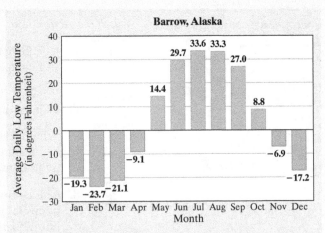

Data from National Climatic Data Center

83. For what month is the graphed temperature the highest?

84. For what month is the graphed temperature the lowest?

85. For what month is the graphed temperature positive *and* closest to 0°?

86. For what month is the graphed temperature negative *and* closest to 0°?

87. Find the average of the temperatures shown for the months of April, May, and October. (To find the average of three temperatures, find their sum and divide by 3.)

88. Find the average of the temperatures shown for the months of January, September, and October.

Each calculation below is incorrect. Find the error and correct it. See the Concept Check in this section.

89. $7 + (-10) \overset{?}{=} 17$ **90.** $-4 + 14 \overset{?}{=} -18$

91. $-10 + (-12) \overset{?}{=} -120$ **92.** $-15 + (-17) \overset{?}{=} 32$

If a is a positive number and b is a negative number, fill in the blanks with the words positive or negative.

93. $-a$ is _____.   **94.** $-b$ is _____.

95. $a + a$ is _____.   **96.** $b + b$ is _____.

For Exercises 97 through 100, determine whether each statement is true or false.

97. The sum of two negative numbers is always a negative number.

98. The sum of two positive numbers is always a positive number.

99. The sum of a positive number and a negative number is always a negative number.

100. The sum of zero and a negative number is always a negative number.

101. In your own words, explain how to find the opposite of a number.

102. In your own words, explain why 0 is the only number that is its own opposite.

103. Explain why adding a negative number to another negative number always gives a negative sum.

104. When a positive and a negative number are added, sometimes the sum is positive, sometimes it is zero, and sometimes it is negative. Explain why and when this happens.

1.6 Subtracting Real Numbers

OBJECTIVES

1 Subtract Real Numbers.

2 Add and Subtract Real Numbers.

3 Evaluate Algebraic Expressions Using Real Numbers.

4 Solve Applications That Involve Subtraction of Real Numbers.

5 Find Complementary and Supplementary Angles.

OBJECTIVE

1   Subtracting Real Numbers

Now that addition of signed numbers has been discussed, we can explore subtraction. We know that $9 - 7 = 2$. Notice that $9 + (-7) = 2$ also. This means that

$$9 - 7 = 9 + (-7)$$

Notice that the difference of 9 and 7 is the same as the sum of 9 and the opposite of 7. In general, we have the following.

> **Subtracting Two Real Numbers**
>
> If a and b are real numbers, then $a - b = a + (-b)$.

In other words, to find the difference of two numbers, add the first number to the opposite of the second number.

EXAMPLE 1 Subtract.

a. $-13 - 4$ **b.** $5 - (-6)$ **c.** $3 - 6$ **d.** $-1 - (-7)$

Solution

a. $-13 - 4 = -13 + (-4)$ Add -13 to the opposite of $+4$, which is -4.

$$= -17$$

b. $5 - (-6) = 5 + (6)$ Add 5 to the opposite of -6, which is 6.

$$= 11$$

c. $3 - 6 = 3 + (-6)$ Add 3 to the opposite of 6, which is -6.

$$= -3$$

d. $-1 - (-7) = -1 + (7) = 6$

PRACTICE

1   Subtract.

a. $-7 - 6$ **b.** $-8 - (-1)$ **c.** $9 - (-3)$ **d.** $5 - 7$

> ▶ **Helpful Hint**
>
> Study the patterns indicated.
>
> No change ⟶   ⟵ Change to addition.
>
>   ⟵ Change to opposite.
>
> $$5 - 11 = 5 + (-11) = -6$$
> $$-3 - 4 = -3 + (-4) = -7$$
> $$7 - (-1) = 7 + (1) = 8$$

EXAMPLE 2 Subtract.

a. $5.3 - (-4.6)$ **b.** $-\dfrac{3}{10} - \dfrac{5}{10}$ **c.** $-\dfrac{2}{3} - \left(-\dfrac{4}{5}\right)$

Solution

a. $5.3 - (-4.6) = 5.3 + (4.6) = 9.9$

b. $-\dfrac{3}{10} - \dfrac{5}{10} = -\dfrac{3}{10} + \left(-\dfrac{5}{10}\right) = -\dfrac{8}{10} = -\dfrac{4}{5}$

c. $-\dfrac{2}{3} - \left(-\dfrac{4}{5}\right) = -\dfrac{2}{3} + \left(\dfrac{4}{5}\right) = -\dfrac{10}{15} + \dfrac{12}{15} = \dfrac{2}{15}$ The common denominator is 15. ☐

PRACTICE
2 Subtract.

a. $8.4 - (-2.5)$ **b.** $-\dfrac{5}{8} - \left(-\dfrac{1}{8}\right)$ **c.** $-\dfrac{3}{4} - \dfrac{1}{5}$

EXAMPLE 3 Subtract 8 from -4.

Solution Be careful when interpreting this: The order of numbers in subtraction is important. 8 is to be subtracted **from** -4.

$$-4 - 8 = -4 + (-8) = -12$$ ☐

PRACTICE
3 Subtract 5 from -2.

OBJECTIVE
2 Adding and Subtracting Real Numbers

If an expression contains additions and subtractions, just write the subtractions as equivalent additions. Then simplify from left to right.

EXAMPLE 4 Simplify each expression.

a. $-14 - 8 + 10 - (-6)$ **b.** $1.6 - (-10.3) + (-5.6)$

Solution

a. $-14 - 8 + 10 - (-6) = -14 + (-8) + 10 + 6$
$$= -6$$

b. $1.6 - (-10.3) + (-5.6) = 1.6 + 10.3 + (-5.6)$
$$= 6.3$$ ☐

PRACTICE
4 Simplify each expression.

a. $-15 - 2 - (-4) + 7$ **b.** $3.5 + (-4.1) - (-6.7)$

When an expression contains parentheses and brackets, remember the order of operations. Start with the innermost set of parentheses or brackets and work your way outward.

EXAMPLE 5   Simplify each expression.

a. $-3 + [(-2 - 5) - 2]$ **b.** $2^3 - |10| + [-6 - (-5)]$

Solution

a. Start with the innermost sets of parentheses. Rewrite $-2 - 5$ as a sum.

$$
\begin{aligned}
-3 + [(-2 - 5) - 2] &= -3 + [(-2 + (-5)) - 2] \\
&= -3 + [(-7) - 2] && \text{Add: } -2 + (-5). \\
&= -3 + [-7 + (-2)] && \text{Write } -7 - 2 \text{ as a sum.} \\
&= -3 + [-9] && \text{Add.} \\
&= -12 && \text{Add.}
\end{aligned}
$$

b. Start simplifying the expression inside the brackets by writing $-6 - (-5)$ as a sum.

$$
\begin{aligned}
2^3 - |10| + [-6 - (-5)] &= 2^3 - |10| + [-6 + 5] \\
&= 2^3 - |10| + [-1] && \text{Add.} \\
&= 8 - 10 + (-1) && \text{Evaluate } 2^3 \text{ and } |10|. \\
&= 8 + (-10) + (-1) && \text{Write } 8 - 10 \text{ as a sum.} \\
&= -2 + (-1) && \text{Add.} \\
&= -3 && \text{Add.} \qquad \square
\end{aligned}
$$

PRACTICE

5   Simplify each expression.

a. $-4 + [(-8 - 3) - 5]$ **b.** $|-13| - 3^2 + [2 - (-7)]$

OBJECTIVE

3   Evaluating Algebraic Expressions

Knowing how to evaluate expressions for given replacement values is helpful when checking solutions of equations and when solving problems whose unknowns satisfy given expressions. The next example illustrates this.

EXAMPLE 6   Find the value of each expression when $x = 2$ and $y = -5$.

a. $\dfrac{x - y}{12 + x}$ **b.** $x^2 - 3y$

Solution

a. Replace x with 2 and y with -5. Be sure to put parentheses around -5 to separate signs. Then simplify the resulting expression.

$$
\begin{aligned}
\frac{x - y}{12 + x} &= \frac{2 - (-5)}{12 + 2} \\
&= \frac{2 + 5}{14} \\
&= \frac{7}{14} = \frac{1}{2}
\end{aligned}
$$

b. Replace x with 2 and y with -5 and simplify.

$$
\begin{aligned}
x^2 - 3y &= 2^2 - 3(-5) \\
&= 4 - 3(-5) \\
&= 4 - (-15) \\
&= 4 + 15 \\
&= 19 \qquad \square
\end{aligned}
$$

PRACTICE
6 Find the value of each expression when $x = -3$ and $y = 4$.

a. $\dfrac{7 - x}{2y + x}$ **b.** $y^2 + x$

▶ **Helpful Hint**

For additional help when replacing variables with replacement values, first place parentheses around any variables.

For Example 6b on the previous page, we have

$x^2 - 3y = \underbrace{(x)^2 - 3(y)}_{\text{Place parentheses around variables}} = \underbrace{(2)^2 - 3(-5)}_{\text{Replace variables with values}} = 4 - 3(-5) = 4 - (-15) = 4 + 15 = 19$

OBJECTIVE
4 Solving Applications by Subtracting Real Numbers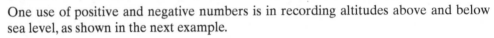

One use of positive and negative numbers is in recording altitudes above and below sea level, as shown in the next example.

EXAMPLE 7 Finding a Change in Elevation

The highest point in the United States is the top of Mount McKinley, at a height of 20,320 feet above sea level. The lowest point is Death Valley, California, which is 282 feet below sea level. How much higher is Mount McKinley than Death Valley? (*Source:* U.S. Geological Survey)

Solution: To find "how much higher," we subtract. Don't forget that since Death Valley is 282 feet *below* sea level, we represent its height by -282. Draw a diagram to help visualize the problem.

Mt. McKinley

20,320 feet

Sea level

Death Valley

-282 feet

In words:	how much higher is Mt. McKinley	=	height of Mt. McKinley	minus	height of Death Valley
Translate:	how much higher is Mt. McKinley	=	20,320	−	(−282)

$$= 20{,}320 + 282$$
$$= 20{,}602$$

Thus, Mount McKinley is 20,602 feet higher than Death Valley.

PRACTICE
7 On Tuesday morning, a bank account balance was $282. On Thursday, the account balance had dropped to $-\$75$. Find the overall change in this account balance.

OBJECTIVE

5 Finding Complementary and Supplementary Angles

A knowledge of geometric concepts is needed by many professionals, such as doctors, carpenters, electronic technicians, gardeners, machinists, and pilots, just to name a few. With this in mind, we review the geometric concepts of **complementary** and **supplementary angles.**

Complementary and Supplementary Angles

Two angles are **complementary** if their sum is 90°.

$x + y = 90°$

Two angles are **supplementary** if their sum is 180°.

$x + y = 180°$

△ **EXAMPLE 8**   Find each unknown complementary or supplementary angle.

a.   **b.**

Solution

a. These angles are complementary, so their sum is 90°. This means that x is 90° − 38°.

$$x = 90° − 38° = 52°$$

b. These angles are supplementary, so their sum is 180°. This means that y is 180° − 62°.

$$y = 180° − 62° = 118°$$

PRACTICE

8   Find each unknown complementary or supplementary angle.

a.   **b.**

Vocabulary, Readiness & Video Check

Translate each phrase. Let x represent "a number." Use the choices below to fill in each blank.

$7 − x \qquad x − 7$

1. 7 minus a number _____

2. 7 subtracted from a number _____

3. A number decreased by 7 _____

4. 7 less a number _____

5. A number less than 7 _____

6. A number subtracted from 7 _____

Multiple choice: Select the correct lettered response following each exercise.

7. To evaluate $x - y$ for $x = -10$ and $y = -14$, we replace x with -10 and y with -14 and evaluate _____.
   a. $10 - 14$ **b.** $-10 - 14$ **c.** $-14 - 10$ **d.** $-10 - (-14)$

8. The expression $-5 - 10$ equals _____.
   a. $5 - 10$ **b.** $5 + 10$ **c.** $-5 + (-10)$ **d.** $10 - 5$

Martin-Gay Interactive Videos

See Video 1.6

Watch the section lecture video and answer the following questions.

OBJECTIVE
1
  9. Complete this statement based on the lecture given before Example 1. To subtract two real numbers, change the operation to _____ and take the _____ of the second number.

OBJECTIVE
2
  10. When simplifying Example 5, what is the result of the first step and why is the expression rewritten in this way?

OBJECTIVE
3
  11. In Example 7, why are you told to be especially careful when working with the replacement value in the numerator?

OBJECTIVE
4
  12. For Example 8, why is the overall vertical change represented as a negative number?

OBJECTIVE
5
  13. The definition of supplementary angles is given just before Example 9. Explain how this definition is used to solve Example 9.

1.6 Exercise Set   MyMathLab®

MIXED PRACTICE

Subtract. See Examples 1 and 2.

1. $-6 - 4$ **2.** $-12 - 8$

3. $4 - 9$ **4.** $8 - 11$

5. $16 - (-3)$ **6.** $12 - (-5)$

7. $\dfrac{1}{2} - \dfrac{1}{3}$ **8.** $\dfrac{3}{4} - \dfrac{7}{8}$

9. $-16 - (-18)$ **10.** $-20 - (-48)$

11. $-6 - 5$ **12.** $-8 - 4$

13. $7 - (-4)$ **14.** $3 - (-6)$

15. $-6 - (-11)$ **16.** $-4 - (-16)$

17. $16 - (-21)$ **18.** $15 - (-33)$

19. $9.7 - 16.1$ **20.** $8.3 - 11.2$

21. $-44 - 27$ **22.** $-36 - 51$

23. $-21 - (-21)$ **24.** $-17 - (-17)$

25. $-2.6 - (-6.7)$ **26.** $-6.1 - (-5.3)$

27. $-\dfrac{3}{11} - \left(-\dfrac{5}{11}\right)$ **28.** $-\dfrac{4}{7} - \left(-\dfrac{1}{7}\right)$

29. $-\dfrac{1}{6} - \dfrac{3}{4}$ **30.** $-\dfrac{1}{10} - \dfrac{7}{8}$

31. $8.3 - (-0.62)$ **32.** $4.3 - (-0.87)$

TRANSLATING

Translate each phrase to an expression and simplify. See Example 3.

33. Subtract -5 from 8.   **34.** Subtract 3 from -2.

35. Subtract -1 from -6.   **36.** Subtract 17 from 1.

37. Subtract 8 from 7.   **38.** Subtract 9 from -4.

39. Decrease -8 by 15.   **40.** Decrease 11 by -14.

Simplify each expression. (Remember the order of operations.) See Examples 4 and 5.

41. $-10 - (-8) + (-4) - 20$

42. $-16 - (-3) + (-11) - 14$

43. $5 - 9 + (-4) - 8 - 8$

44. $7 - 12 + (-5) - 2 + (-2)$

45. $-6 - (2 - 11)$ **46.** $-9 - (3 - 8)$

47. $3^3 - 8 \cdot 9$ **48.** $2^3 - 6 \cdot 3$

49. $2 - 3(8 - 6)$ **50.** $4 - 6(7 - 3)$

51. $(3 - 6) + 4^2$ **52.** $(2 - 3) + 5^2$

53. $-2 + [(8 - 11) - (-2 - 9)]$

54. $-5 + [(4 - 15) - (-6) - 8]$

55. $|-3| + 2^2 + [-4 - (-6)]$

56. $|-2| + 6^2 + (-3 - 8)$

Evaluate each expression when x = −5, y = 4, and t = 10.
See Example 6.

57. $x - y$

58. $y - x$

59. $|x| + 2t - 8y$

60. $|x + t - 7y|$

61. $\dfrac{9 - x}{y + 6}$

62. $\dfrac{15 - x}{y + 2}$

63. $y^2 - x$

64. $t^2 - x$

65. $\dfrac{|x - (-10)|}{2t}$

66. $\dfrac{|5y - x|}{6t}$

Solve. See Example 7.

67. Within 24 hours in 1916, the temperature in Browning, Montana, fell from 44°F to −56°F. How large a drop in temperature was this?

68. Much of New Orleans is below sea level. If George descends 12 feet from an elevation of 5 feet above sea level, what is his new elevation?

69. The coldest temperature ever recorded on Earth was −129°F in Antarctica. The warmest temperature ever recorded was 136°F in the Sahara Desert. How many degrees warmer is 136°F than −129°F? (*Source: Questions Kids Ask,* Grolier Limited, 1991, and *The World Almanac*)

70. The coldest temperature ever recorded in the United States was −80°F in Alaska. The warmest temperature ever recorded was 134°F in California. How many degrees warmer is 134°F than −80°F? (*Source: The World Almanac*)

71. Mauna Kea in Hawaii has an elevation of 13,796 feet above sea level. The Mid-America Trench in the Pacific Ocean has an elevation of 21,857 feet below sea level. Find the difference in elevation between those two points. (*Source:* National Geographic Society and Defense Mapping Agency)

72. A woman received a statement of her charge account at Old Navy. She spent $93 on purchases last month. She returned an $18 top because she didn't like the color. She also returned a $26 nightshirt because it was damaged. What does she actually owe on her account?

73. A commercial jetliner hits an air pocket and drops 250 feet. After climbing 120 feet, it drops another 178 feet. What is its overall vertical change?

74. In some card games, it is possible to have a negative score. Lavonne Schultz currently has a score of 15 points. She then loses 24 points. What is her new score?

75. The highest point in Africa is Mt. Kilimanjaro, Tanzania, at an elevation of 19,340 feet. The lowest point is Lake Assal, Djibouti, at 512 feet below sea level. How much higher is Mt. Kilimanjaro than Lake Assal? (*Source:* National Geographic Society)

76. The airport in Bishop, California, is at an elevation of 4101 feet above sea level. The nearby Furnace Creek Airport in Death Valley, California, is at an elevation of 226 feet below sea level. How much higher in elevation is the Bishop Airport than the Furnace Creek Airport? (*Source:* National Climatic Data Center)

Find each unknown complementary or supplementary angle.
See Example 8.

77.

78.

79.

80.

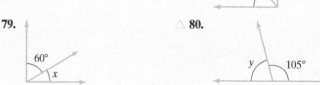

Decide whether the given number is a solution of the given equation.

81. Is −4 a solution of $x - 9 = 5$?

82. Is 3 a solution of $x - 10 = -7$?

83. Is −2 a solution of $-x + 6 = -x - 1$?

84. Is −10 a solution of $-x - 6 = -x - 1$?

85. Is 2 a solution of $-x - 13 = -15$?

86. Is 5 a solution of $4 = 1 - x$?

MIXED PRACTICE—TRANSLATING (*SECTIONS 1.5, 1.6*)

Translate each phrase to an algebraic expression. Use "x" to represent "a number."

87. The sum of −5 and a number.

88. The difference of −3 and a number.

89. Subtract a number from −20.

90. Add a number and −36.

CONCEPT EXTENSIONS

Recall the bar graph from Section 1.5. It shows each month's average daily low temperature in degrees Fahrenheit for Barrow, Alaska. Use this graph to answer Exercises 91 through 94.

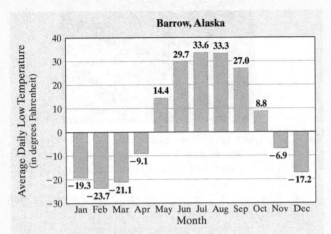

Data from National Climatic Data Center

91. Record the monthly increases and decreases in the low temperature from the previous month.

Month	Monthly Increase or Decrease (from the previous month)
February	
March	
April	
May	
June	

92. Record the monthly increases and decreases in the low temperature from the previous month.

Month	Monthly Increase or Decrease (from the previous month)
July	
August	
September	
October	
November	
December	

93. Which month had the greatest increase in temperature?

94. Which month had the greatest decrease in temperature?

95. Find two numbers whose difference is -5.

96. Find two numbers whose difference is -9.

*Each calculation below is **incorrect**. Find the error and correct it.*

97. $9 - (-7) \overset{?}{=} 2$

98. $-4 - 8 \overset{?}{=} 4$

99. $10 - 30 \overset{?}{=} 20$

100. $-3 - (-10) \overset{?}{=} -13$

If p is a positive number and n is a negative number, determine whether each statement is true or false. Explain your answer.

101. $p - n$ is always a positive number.

102. $n - p$ is always a negative number.

103. $|n| - |p|$ is always a positive number.

104. $|n - p|$ is always a positive number.

Without calculating, determine whether each answer is positive or negative. Then use a calculator to find the exact difference.

105. $56,875 - 87,262$

106. $4.362 - 7.0086$

Integrated Review OPERATIONS ON REAL NUMBERS

Sections 1.1–1.6

Answer the following with positive, negative, or 0.

1. The opposite of a positive number is a _____ number.

2. The sum of two negative numbers is a _____ number.

3. The absolute value of a negative number is a _____ number.

4. The absolute value of zero is _____.

5. The reciprocal of a positive number is a _____ number.

6. The sum of a number and its opposite is _____.

7. The absolute value of a positive number is a _____ number.

8. The opposite of a negative number is a _____ number.

Fill in the chart:

	Number	Opposite	Absolute Value
9.	$\frac{1}{7}$		
10.	$-\frac{12}{5}$		
11.		-3	
12.		$\frac{9}{11}$	

Perform each indicated operation and simplify.

13. $-19 + (-23)$

14. $7 - (-3)$

15. $-15 + 17$

16. $-8 - 10$

17. $18 + (-25)$

18. $-2 + (-37)$

34. $-6 + [(-3 + 7) + (4 - 15)]$

19. $-14 - (-12)$

20. $5 - 14$

35. Subtract 5 from 1.

21. $4.5 - 7.9$

22. $-8.6 - 1.2$

36. Subtract -2 from -3.

23. $-\dfrac{3}{4} - \dfrac{1}{7}$

24. $\dfrac{2}{3} - \dfrac{7}{8}$

37. Subtract $-\dfrac{2}{5}$ from $\dfrac{1}{4}$.

25. $-9 - (-7) + 4 - 6$

38. Subtract $\dfrac{1}{10}$ from $-\dfrac{5}{8}$.

26. $11 - 20 + (-3) - 12$

27. $24 - 6(14 - 11)$

39. $2(19 - 17)^3 - 3(-7 + 9)^2$

28. $30 - 5(10 - 8)$

40. $3(10 - 9)^2 + 6(20 - 19)^3$

29. $(7 - 17) + 4^2$

Evaluate each expression when $x = -2, y = -1,$ and $z = 9$.

30. $9^2 + (10 - 30)$

41. $x - y$

42. $x + y$

31. $|-9| + 3^2 + (-4 - 20)$

43. $y + z$

44. $z - y$

32. $|-4 - 5| + 5^2 + (-50)$

45. $\dfrac{|5z - x|}{y - x}$

46. $\dfrac{|-x - y + z|}{2z}$

33. $-7 + [(1 - 2) + (-2 - 9)]$

1.7 Multiplying and Dividing Real Numbers

OBJECTIVES

1. Multiply Real Numbers.
2. Find the Reciprocal of a Real Number.
3. Divide Real Numbers.
4. Evaluate Expressions Using Real Numbers.
5. Solve Applications That Involve Multiplication or Division of Real Numbers.

OBJECTIVE

1   Multiplying Real Numbers

In this section, we discover patterns for multiplying and dividing real numbers. To discover sign rules for multiplication, recall that multiplication is repeated addition. Thus $3 \cdot 2$ means that 2 is an addend 3 times. That is,

$$2 + 2 + 2 = 3 \cdot 2$$

which equals 6. Similarly, $3 \cdot (-2)$ means -2 is an addend 3 times. That is,

$$(-2) + (-2) + (-2) = 3 \cdot (-2)$$

Since $(-2) + (-2) + (-2) = -6, 3 \cdot (-2) = -6$. This suggests that the product of a positive number and a negative number is a negative number.

What about the product of two negative numbers? To find out, consider the following pattern.

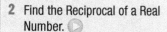

— Factor decreases by 1 each time

$$\begin{aligned} -3 \cdot 2 &= -6 \\ -3 \cdot 1 &= -3 \\ -3 \cdot 0 &= 0 \end{aligned} \Bigg\} \text{ Product increases by 3 each time.}$$

This pattern continues as

— Factor decreases by 1 each time

$$\begin{aligned} -3 \cdot -1 &= 3 \\ -3 \cdot -2 &= 6 \end{aligned} \Bigg\} \text{ Product increases by 3 each time.}$$

This suggests that the product of two negative numbers is a positive number.

Multiplying Real Numbers

1. The product of two numbers with the *same* sign is a positive number.

2. The product of two numbers with *different* signs is a negative number.

EXAMPLE 1   Multiply.

a. $(-8)(4)$ **b.** $14(-1)$ **c.** $-9(-10)$

Solution

a. $-8(4) = -32$ **b.** $14(-1) = -14$ **c.** $-9(-10) = 90$ □

PRACTICE
1   Multiply.

a. $8(-5)$ **b.** $(-3)(-4)$ **c.** $(-6)(9)$

We know that every whole number multiplied by zero equals zero. This remains true for real numbers.

Zero as a Factor

If b is a real number, then $b \cdot 0 = 0$. Also, $0 \cdot b = 0$.

EXAMPLE 2   Perform the indicated operations.

a. $(7)(0)(-6)$ **b.** $(-2)(-3)(-4)$ **c.** $(-1)(5)(-9)$ **d.** $(-4)(-11) - (5)(-2)$

Solution

a. By the order of operations, we multiply from left to right. Notice that, because one of the factors is 0, the product is 0.

$$(7)(0)(-6) = 0(-6) = 0$$

b. Multiply two factors at a time, from left to right.

$$(-2)(-3)(-4) = (6)(-4) \quad \text{Multiply } (-2)(-3).$$
$$= -24$$

c. Multiply from left to right.

$$(-1)(5)(-9) = (-5)(-9) \quad \text{Multiply } (-1)(5).$$
$$= 45$$

d. Follow the rules for order of operations.

$$(-4)(-11) - (5)(-2) = 44 - (-10) \quad \text{Find each product.}$$
$$= 44 + 10 \quad \text{Add 44 to the opposite of } -10.$$
$$= 54 \quad \text{Add.} \quad □$$

PRACTICE
2   Perform the indicated operations.

a. $(-1)(-5)(-6)$ **b.** $(-3)(-2)(4)$

c. $(-4)(0)(5)$ **d.** $(-2)(-3) - (-4)(5)$

▶ Helpful Hint

You may have noticed from the example that if we multiply:

- an *even* number of negative numbers, the product is *positive*.
- an *odd* number of negative numbers, the product is *negative*.

Answer to Concept Check
negative

✓CONCEPT CHECK
What is the sign of the product of five negative numbers? Explain.

Multiplying signed decimals or fractions is carried out exactly the same way as multiplying integers.

EXAMPLE 3   Multiply.

a. $(-1.2)(0.05)$ **b.** $\dfrac{2}{3} \cdot \left(-\dfrac{7}{10}\right)$ **c.** $\left(-\dfrac{4}{5}\right)(-20)$

Solution

a. The product of two numbers with different signs is negative.

$$(-1.2)(0.05) = -[(1.2)(0.05)]$$
$$= -0.06$$

b. $\dfrac{2}{3} \cdot \left(-\dfrac{7}{10}\right) = -\dfrac{2 \cdot 7}{3 \cdot 10} = -\dfrac{2 \cdot 7}{3 \cdot 2 \cdot 5} = -\dfrac{7}{15}$

c. $\left(-\dfrac{4}{5}\right)(-20) = \dfrac{4 \cdot 20}{5 \cdot 1} = \dfrac{4 \cdot 4 \cdot 5}{5 \cdot 1} = \dfrac{16}{1}$ or 16

PRACTICE
3   Multiply.

a. $(0.23)(-0.2)$ **b.** $\left(-\dfrac{3}{5}\right) \cdot \left(\dfrac{4}{9}\right)$ **c.** $\left(-\dfrac{7}{12}\right)(-24)$

Now that we know how to multiply positive and negative numbers, let's see how we find the values of $(-4)^2$ and -4^2, for example. Although these two expressions look similar, the difference between the two is the parentheses. In $(-4)^2$, the parentheses tell us that the base, or repeated factor, is -4. In -4^2, only 4 is the base. Thus,

$$(-4)^2 = (-4)(-4) = 16 \quad \text{The base is } -4.$$
$$-4^2 = -(4 \cdot 4) = -16 \quad \text{The base is } 4.$$

EXAMPLE 4   Evaluate.

a. $(-2)^3$ **b.** -2^3 **c.** $(-3)^2$ **d.** -3^2

Solution

a. $(-2)^3 = (-2)(-2)(-2) = -8$ The base is -2.
b. $-2^3 = -(2 \cdot 2 \cdot 2) = -8$ The base is 2.
c. $(-3)^2 = (-3)(-3) = 9$ The base is -3.
d. $-3^2 = -(3 \cdot 3) = -9$ The base is 3.

PRACTICE
4   Evaluate.

a. $(-6)^2$ **b.** -6^2 **c.** $(-4)^3$ **d.** -4^3

▶ **Helpful Hint**
Be careful when identifying the base of an exponential expression.

$$(-3)^2 \qquad\qquad -3^2$$
Base is -3 \qquad\qquad Base is 3
$$(-3)^2 = (-3)(-3) = 9 \qquad -3^2 = -(3 \cdot 3) = -9$$

OBJECTIVE

2 Finding Reciprocals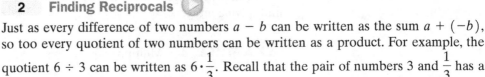

Just as every difference of two numbers $a - b$ can be written as the sum $a + (-b)$, so too every quotient of two numbers can be written as a product. For example, the quotient $6 \div 3$ can be written as $6 \cdot \frac{1}{3}$. Recall that the pair of numbers 3 and $\frac{1}{3}$ has a special relationship. Their product is 1 and they are called reciprocals or **multiplicative inverses** of each other.

> **Reciprocals or Multiplicative Inverses**
>
> Two numbers whose product is 1 are called reciprocals or multiplicative inverses of each other.

Notice that **0 has no multiplicative inverse** since 0 multiplied by any number is never 1 but always 0.

EXAMPLE 5 Find the reciprocal of each number.

a. 22 **b.** $\frac{3}{16}$ **c.** -10 **d.** $-\frac{9}{13}$

Solution

a. The reciprocal of 22 is $\frac{1}{22}$ since $22 \cdot \frac{1}{22} = 1$.

b. The reciprocal of $\frac{3}{16}$ is $\frac{16}{3}$ since $\frac{3}{16} \cdot \frac{16}{3} = 1$.

c. The reciprocal of -10 is $-\frac{1}{10}$.

d. The reciprocal of $-\frac{9}{13}$ is $-\frac{13}{9}$.

PRACTICE

5 Find the reciprocal of each number.

a. $\frac{8}{3}$ **b.** 15 **c.** $-\frac{2}{7}$ **d.** -5

OBJECTIVE

3 Dividing Real Numbers

We may now write a quotient as an equivalent product.

> **Quotient of Two Real Numbers**
>
> If a and b are real numbers and b is not 0, then
>
> $$a \div b = \frac{a}{b} = a \cdot \frac{1}{b}$$

In other words, the quotient of two real numbers is the product of the first number and the multiplicative inverse or reciprocal of the second number.

EXAMPLE 6 Use the definition of the quotient of two numbers to divide.

a. $-18 \div 3$ **b.** $\frac{-14}{-2}$ **c.** $\frac{20}{-4}$

Solution

a. $-18 \div 3 = -18 \cdot \frac{1}{3} = -6$ **b.** $\frac{-14}{-2} = -14 \cdot -\frac{1}{2} = 7$

c. $\frac{20}{-4} = 20 \cdot -\frac{1}{4} = -5$

PRACTICE
6   Use the definition of the quotient of two numbers to divide.

a. $\dfrac{16}{-2}$ **b.** $24 \div (-6)$ **c.** $\dfrac{-35}{-7}$

Since the quotient $a \div b$ can be written as the product $a \cdot \dfrac{1}{b}$, it follows that sign patterns for dividing two real numbers are the same as sign patterns for multiplying two real numbers.

> **Multiplying and Dividing Real Numbers**
>
> **1.** The product or quotient of two numbers with the *same* sign is a positive number.
> **2.** The product or quotient of two numbers with *different* signs is a negative number.

EXAMPLE 7   Divide.

a. $\dfrac{-24}{-4}$ **b.** $\dfrac{-36}{3}$ **c.** $\dfrac{2}{3} \div \left(-\dfrac{5}{4}\right)$ **d.** $-\dfrac{3}{2} \div 9$

Solution

a. $\dfrac{-24}{-4} = 6$ **b.** $\dfrac{-36}{3} = -12$ **c.** $\dfrac{2}{3} \div \left(-\dfrac{5}{4}\right) = \dfrac{2}{3} \cdot \left(-\dfrac{4}{5}\right) = -\dfrac{8}{15}$

d. $-\dfrac{3}{2} \div 9 = -\dfrac{3}{2} \cdot \dfrac{1}{9} = -\dfrac{3 \cdot 1}{2 \cdot 9} = -\dfrac{3 \cdot 1}{2 \cdot 3 \cdot 3} = -\dfrac{1}{6}$

PRACTICE
7   Divide.

a. $\dfrac{-18}{-6}$ **b.** $\dfrac{-48}{3}$ **c.** $\dfrac{3}{5} \div \left(-\dfrac{1}{2}\right)$ **d.** $-\dfrac{4}{9} \div 8$

✓ CONCEPT CHECK
What is wrong with the following calculation?

$$\dfrac{-36}{-9} = -4$$

The definition of the quotient of two real numbers does not allow for division by 0 because 0 does not have a multiplicative inverse. There is no number we can multiply 0 by to get 1. How then do we interpret $\dfrac{3}{0}$? We say that division by 0 is not allowed or not defined and that $\dfrac{3}{0}$ does not represent a real number. The denominator of a fraction can never be 0.

Can the numerator of a fraction be 0? Can we divide 0 by a number? Yes. For example,

$$\dfrac{0}{3} = 0 \cdot \dfrac{1}{3} = 0$$

In general, the quotient of 0 and any nonzero number is 0.

> **Zero as a Divisor or Dividend**
>
> **1.** The quotient of any nonzero real number and 0 is undefined. In symbols, if
> $a \neq 0, \dfrac{a}{0}$ is **undefined.**
>
> **2.** The quotient of 0 and any real number except 0 is 0. In symbols, if $a \neq 0, \dfrac{0}{a} = 0.$

Answer to Concept Check
$\dfrac{-36}{-9} = 4$

EXAMPLE 8 Perform the indicated operations.

a. $\dfrac{1}{0}$ b. $\dfrac{0}{-3}$ c. $\dfrac{0(-8)}{2}$

Solution

a. $\dfrac{1}{0}$ is undefined   b. $\dfrac{0}{-3} = 0$ c. $\dfrac{0(-8)}{2} = \dfrac{0}{2} = 0$

PRACTICE
8 Perform the indicated operations.

a. $\dfrac{0}{-2}$ b. $\dfrac{-4}{0}$ c. $\dfrac{-5}{6(0)}$

Notice that $\dfrac{12}{-2} = -6$, $-\dfrac{12}{2} = -6$, and $\dfrac{-12}{2} = -6$. This means that

$$\dfrac{12}{-2} = -\dfrac{12}{2} = \dfrac{-12}{2}$$

In words, a single negative sign in a fraction can be written in the denominator, in the numerator, or in front of the fraction without changing the value of the fraction. Thus,

$$\dfrac{1}{-7} = \dfrac{-1}{7} = -\dfrac{1}{7}$$

> In general, if a and b are real numbers, $b \neq 0$, then $\dfrac{a}{-b} = \dfrac{-a}{b} = -\dfrac{a}{b}$.

OBJECTIVE
4 Evaluating Expressions

Examples combining basic arithmetic operations along with the principles of order of operations help us review these concepts.

EXAMPLE 9 Simplify each expression.

a. $\dfrac{(-12)(-3) + 3}{-7 - (-2)}$ b. $\dfrac{2(-3)^2 - 20}{-5 + 4}$

Solution

a. First, simplify the numerator and denominator separately, then divide.

$$\dfrac{(-12)(-3) + 3}{-7 - (-2)} = \dfrac{36 + 3}{-7 + 2}$$
$$= \dfrac{39}{-5} \text{ or } -\dfrac{39}{5}$$

b. Simplify the numerator and denominator separately, then divide.

$$\dfrac{2(-3)^2 - 20}{-5 + 4} = \dfrac{2 \cdot 9 - 20}{-5 + 4} = \dfrac{18 - 20}{-5 + 4} = \dfrac{-2}{-1} = 2$$

PRACTICE
9 Simplify each expression.

a. $\dfrac{(-8)(-11) - 4}{-9 - (-4)}$ b. $\dfrac{3(-2)^3 - 9}{-6 + 3}$

Using what we have learned about multiplying and dividing real numbers, we continue to practice evaluating algebraic expressions.

EXAMPLE 10   If $x = -2$ and $y = -4$, evaluate each expression.

a. $5x - y$ **b.** $x^4 - y^2$ **c.** $\dfrac{3x}{2y}$

Solution

a. Replace x with -2 and y with -4 and simplify.

$$5x - y = 5(-2) - (-4) = -10 - (-4) = -10 + 4 = -6$$

b. Replace x with -2 and y with -4.

$$
\begin{aligned}
x^4 - y^2 &= (-2)^4 - (-4)^2 & \text{Substitute the given values for the variables.}\\
&= 16 - (16) & \text{Evaluate exponential expressions.}\\
&= 0 & \text{Subtract.}
\end{aligned}
$$

c. Replace x with -2 and y with -4 and simplify.

$$\frac{3x}{2y} = \frac{3(-2)}{2(-4)} = \frac{-6}{-8} = \frac{3}{4}$$

PRACTICE
10   If $x = -5$ and $y = -2$, evaluate each expression.

a. $7y - x$ **b.** $x^2 - y^3$ **c.** $\dfrac{2x}{3y}$

OBJECTIVE
5   Solving Applications That Involve Multiplying or Dividing Numbers

Many real-life problems involve multiplication and division of numbers.

EXAMPLE 11   Calculating a Total Golf Score

A professional golfer finished seven strokes under par (-7) for each of three days of a tournament. What was her total score for the tournament?

Solution   Although the key word is "total," since this is repeated addition of the same number, we multiply.

In words:	golfer's total score	=	number of days	·	score each day
	↓	↓	↓	↓	↓
Translate:	golfer's total	=	3	·	(−7)
		= −21			

Thus, the golfer's total score was -21, or 21 strokes under par.

PRACTICE
11   A card player had a score of -13 for each of four games. Find the total score.

Graphing Calculator Explorations

Entering Negative Numbers on a Scientific Calculator

To enter a negative number on a scientific calculator, find a key marked $\boxed{+/-}$. (On some calculators, this key is marked $\boxed{\text{CHS}}$ for "change sign.") To enter -8, for example, press the keys $\boxed{8}$ $\boxed{+/-}$. The display will read $\boxed{-8}$.

(Continued on next page)

Entering Negative Numbers on a Graphing Calculator

To enter a negative number on a graphing calculator, find a key marked $\boxed{(-)}$. Do not confuse this key with the key $\boxed{-}$, which is used for subtraction. To enter -8, for example, press the keys $\boxed{(-)}$ $\boxed{8}$. The display will read $\boxed{-8}$.

Operations with Real Numbers

To evaluate $-2(7 - 9) - 20$ on a calculator, press the keys

$\boxed{2}\boxed{+/-}\boxed{\times}\boxed{(}\boxed{(}\boxed{7}\boxed{-}\boxed{9}\boxed{)}\boxed{)}\boxed{-}\boxed{2}\boxed{0}\boxed{=}$ or

$\boxed{(-)}\boxed{2}\boxed{(}\boxed{(}\boxed{7}\boxed{-}\boxed{9}\boxed{)}\boxed{)}\boxed{-}\boxed{2}\boxed{0}\boxed{ENTER}$

The display will read $\boxed{-16}$ or $\boxed{\begin{array}{l} -2(7 - 9) - 20 \\ \hphantom{-2(7 - 9) - 2}-16 \end{array}}$.

Use a calculator to simplify each expression.

1. $-38(26 - 27)$
2. $-59(-8) + 1726$
3. $134 + 25(68 - 91)$
4. $45(32) - 8(218)$
5. $\dfrac{-50(294)}{175 - 265}$
6. $\dfrac{-444 - 444.8}{-181 - 324}$
7. $9^5 - 4550$
8. $5^8 - 6259$
9. $(-125)^2$ (Be careful.)
10. -125^2 (Be careful.)

Vocabulary, Readiness & Video Check

Use the choices below to fill in each blank.

positive   0   negative   undefined

1. If n is a real number, then $n \cdot 0 = $ _____ and $0 \cdot n = $ _____.

2. If n is a real number, but not 0, then $\dfrac{0}{n} = $ _____ and we say $\dfrac{n}{0}$ is _____.

3. The product of two negative numbers is a _____ number.

4. The quotient of two negative numbers is a _____ number.

5. The quotient of a positive number and a negative number is a _____ number.

6. The product of a positive number and a negative number is a _____ number.

7. The reciprocal of a positive number is a _____ number.

8. The opposite of a positive number is a _____ number.

Martin-Gay Interactive Videos

See Video 1.7

Watch the section lecture video and answer the following questions.

OBJECTIVE
1
9. Explain the significance of the use of parentheses when comparing Examples 6 and 7.

OBJECTIVE
2
10. In Example 9, why is the reciprocal equal to $\dfrac{3}{2}$ and not $-\dfrac{3}{2}$?

OBJECTIVE
3
11. Before Example 11, the sign rules for division of real numbers are discussed. Are the sign rules for division the same as for multiplication? Why or why not?

OBJECTIVE
4
12. In Example 17, the importance of placing the replacement values in parentheses when evaluating is emphasized. Why?

OBJECTIVE
5
13. In Example 18, explain why each loss of 4 yards is represented by -4 and not 4.

1.7 Exercise Set MyMathLab®

Multiply. See Examples 1 through 3.

1. $-6(4)$

2. $-8(5)$

3. $2(-1)$

4. $7(-4)$

5. $-5(-10)$

6. $-6(-11)$

7. $-3 \cdot 4$

8. $-2 \cdot 8$

9. $-7 \cdot 0$

10. $-6 \cdot 0$

11. $2(-9)$

12. $3(-5)$

13. $-\dfrac{1}{2}\left(-\dfrac{3}{5}\right)$

14. $-\dfrac{1}{8}\left(-\dfrac{1}{3}\right)$

15. $-\dfrac{3}{4}\left(-\dfrac{8}{9}\right)$

16. $-\dfrac{5}{6}\left(-\dfrac{3}{10}\right)$

17. $5(-1.4)$

18. $6(-2.5)$

19. $-0.2(-0.7)$

20. $-0.5(-0.3)$

21. $-10(80)$

22. $-20(60)$

23. $4(-7)$

24. $5(-9)$

25. $(-5)(-5)$

26. $(-7)(-7)$

27. $\dfrac{2}{3}\left(-\dfrac{4}{9}\right)$

28. $\dfrac{2}{7}\left(-\dfrac{2}{11}\right)$

29. $-11(11)$

30. $-12(12)$

31. $-\dfrac{20}{25}\left(\dfrac{5}{16}\right)$

32. $-\dfrac{25}{36}\left(\dfrac{6}{15}\right)$

33. $(-1)(2)(-3)(-5)$

34. $(-2)(-3)(-4)(-2)$

Perform the indicated operations. See Example 2.

35. $(-2)(5) - (-11)(3)$

36. $8(-3) - 4(-5)$

37. $(-6)(-1)(-2) - (-5)$

38. $20 - (-4)(3)(-2)$

Decide whether each statement is true or false.

39. The product of three negative integers is negative.

40. The product of three positive integers is positive.

41. The product of four negative integers is negative.

42. The product of four positive integers is positive.

Evaluate. See Example 4.

43. $(-2)^4$

44. -2^4

45. -1^5

46. $(-1)^5$

47. $(-5)^2$

48. -5^2

49. -7^2

50. $(-7)^2$

Find each reciprocal or multiplicative inverse. See Example 5.

51. 9

52. 100

53. $\dfrac{2}{3}$

54. $\dfrac{1}{7}$

55. -14

56. -8

57. $-\dfrac{3}{11}$

58. $-\dfrac{6}{13}$

59. 0.2

60. 1.5

61. $\dfrac{1}{-6.3}$

62. $\dfrac{1}{-8.9}$

Divide. See Examples 6 through 8.

63. $\dfrac{18}{-2}$

64. $\dfrac{20}{-10}$

65. $\dfrac{-16}{-4}$

66. $\dfrac{-18}{-6}$

67. $\dfrac{-48}{12}$

68. $\dfrac{-60}{5}$

69. $\dfrac{0}{-4}$

70. $\dfrac{0}{-9}$

71. $-\dfrac{15}{3}$

72. $-\dfrac{24}{8}$

73. $\dfrac{5}{0}$

74. $\dfrac{3}{0}$

75. $\dfrac{-12}{-4}$

76. $\dfrac{-45}{-9}$

77. $\dfrac{30}{-2}$

78. $\dfrac{14}{-2}$

79. $\dfrac{6}{7} \div \left(-\dfrac{1}{3}\right)$

80. $\dfrac{4}{5} \div \left(-\dfrac{1}{2}\right)$

81. $-\dfrac{5}{9} \div \left(-\dfrac{3}{4}\right)$

82. $-\dfrac{1}{10} \div \left(-\dfrac{8}{11}\right)$

83. $-\dfrac{4}{9} \div \dfrac{4}{9}$

84. $-\dfrac{5}{12} \div \dfrac{5}{12}$

MIXED PRACTICE

Simplify. See Examples 1 through 9.

85. $\dfrac{-9(-3)}{-6}$

86. $\dfrac{-6(-3)}{-4}$

87. $\dfrac{12}{9 - 12}$

88. $\dfrac{-15}{1 - 4}$

89. $\dfrac{-6^2 + 4}{-2}$

90. $\dfrac{3^2 + 4}{5}$

91. $\dfrac{8 + (-4)^2}{4 - 12}$

92. $\dfrac{6 + (-2)^2}{4 - 9}$

93. $\dfrac{22 + (3)(-2)}{-5 - 2}$

94. $\dfrac{-20 + (-4)(3)}{1 - 5}$

95. $\dfrac{-3 - 5^2}{2(-7)}$

96. $\dfrac{-2 - 4^2}{3(-6)}$

97. $\dfrac{6 - 2(-3)}{4 - 3(-2)}$

98. $\dfrac{8 - 3(-2)}{2 - 5(-4)}$

99. $\dfrac{-3 - 2(-9)}{-15 - 3(-4)}$

100. $\dfrac{-4 - 8(-2)}{-9 - 2(-3)}$

101. $\dfrac{|5 - 9| + |10 - 15|}{|2(-3)|}$

102. $\dfrac{|-3 + 6| + |-2 + 7|}{|-2 \cdot 2|}$

If $x = -5$ and $y = -3$, evaluate each expression. See Example 10.

103. $3x + 2y$

104. $4x + 5y$

105. $2x^2 - y^2$

106. $x^2 - 2y^2$

107. $x^3 + 3y$

108. $y^3 + 3x$

109. $\dfrac{2x - 5}{y - 2}$

110. $\dfrac{2y - 12}{x - 4}$

111. $\dfrac{-3 - y}{x - 4}$

112. $\dfrac{4 - 2x}{y + 3}$

TRANSLATING

Translate each phrase to an expression. Use x to represent "a number." See Example 11.

113. The product of −71 and a number

114. The quotient of −8 and a number

115. Subtract a number from −16.

116. The sum of a number and −12

117. −29 increased by a number

118. The difference of a number and −10

119. Divide a number by −33.

120. Multiply a number by −17.

Solve. See Example 11.

121. A football team lost four yards on each of three consecutive plays. Represent the total loss as a product of signed numbers and find the total loss.

122. Joe Norstrom lost $400 on each of seven consecutive days in the stock market. Represent his total loss as a product of signed numbers and find his total loss.

123. A deep-sea diver must move up or down in the water in short steps to keep from getting a physical condition called the "bends." Suppose a diver moves down from the surface in five steps of 20 feet each. Represent his total movement as a product of signed numbers and find the total depth.

124. A weather forecaster predicts that the temperature will drop five degrees each hour for the next six hours. Represent this drop as a product of signed numbers and find the total drop in temperature.

Decide whether the given number is a solution of the given equation.

125. Is 7 a solution of $-5x = -35$?

126. Is −4 a solution of $2x = x - 1$?

127. Is −20 a solution of $\frac{x}{10} = 2$?

128. Is −3 a solution of $\frac{45}{x} = -15$?

129. Is 5 a solution of $-3x - 5 = -20$?

130. Is −4 a solution of $2x + 4 = x + 8$?

CONCEPT EXTENSIONS

Study the bar graph below showing the average surface temperatures of planets. Use Exercises 131 and 132 to complete the planet temperatures on the graph. (Pluto is now classified as a dwarf planet.)

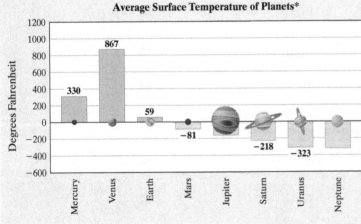

Average Surface Temperature of Planets*

*For some planets, the temperature given is the temperature where the atmosphere pressure equals 1 Earth atmosphere; data from *The World Almanac*

131. The surface temperature of Jupiter is twice the temperature of Mars. Find this temperature.

132. The surface temperature of Neptune is equal to the temperature of Mercury divided by −1. Find this temperature.

133. Explain why the product of an even number of negative numbers is a positive number.

134. If *a* and *b* are any real numbers, is the statement $a \cdot b = b \cdot a$ always true? Why or why not?

135. Find any real numbers that are their own reciprocal.

136. Explain why 0 has no reciprocal.

If q is a negative number, r is a negative number, and t is a positive number, determine whether each expression simplifies to a positive or negative number. If it is not possible to determine, state so.

137. $\frac{q}{r \cdot t}$

138. $q^2 \cdot r \cdot t$

139. $q + t$

140. $t + r$

141. $t(q + r)$

142. $r(q - t)$

Write each of the following as an expression and evaluate.

143. The sum of −2 and the quotient of −15 and 3

144. The sum of 1 and the product of −8 and −5

145. Twice the sum of −5 and −3

146. 7 subtracted from the quotient of 0 and 5

Properties of Real Numbers

OBJECTIVES

1   Use the Commutative and Associative Properties.

2   Use the Distributive Property.

3   Use the Identity and Inverse Properties.

OBJECTIVE

1   Using the Commutative and Associative Properties

In this section, we give names to properties of real numbers with which we are already familiar. Throughout this section, the variables a, b, and c represent real numbers.

We know that order does not matter when adding numbers. For example, we know that $7 + 5$ is the same as $5 + 7$. This property is given a special name—the **commutative property of addition.** We also know that order does not matter when multiplying numbers. For example, we know that $-5(6) = 6(-5)$. This property means that multiplication is commutative also and is called the **commutative property of multiplication.**

Commutative Properties

Addition: $a + b = b + a$

Multiplication: $a \cdot b = b \cdot a$

These properties state that the *order* in which any two real numbers are added or multiplied does not change their sum or product. For example, if we let $a = 3$ and $b = 5$, then the commutative properties guarantee that

$$3 + 5 = 5 + 3 \quad \text{and} \quad 3 \cdot 5 = 5 \cdot 3$$

> ▶ Helpful Hint
>
> Is subtraction also commutative? Try an example. Does $3 - 2 = 2 - 3$? **No!** The left side of this statement equals 1; the right side equals -1. There is no commutative property of subtraction. Similarly, there is no commutative property for division. For example, $10 \div 2$ does not equal $2 \div 10$.

EXAMPLE 1   Use a commutative property to complete each statement.

a. $x + 5 = $ _____

b. $3 \cdot x = $ _____

Solution

a. $x + 5 = 5 + x$ By the commutative property of addition

b. $3 \cdot x = x \cdot 3$ By the commutative property of multiplication

PRACTICE

1   Use a commutative property to complete each statement.

a. $x \cdot 8 = $ ___

b. $x + 17 = $ _____

✓CONCEPT CHECK

Which of the following pairs of actions are commutative?

a. "raking the leaves" and "bagging the leaves"

b. "putting on your left glove" and "putting on your right glove"

c. "putting on your coat" and "putting on your shirt"

d. "reading a novel" and "reading a newspaper"

Let's now discuss grouping numbers. We know that when we add three numbers, the way in which they are grouped or associated does not change their sum. For example, we know that $2 + (3 + 4) = 2 + 7 = 9$. This result is the same if we group the numbers differently. In other words, $(2 + 3) + 4 = 5 + 4 = 9$ also. Thus, ▶ $2 + (3 + 4) = (2 + 3) + 4$. This property is called the **associative property of addition.**

We also know that changing the grouping of numbers when multiplying does not change their product. For example, $2 \cdot (3 \cdot 4) = (2 \cdot 3) \cdot 4$ (check it). This is the **associative property of multiplication.**

> **Associative Properties**
> *Addition:* $(a + b) + c = a + (b + c)$
> *Multiplication:* $(a \cdot b) \cdot c = a \cdot (b \cdot c)$

These properties state that the way in which three numbers are *grouped* does not change their sum or their product.

EXAMPLE 2 Use an associative property to complete each statement.

a. $5 + (4 + 6) =$ _____

b. $(-1 \cdot 2) \cdot 5 =$ _____

Solution

a. $5 + (4 + 6) = (5 + 4) + 6$ By the associative property of addition

b. $(-1 \cdot 2) \cdot 5 = -1 \cdot (2 \cdot 5)$ By the associative property of multiplication   ☐

PRACTICE
2 Use an associative property to complete each statement.

a. $(2 + 9) + 7 =$ _____

b. $-4 \cdot (2 \cdot 7) =$ _____

> ▶ Helpful Hint
> Remember the difference between the commutative properties and the associative properties. The commutative properties have to do with the *order* of numbers, and the associative properties have to do with the *grouping* of numbers.

Let's now illustrate how these properties can help us simplify expressions.

EXAMPLE 3 Simplify each expression.

a. $10 + (x + 12)$

b. $-3(7x)$

Solution

a. $10 + (x + 12) = 10 + (12 + x)$ By the commutative property of addition
$\qquad\qquad\qquad = (10 + 12) + x$ By the associative property of addition
$\qquad\qquad\qquad = 22 + x$ Add.

b. $-3(7x) = (-3 \cdot 7)x$ By the associative property of multiplication
$\qquad\quad = -21x$ Multiply.   ☐

PRACTICE
3 Simplify each expression.

a. $(5 + x) + 9$

b. $5(-6x)$

OBJECTIVE
2 Using the Distributive Property

The **distributive property of multiplication over addition** is used repeatedly throughout algebra. It is useful because it allows us to write a product as a sum or a sum as a product.

We know that $7(2 + 4) = 7(6) = 42$. Compare that with $7(2) + 7(4) = 14 + 28 = 42$. Since both original expressions equal 42, they must equal each other, or

$$7(2 + 4) = 7(2) + 7(4)$$

This is an example of the distributive property. The product on the left side of the equal sign is equal to the sum on the right side. We can think of the 7 as being distributed to each number inside the parentheses.

Distributive Property of Multiplication Over Addition

$$a(b + c) = ab + ac$$

Since multiplication is commutative, this property can also be written as

$$(b + c)a = ba + ca$$

The distributive property can also be extended to more than two numbers inside the parentheses. For example,

$$3(x + y + z) = 3(x) + 3(y) + 3(z)$$
$$= 3x + 3y + 3z$$

Since we define subtraction in terms of addition, the distributive property is also true for subtraction. For example

$$2(x - y) = 2(x) - 2(y)$$
$$= 2x - 2y$$

EXAMPLE 4   Use the distributive property to write each expression without parentheses. Then simplify if possible.

a. $2(x + y)$ **b.** $-5(-3 + 2z)$ **c.** $5(x + 3y - z)$

d. $-1(2 - y)$ **e.** $-(3 + x - w)$ **f.** $\frac{1}{2}(6x + 14) + 10$

Solution

a. $2(x + y) = 2 \cdot x + 2 \cdot y$
$$= 2x + 2y$$

b. $-5(-3 + 2z) = -5(-3) + (-5)(2z)$
$$= 15 - 10z$$

c. $5(x + 3y - z) = 5(x) + 5(3y) - 5(z)$
$$= 5x + 15y - 5z$$

d. $-1(2 - y) = (-1)(2) - (-1)(y)$
$$= -2 + y$$

e. $-(3 + x - w) = -1(3 + x - w)$
$$= (-1)(3) + (-1)(x) - (-1)(w)$$
$$= -3 - x + w$$

> ▶ Helpful Hint
> Notice in part **(e)** that $-(3 + x - w)$ is first rewritten as $-1(3 + x - w)$.

f. $\frac{1}{2}(6x + 14) + 10 = \frac{1}{2}(6x) + \frac{1}{2}(14) + 10$ Apply the distributive property.
$$= 3x + 7 + 10$$ Multiply.
$$= 3x + 17$$ Add.

4 Use the distributive property to write each expression without parentheses. Then simplify if possible.

a. $5(x - y)$

b. $-6(4 + 2t)$

c. $2(3x - 4y - z)$

d. $(3 - y) \cdot (-1)$

e. $-(x - 7 + 2s)$

f. $\frac{1}{2}(2x + 4) + 9$

We can use the distributive property in reverse to write a sum as a product.

EXAMPLE 5 Use the distributive property to write each sum as a product.

a. $8 \cdot 2 + 8 \cdot x$

b. $7s + 7t$

Solution

a. $8 \cdot 2 + 8 \cdot x = 8(2 + x)$

b. $7s + 7t = 7(s + t)$

5 Use the distributive property to write each sum as a product.

a. $5 \cdot w + 5 \cdot 3$

b. $9w + 9z$

3 Using the Identity and Inverse Properties

Next, we look at the **identity properties.**

The number 0 is called the identity for addition because when 0 is added to any real number, the result is the same real number. In other words, the *identity* of the real number is not changed.

The number 1 is called the identity for multiplication because when a real number is multiplied by 1, the result is the same real number. In other words, the *identity* of the real number is not changed.

Identities for Addition and Multiplication

0 is the identity element for addition.

$$a + 0 = a \quad \text{and} \quad 0 + a = a$$

1 is the identity element for multiplication.

$$a \cdot 1 = a \quad \text{and} \quad 1 \cdot a = a$$

Notice that 0 is the *only* number that can be added to any real number with the result that the sum is the same real number. Also, 1 is the *only* number that can be multiplied by any real number with the result that the product is the same real number.

Additive inverses or **opposites** were introduced in Section 1.5. Two numbers are called additive inverses or opposites if their sum is 0. The additive inverse or opposite of 6 is -6 because $6 + (-6) = 0$. The additive inverse or opposite of -5 is 5 because $-5 + 5 = 0$.

Reciprocals or **multiplicative inverses** were introduced in Section 1.3. Two nonzero numbers are called reciprocals or multiplicative inverses if their product is 1. The reciprocal or multiplicative inverse of $\frac{2}{3}$ is $\frac{3}{2}$ because $\frac{2}{3} \cdot \frac{3}{2} = 1$. Likewise, the reciprocal of -5 is $-\frac{1}{5}$ because $-5\left(-\frac{1}{5}\right) = 1$.

✓CONCEPT CHECK

Which of the following, $1, -\frac{10}{3}, \frac{3}{10}, 0, \frac{10}{3}, -\frac{3}{10}$, is the

a. opposite of $-\frac{3}{10}$?

b. reciprocal of $-\frac{3}{10}$?

Additive or Multiplicative Inverses

The numbers a and $-a$ are additive inverses or opposites of each other because their sum is 0; that is,

$$a + (-a) = 0$$

The numbers b and $\frac{1}{b}$ (for $b \neq 0$) are reciprocals or multiplicative inverses of each other because their product is 1; that is,

$$b \cdot \frac{1}{b} = 1$$

EXAMPLE 6   Name the property or properties illustrated by each true statement.

Solution

a. $3 \cdot y = y \cdot 3$ Commutative property of multiplication (order changed)

b. $(x + 7) + 9 = x + (7 + 9)$ Associative property of addition (grouping changed)

c. $(b + 0) + 3 = b + 3$ Identity element for addition

d. $0.2 \cdot (z \cdot 5) = 0.2 \cdot (5 \cdot z)$ Commutative property of multiplication (order changed)

e. $-2 \cdot \left(-\frac{1}{2}\right) = 1$ Multiplicative inverse property

f. $-2 + 2 = 0$ Additive inverse property

g. $-6 \cdot (y \cdot 2) = (-6 \cdot 2) \cdot y$ Commutative and associative properties of multiplication (order and grouping changed) ☐

PRACTICE

6   Name the property or properties illustrated by each true statement.

a. $(7 \cdot 3x) \cdot 4 = (3x \cdot 7) \cdot 4$ Commutative property of multiplication

b. $6 + (3 + y) = (6 + 3) + y$ Associative property of addition

c. $8 + (t + 0) = 8 + t$ Identity element for addition

d. $-\frac{3}{4} \cdot \left(-\frac{4}{3}\right) = 1$ Multiplicative inverse property

e. $(2 + x) + 5 = 5 + (2 + x)$ Commutative property of addition

f. $3 + (-3) = 0$ Additive inverse property

g. $(-3b) \cdot 7 = (-3 \cdot 7) \cdot b$ Commutative and associative properties of multiplication

Answers to Concept Check:

a. $\frac{3}{10}$ **b.** $-\frac{10}{3}$

Vocabulary, Readiness & Video Check

Use the choices below to fill in each blank.

distributive property   associative property of multiplication   commutative property of addition
opposites or additive inverses   associative property of addition
reciprocals or multiplicative inverses   commutative property of multiplication

1. $x + 5 = 5 + x$ is a true statement by the _____.

2. $x \cdot 5 = 5 \cdot x$ is a true statement by the _____.

3. $3(y + 6) = 3 \cdot y + 3 \cdot 6$ is true by the _____.

4. $2 \cdot (x \cdot y) = (2 \cdot x) \cdot y$ is a true statement by the _____.

5. $x + (7 + y) = (x + 7) + y$ is a true statement by the _____.

6. The numbers $-\dfrac{2}{3}$ and $-\dfrac{3}{2}$ are called _____.

7. The numbers $-\dfrac{2}{3}$ and $\dfrac{2}{3}$ are called _____.

Martin-Gay Interactive Videos

See Video 1.8

Watch the section lecture video and answer the following questions.

OBJECTIVE 1

8. The commutative properties are discussed in ▣ Examples 1 and 2 and the associative properties are discussed in ▣ Examples 3–7. What's the one word used again and again to describe the commutative property? The associative property?

OBJECTIVE 2

9. In ▣ Example 10, what point is made about the term 2?

OBJECTIVE 3

10. Complete these statements based on the lecture given before ▣ Example 12.

• The identify element for addition is ____ because if we add ____ to any real number, the result is that real number.

• The identify element for multiplication is ____ because any real number times ____ gives a result of that original real number.

1.8 Exercise Set   MyMathLab®

Use a commutative property to complete each statement. See Example 1.

1. $x + 16 =$ _____
2. $4 + y =$ _____
3. $-4 \cdot y =$ _____
4. $-2 \cdot x =$ _____
5. $xy =$ _____
6. $ab =$ _____
7. $2x + 13 =$ _____
8. $19 + 3y =$ _____

Use an associative property to complete each statement. See Example 2.

9. $(xy) \cdot z =$ _____
10. $3 \cdot (xy) =$ _____
11. $2 + (a + b) =$ _____
12. $(y + 4) + z =$ _____
13. $4 \cdot (ab) =$ _____
14. $(-3y) \cdot z =$ _____
15. $(a + b) + c =$ _____
16. $6 + (r + s) =$ _____

Use the commutative and associative properties to simplify each expression. See Example 3.

17. $8 + (9 + b)$
18. $(r + 3) + 11$
19. $4(6y)$
20. $2(42x)$
21. $\dfrac{1}{5}(5y)$
22. $\dfrac{1}{8}(8z)$
23. $(13 + a) + 13$
24. $7 + (x + 4)$
25. $-9(8x)$
26. $-3(12y)$
27. $\dfrac{3}{4}\left(\dfrac{4}{3}s\right)$
28. $\dfrac{2}{7}\left(\dfrac{7}{2}r\right)$
29. $\dfrac{2}{3} + \left(\dfrac{4}{3} + x\right)$
30. $\dfrac{7}{9} + \left(\dfrac{2}{9} + y\right)$

Use the distributive property to write each expression without parentheses. Then simplify the result. See Example 4.

31. $4(x + y)$ **32.** $7(a + b)$

33. $9(x - 6)$ **34.** $11(y - 4)$

35. $2(3x + 5)$ **36.** $5(7 + 8y)$

37. $7(4x - 3)$ **38.** $3(8x - 1)$

39. $3(6 + x)$ **40.** $2(x + 5)$

41. $-2(y - z)$ **42.** $-3(z - y)$

43. $-7(3y + 5)$

44. $-5(2r + 11)$

45. $5(x + 4m + 2)$

46. $8(3y + z - 6)$

47. $-4(1 - 2m + n)$

48. $-4(4 + 2p + 5q)$

49. $-(5x + 2)$

50. $-(9r + 5)$

51. $-(r - 3 - 7p)$

52. $-(q - 2 + 6r)$

53. $\frac{1}{2}(6x + 8)$

54. $\frac{1}{4}(4x - 2)$

55. $-\frac{1}{3}(3x - 9y)$

56. $-\frac{1}{5}(10a - 25b)$

57. $3(2r + 5) - 7$

58. $10(4s + 6) - 40$

59. $-9(4x + 8) + 2$

60. $-11(5x + 3) + 10$

61. $-4(4x + 5) - 5$

62. $-6(2x + 1) - 1$

Use the distributive property to write each sum as a product. See Example 5.

63. $4 \cdot 1 + 4 \cdot y$ **64.** $14 \cdot z + 14 \cdot 5$

65. $11x + 11y$ **66.** $9a + 9b$

67. $(-1) \cdot 5 + (-1) \cdot x$ **68.** $(-3)a + (-3)b$

69. $30a + 30b$ **70.** $25x + 25y$

Name the properties illustrated by each true statement. See Example 6.

71. $3 \cdot 5 = 5 \cdot 3$

72. $4(3 + 8) = 4 \cdot 3 + 4 \cdot 8$

73. $2 + (x + 5) = (2 + x) + 5$

74. $(x + 9) + 3 = (9 + x) + 3$

75. $9(3 + 7) = 9 \cdot 3 + 9 \cdot 7$

76. $1 \cdot 9 = 9$

77. $(4 \cdot y) \cdot 9 = 4 \cdot (y \cdot 9)$

78. $6 \cdot \frac{1}{6} = 1$

79. $0 + 6 = 6$

80. $(a + 9) + 6 = a + (9 + 6)$

81. $-4(y + 7) = -4 \cdot y + (-4) \cdot 7$

82. $(11 + r) + 8 = (r + 11) + 8$

83. $-4 \cdot (8 \cdot 3) = (8 \cdot -4) \cdot 3$

84. $r + 0 = r$

CONCEPT EXTENSIONS

Fill in the table with the opposite (additive inverse), and the reciprocal (multiplicative inverse). Assume that the value of each expression is not 0.

	Expression	*Opposite*	*Reciprocal*
85.	8		
86.	$-\dfrac{2}{3}$		
87.	x		
88.	$4y$		
89.			$\dfrac{1}{2x}$
90.		$7x$	

Decide whether each statement is true or false. See the second Concept Check in this section.

91. The opposite of $-\dfrac{a}{2}$ is $-\dfrac{2}{a}$.

92. The reciprocal of $-\dfrac{a}{2}$ is $\dfrac{a}{2}$.

Determine which pairs of actions are commutative. See the first Concept Check in this section.

93. "taking a test" and "studying for the test"

94. "putting on your shoes" and "putting on your socks"

95. "putting on your left shoe" and "putting on your right shoe"

96. "reading the sports section" and "reading the comics section"

97. "mowing the lawn" and "trimming the hedges"

98. "baking a cake" and "eating the cake"

99. "dialing a number" and "turning on the cell phone"

100. "feeding the dog" and "feeding the cat"

Name the property illustrated by each step.

101. a. $\triangle + (\square + \bigcirc) = (\square + \bigcirc) + \triangle$

    b. $= (\bigcirc + \square) + \triangle$

    c. $= \bigcirc + (\square + \triangle)$

102. a. $(x + y) + z = x + (y + z)$
  b. $\qquad = (y + z) + x$
  c. $\qquad = (z + y) + x$

103. Explain why 0 is called the identity element for addition.

104. Explain why 1 is called the identity element for multiplication.

105. Write an example that shows that division is not commutative.

106. Write an example that shows that subtraction is not commutative.

Chapter 1 Vocabulary Check

Fill in each blank with one of the words or phrases listed below.

set	inequality symbols	opposites	absolute value	numerator
denominator	grouping symbols	exponent	base	reciprocals
variable	equation	solution		

1. The symbols $\neq$, $<$, and $>$ are called _____.
2. A mathematical statement that two expressions are equal is called a(n) _____.
3. The _____ of a number is the distance between that number and 0 on the number line.
4. A symbol used to represent a number is called a(n) _____.
5. Two numbers that are the same distance from 0 but lie on opposite sides of 0 are called _____.
6. The number in a fraction above the fraction bar is called the _____.
7. A(n) _____ of an equation is a value for the variable that makes the equation a true statement.
8. Two numbers whose product is 1 are called _____.
9. In 2^3, the 2 is called the _____ and the 3 is called the _____.
10. The number in a fraction below the fraction bar is called the _____.
11. Parentheses and brackets are examples of _____.
12. A(n) _____ is a collection of objects.

Chapter 1 Highlights

DEFINITIONS AND CONCEPTS	EXAMPLES
Section 1.2 Symbols and Sets of Numbers	
A **set** is a collection of objects, called **elements**, enclosed in braces.	$\{a, c, e\}$
Natural Numbers: $\{1, 2, 3, 4, \dots\}$ **Whole Numbers:** $\{0, 1, 2, 3, 4, \dots\}$	Given the set $\left\{-3.4, \sqrt{3}, 0, \frac{2}{3}, 5, -4\right\}$, list the numbers that belong to the set of
Integers: $\{\dots, -3, -2, -1, 0, 1, 2, 3, \dots\}$	Natural numbers: 5 Whole numbers: 0, 5 Integers: $-4, 0, 5$
Rational Numbers: {real numbers that can be expressed as a quotient of integers}	
Irrational Numbers: {real numbers that cannot be expressed as a quotient of integers}	Rational numbers: $-4, -3.4, 0, \frac{2}{3}, 5$ Irrational Numbers: $\sqrt{3}$
Real Numbers: {all numbers that correspond to a point on the number line}	Real numbers: $-4, -3.4, 0, \frac{2}{3}, \sqrt{3}, 5$

DEFINITIONS AND CONCEPTS	EXAMPLES

Section 1.2   Symbols and Sets of Numbers (continued)

A line used to picture numbers is called a **number line.**

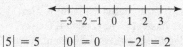

The **absolute value** of a real number a, denoted by $|a|$, is the distance between a and 0 on the number line.

$$|5| = 5 \qquad |0| = 0 \qquad |-2| = 2$$

Symbols: $=$ is equal to

$\neq$ is not equal to

$>$ is greater than

$<$ is less than

$\leq$ is less than or equal to

$\geq$ is greater than or equal to

$-7 = -7$

$3 \neq -3$

$4 > 1$

$1 < 4$

$6 \leq 6$

$18 \geq -\dfrac{1}{3}$

Order Property for Real Numbers

For any two real numbers a and b, a is less than b if a is to the left of b on a number line.

$$-3 < 0 \qquad 0 > -3 \qquad 0 < 2.5 \qquad 2.5 > 0$$

Section 1.3   Fractions and Mixed Numbers

A quotient of two integers is called a **fraction.** The **numerator** of a fraction is the top number. The **denominator** of a fraction is the bottom number.

$\dfrac{13}{17}$ $\leftarrow$ numerator
$\phantom{\dfrac{13}{17}}$ $\leftarrow$ denominator

If $a \cdot b = c$, then a and b are **factors** and c is the **product.**

$$\underset{\underset{\text{factor}}{\downarrow}}{7} \quad \cdot \quad \underset{\underset{\text{factor}}{\downarrow}}{9} \quad = \quad \underset{\underset{\text{product}}{\downarrow}}{63}$$

A fraction is in **lowest terms** or **simplest form** when the numerator and the denominator have no factors in common other than 1.

$\dfrac{13}{17}$ is in simplest form.

To write a fraction in simplest form, factor the numerator and the denominator; then apply the fundamental principle.

Write in simplest form.

$$\frac{6}{14} = \frac{2 \cdot 3}{2 \cdot 7} = \frac{3}{7}$$

Two fractions are **reciprocals** if their product is 1. The reciprocal of $\dfrac{a}{b}$ is $\dfrac{b}{a}$.

The reciprocal of $\dfrac{6}{25}$ is $\dfrac{25}{6}$.

To multiply fractions, numerator times numerator is the numerator of the product and denominator times denominator is the denominator of the product.

Perform the indicated operations.

$$\frac{2}{5} \cdot \frac{3}{7} = \frac{6}{35}$$

To divide fractions, multiply the first fraction by the reciprocal of the second fraction.

$$\frac{5}{9} \div \frac{2}{7} = \frac{5}{9} \cdot \frac{7}{2} = \frac{35}{18}$$

To add fractions with the same denominator, add the numerators and place the sum over the common denominator.

$$\frac{5}{11} + \frac{3}{11} = \frac{8}{11}$$

To subtract fractions with the same denominator, subtract the numerators and place the difference over the common denominator.

$$\frac{13}{15} - \frac{3}{15} = \frac{10}{15} = \frac{2}{3}$$

Fractions that represent the same quantity are called **equivalent fractions.**

$$\frac{1}{5} = \frac{1 \cdot 4}{5 \cdot 4} = \frac{4}{20}$$

$\dfrac{1}{5}$ and $\dfrac{4}{20}$ are equivalent fractions.

DEFINITIONS AND CONCEPTS	EXAMPLES

Section 1.4 Exponents, Order of Operations, Variable Expressions, and Equations

The expression a^n is an **exponential expression.** The number a is called the **base;** it is the repeated factor. The number n is called the **exponent;** it is the number of times that the base is a factor.

$$4^3 = 4 \cdot 4 \cdot 4 = 64$$
$$7^2 = 7 \cdot 7 = 49$$

Order of Operations

Simplify expressions in the following order. If grouping symbols are present, simplify expressions within those first, starting with the innermost set. Also, simplify the numerator and the denominator of a fraction separately.

$$\frac{8^2 + 5(7-3)}{3 \cdot 7} = \frac{8^2 + 5(4)}{21}$$
$$= \frac{64 + 5(4)}{21}$$
$$= \frac{64 + 20}{21}$$
$$= \frac{84}{21}$$
$$= 4$$

1. Simplify exponential expressions.
2. Multiply or divide in order from left to right.
3. Add or subtract in order from left to right.

A symbol used to represent a number is called a **variable.**

Examples of variables are:
$$q, x, z$$

An **algebraic expression** is a collection of numbers, variables, operation symbols, and grouping symbols.

Examples of algebraic expressions are:
$$5x, 2(y-6), \frac{q^2 - 3q + 1}{6}$$

To evaluate an algebraic expression containing a variable, substitute a given number for the variable and simplify.

Evaluate $x^2 - y^2$ if $x = 5$ and $y = 3$.
$$x^2 - y^2 = (5)^2 - 3^2$$
$$= 25 - 9$$
$$= 16$$

A mathematical statement that two expressions are equal is called an **equation.**

Examples of equations are:
$$3x - 9 = 20$$
$$A = \pi r^2$$

A **solution** of an equation is a value for the variable that makes the equation a true statement.

Determine whether 4 is a solution of $5x + 7 = 27$.
$$5x + 7 = 27$$
$$5(4) + 7 \stackrel{?}{=} 27$$
$$20 + 7 \stackrel{?}{=} 27$$
$$27 = 27 \quad \text{True}$$
4 is a solution.

Section 1.5 Adding Real Numbers

To Add Two Numbers with the Same Sign

1. Add their absolute values.
2. Use their common sign as the sign of the sum.

Add.
$$10 + 7 = 17$$
$$-3 + (-8) = -11$$

To Add Two Numbers with Different Signs

1. Subtract their absolute values.
2. Use the sign of the number whose absolute value is larger as the sign of the sum.

$$-25 + 5 = -20$$
$$14 + (-9) = 5$$

DEFINITIONS AND CONCEPTS	EXAMPLES

Section 1.5 Adding Real Numbers (continued)

Two numbers that are the same distance from 0 but lie on opposite sides of 0 are called **opposites** or **additive inverses**. The opposite of a number a is denoted by $-a$.

The sum of a number a and its opposite, $-a$, is 0.

$$a + (-a) = 0$$

If a is a number, then $-(-a) = a$.

The opposite of -7 is 7.
The opposite of 123 is -123.

$$-4 + 4 = 0$$
$$12 + (-12) = 0$$
$$-(-8) = 8$$
$$-(-14) = 14$$

Section 1.6 Subtracting Real Numbers

To subtract two numbers a and b, add the first number a to the opposite of the second number b.

$$a - b = a + (-b)$$

Subtract.

$$3 - (-44) = 3 + 44 = 47$$
$$-5 - 22 = -5 + (-22) = -27$$
$$-30 - (-30) = -30 + 30 = 0$$

Section 1.7 Multiplying and Dividing Real Numbers

Quotient of two real numbers

$$\frac{a}{b} = a \cdot \frac{1}{b}$$

Multiplying and Dividing Real Numbers

The product or quotient of two numbers with the same sign is a positive number. The product or quotient of two numbers with different signs is a negative number.

Multiply or divide.

$$\frac{42}{2} = 42 \cdot \frac{1}{2} = 21$$

$$7 \cdot 8 = 56 \quad -7 \cdot (-8) = 56$$
$$-2 \cdot 4 = -8 \quad 2 \cdot (-4) = -8$$
$$\frac{90}{10} = 9 \quad \frac{-90}{-10} = 9$$
$$\frac{42}{-6} = -7 \quad \frac{-42}{6} = -7$$

Products and Quotients Involving Zero

The product of 0 and any number is 0.

$$b \cdot 0 = 0 \quad \text{and} \quad 0 \cdot b = 0$$

The quotient of a nonzero number and 0 is undefined.

$$\frac{b}{0} \text{ is undefined.}$$

The quotient of 0 and any nonzero number is 0.

$$\frac{0}{b} = 0$$

$$-4 \cdot 0 = 0 \quad 0 \cdot \left(-\frac{3}{4}\right) = 0$$

$$\frac{-85}{0} \text{ is undefined.}$$

$$\frac{0}{18} = 0 \quad \frac{0}{-47} = 0$$

Section 1.8 Properties of Real Numbers

Commutative Properties

Addition: $a + b = b + a$
Multiplication: $a \cdot b = b \cdot a$

Associative Properties

Addition: $(a + b) + c = a + (b + c)$
Multiplication: $(a \cdot b) \cdot c = a \cdot (b \cdot c)$

$$3 + (-7) = -7 + 3$$
$$-8 \cdot 5 = 5 \cdot (-8)$$

$$(5 + 10) + 20 = 5 + (10 + 20)$$
$$(-3 \cdot 2) \cdot 11 = -3 \cdot (2 \cdot 11)$$

(continued)

DEFINITIONS AND CONCEPTS	EXAMPLES
Section 1.8 Properties of Real Numbers (continued)	

Two numbers whose product is 1 are called **multiplicative inverses** or **reciprocals.** The reciprocal of a nonzero number a is $\frac{1}{a}$ because $a \cdot \frac{1}{a} = 1$.

The reciprocal of 3 is $\frac{1}{3}$.

The reciprocal of $-\frac{2}{5}$ is $-\frac{5}{2}$.

Distributive Property $\quad a(b + c) = a \cdot b + a \cdot c$

$$5(6 + 10) = 5 \cdot 6 + 5 \cdot 10$$
$$-2(3 + x) = -2 \cdot 3 + (-2)(x)$$

Identities $\quad a + 0 = a \qquad 0 + a = a$

$\qquad\qquad\quad a \cdot 1 = a \qquad 1 \cdot a = a$

$$5 + 0 = 5 \qquad 0 + (-2) = -2$$
$$-14 \cdot 1 = -14 \qquad 1 \cdot 27 = 27$$

Inverses

Additive or opposite: $\quad a + (-a) = 0$

$$7 + (-7) = 0$$

Multiplicative or reciprocal: $\quad b \cdot \frac{1}{b} = 1$

$$3 \cdot \frac{1}{3} = 1$$

Chapter 1 Review

(1.2) *Insert* $<, >,$ *or* $=$ *in the appropriate space to make the following statements true.*

1. 8   10

2. 7   2

3. -4 -5

4. $\frac{12}{2}$ -8

5. $|-7|$ $|-8|$

6. $|-9|$ -9

7. $-|-1|$ -1

8. $|-14|$ $-(-14)$

9. 1.2   1.02

10. $-\frac{3}{2}$ $-\frac{3}{4}$

TRANSLATING

Translate each statement into symbols.

11. Four is greater than or equal to negative three.

12. Six is not equal to five.

13. 0.03 is less than 0.3.

14. New York City has 155 museums and 400 art galleries. Write an inequality comparing the numbers 155 and 400. (*Source: Absolute Trivia.com*)

Given the following sets of numbers, list the numbers in each set that also belong to the set of:

a. Natural numbers

b. Whole numbers

c. Integers

d. Rational numbers

e. Irrational numbers

f. Real numbers

15. $\left\{ -6, 0, 1, 1\frac{1}{2}, 3, \pi, 9.62 \right\}$

16. $\left\{ -3, -1.6, 2, 5, \frac{11}{2}, 15.1, \sqrt{5}, 2\pi \right\}$

The following chart shows the gains and losses in dollars of Density Oil and Gas stock for a particular week.

Day	Gain or Loss in Dollars
Monday	$+1$
Tuesday	-2
Wednesday	$+5$
Thursday	$+1$
Friday	-4

17. Which day showed the greatest loss?

18. Which day showed the greatest gain?

(1.3) *Write the number as a product of prime factors.*

19. 36

20. 120

Perform the indicated operations. Write results in lowest terms.

21. $\frac{8}{15} \cdot \frac{27}{30}$

22. $\frac{7}{8} \div \frac{21}{32}$

23. $\frac{7}{15} + \frac{5}{6}$

24. $\frac{3}{4} - \frac{3}{20}$

25. $2\frac{3}{4} + 6\frac{5}{8}$

26. $7\frac{1}{6} - 2\frac{2}{3}$

27. $5 \div \frac{1}{3}$

28. $2 \cdot 8\frac{3}{4}$

Each circle represents a whole, or 1. Determine the unknown part of the circle.

29.

30.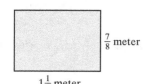

Find the area and the perimeter of each figure.

31. **△ 32.**

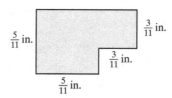

$\frac{7}{8}$ meter

$1\frac{1}{3}$ meter

$\frac{5}{11}$ in. $\frac{3}{11}$ in.

$\frac{3}{11}$ in.

$\frac{5}{11}$ in.

Octuplets were born in the U.S. in 2009. The following chart gives the octuplets' birthweights. The babies are listed in order of birth.

Baby	Gender	Birthweight (pounds)
Baby A	boy	$2\frac{1}{2}$
Baby B	girl	$2\frac{1}{8}$
Baby C	boy	$3\frac{1}{16}$
Baby D	girl	$2\frac{3}{16}$
Baby E	boy	$1\frac{3}{4}$
Baby F	boy	$2\frac{9}{16}$
Baby G	boy	$1\frac{13}{16}$
Baby H	boy	$2\frac{7}{16}$

33. What was the total weight of the boy octuplets?

34. What was the total weight of the girl octuplets?

35. Find the combined weight of all eight octuplets.

36. Which baby weighed the most?

37. Which baby weighed the least?

38. How much more did the heaviest baby weigh than the lightest baby?

(1.4) Choose the correct answer for each statement.

39. The expression $6 \cdot 3^2 + 2 \cdot 8$ simplifies to

   a. -52 **b.** 448 **c.** 70 **d.** 64

40. The expression $68 - 5 \cdot 2^3$ simplifies to

   a. -232 **b.** 28 **c.** 38 **d.** 504

Simplify each expression.

41. $\left(\frac{2}{7}\right)^2$ **42.** $\left(\frac{3}{4}\right)^3$

43. $3(1 + 2\cdot5) + 4$ **44.** $8 + 3(2\cdot6 - 1)$

45. $\dfrac{4 + |6 - 2| + 8^2}{4 + 6\cdot4}$ **46.** $5[3(2 + 5) - 5]$

TRANSLATING

Translate each word statement to symbols.

47. The difference of twenty and twelve is equal to the product of two and four.

48. The quotient of nine and two is greater than negative five.

Evaluate each expression if $x = 6$, $y = 2$, and $z = 8$.

49. $2x + 3y$ **50.** $x(y + 2z)$

51. $\dfrac{x}{y} + \dfrac{z}{2y}$ **52.** $x^2 - 3y^2$

△ 53. The expression $180 - a - b$ represents the measure of the unknown angle of the given triangle. Replace a with 37 and b with 80 to find the measure of the unknown angle.

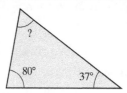

△ 54. The expression $360 - a - b - c$ represents the measure of the unknown angle of the given quadrilateral. Replace a with 93, b with 80, and c with 82 to find the measure of the unknown angle.

Decide whether the given number is a solution to the given equation.

55. Is $x = 3$ a solution of $7x - 3 = 18$?

56. Is $x = 1$ a solution of $3x^2 + 4 = x - 1$?

(1.5) Find the additive inverse or the opposite.

57. -9 **58.** $\dfrac{2}{3}$

59. $|-2|$ **60.** $-|-7|$

Find the following sums.

61. $-15 + 4$ **62.** $-6 + (-11)$

63. $\dfrac{1}{16} + \left(-\dfrac{1}{4}\right)$ **64.** $-8 + |-3|$

65. $-4.6 + (-9.3)$ **66.** $-2.8 + 6.7$

(1.6) *Perform the indicated operations.*

67. $6 - 20$

68. $-3.1 - 8.4$

69. $-6 - (-11)$

70. $4 - 15$

71. $-21 - 16 + 3(8 - 2)$

72. $\dfrac{11 - (-9) + 6(8 - 2)}{2 + 3 \cdot 4}$

Evaluate each expression for $x = 3$, $y = -6$, and $z = -9$. Then choose the correct evaluation.

73. $2x^2 - y + z$

    a. 15   **b.** 3   **c.** 27   **d.** -3

74. $\dfrac{|y - 4x|}{2x}$

    a. 3   **b.** 1   **c.** -1 **d.** -3

75. At the beginning of the week, the price of Density Oil and Gas stock from Exercises 17 and 18 is $50 per share. Find the price of a share of stock at the end of the week.

76. Find the price of a share of stock by the end of the day on Wednesday.

(1.7) *Find the multiplicative inverse or reciprocal.*

77. -6

78. $\dfrac{3}{5}$

Simplify each expression.

79. $6(-8)$

80. $(-2)(-14)$

81. $\dfrac{-18}{-6}$

82. $\dfrac{42}{-3}$

83. $\dfrac{4(-3) + (-8)}{2 + (-2)}$

84. $\dfrac{3(-2)^2 - 5}{-14}$

85. $\dfrac{-6}{0}$

86. $\dfrac{0}{-2}$

87. $-4^2 - (-3 + 5) \div (-1) \cdot 2$

88. $-5^2 - (2 - 20) \div (-3) \cdot 3$

If $x = -5$ and $y = -2$, evaluate each expression.

89. $x^2 - y^4$

90. $x^2 - y^3$

TRANSLATING

Translate each phrase to an expression. Use x to represent a number.

91. The product of -7 and a number

92. The quotient of a number and -13

93. Subtract a number from -20

94. The sum of -1 and a number

(1.8) *Name the property illustrated.*

95. $-6 + 5 = 5 + (-6)$

96. $6 \cdot 1 = 6$

97. $3(8 - 5) = 3 \cdot 8 - 3 \cdot (5)$

98. $4 + (-4) = 0$

99. $2 + (3 + 9) = (2 + 3) + 9$

100. $2 \cdot 8 = 8 \cdot 2$

101. $6(8 + 5) = 6 \cdot 8 + 6 \cdot 5$

102. $(3 \cdot 8) \cdot 4 = 3 \cdot (8 \cdot 4)$

103. $4 \cdot \dfrac{1}{4} = 1$

104. $8 + 0 = 8$

Use the distributive property to write each expression without parentheses.

105. $5(y - 2)$

106. $-3(z + y)$

107. $-(7 - x + 4z)$

108. $\dfrac{1}{2}(6z - 10)$

109. $-4(3x + 5) - 7$

110. $-8(2y + 9) - 1$

MIXED REVIEW

Insert $<$, $>$, or $=$ in the space between each pair of numbers.

111. $-|-11|$ $|11.4|$

112. $-1\dfrac{1}{2}$ $-2\dfrac{1}{2}$

Perform the indicated operations.

113. $-7.2 + (-8.1)$

114. $14 - 20$

115. $4(-20)$

116. $\dfrac{-20}{4}$

117. $-\dfrac{4}{5}\left(\dfrac{5}{16}\right)$

118. $-0.5(-0.3)$

119. $8 \div 2 \cdot 4$

120. $(-2)^4$

121. $\dfrac{-3 - 2(-9)}{-15 - 3(-4)}$

122. $5 + 2[(7 - 5)^2 + (1 - 3)]$

123. $-\dfrac{5}{8} \div \dfrac{3}{4}$

124. $\dfrac{-15 + (-4)^2 + |-9|}{10 - 2 \cdot 5}$

△ **125.** A trim carpenter needs a piece of quarter round molding $6\dfrac{1}{8}$ feet long for a bathroom. She finds a piece $7\dfrac{1}{2}$ feet long. How long a piece does she need to cut from the $7\dfrac{1}{2}$-foot-long molding in order to use it in the bathroom?

Chapter 1 Test   MyMathLab®   Test Prep VIDEOS   ▶   You Tube

Translate the statement into symbols.

1. The absolute value of negative seven is greater than five.

2. The sum of nine and five is greater than or equal to four.

Simplify the expression.

3. $-13 + 8$

4. $-13 - (-2)$

5. $12 \div 4 \cdot 3 - 6 \cdot 2$

6. $(13)(-3)$

7. $(-6)(-2)$

8. $\dfrac{|-16|}{-8}$

9. $\dfrac{-8}{0}$

10. $\dfrac{|-6| + 2}{5 - 6}$

11. $\dfrac{1}{2} - \dfrac{5}{6}$

12. $5\dfrac{3}{4} - 1\dfrac{1}{8}$

13. $-0.6 + 1.875$

14. $3(-4)^2 - 80$

15. $6[5 + 2(3 - 8) - 3]$

16. $\dfrac{-12 + 3 \cdot 8}{4}$

17. $\dfrac{(-2)(0)(-3)}{-6}$

Insert $<$, $>$, or $=$ in the appropriate space to make each of the following statements true.

18. $-3 \quad -7$

19. $4 \quad -8$

20. $2 \quad |-3|$

21. $|-2| \quad -1 - (-3)$

22. In the state of Massachusetts, there are 2221 licensed child care centers and 10,993 licensed home-based child care providers. Write an inequality statement comparing the numbers 2221 and 10,993. (*Source:* Children's Foundation)

23. Given $\left\{-5, -1, 0, \dfrac{1}{4}, 1, 7, 11.6, \sqrt{7}, 3\pi\right\}$, list the numbers in this set that also belong to the set of:
 a. Natural numbers
 b. Whole numbers
 c. Integers
 d. Rational numbers
 e. Irrational numbers
 f. Real numbers

If $x = 6$, $y = -2$, and $z = -3$, evaluate each expression.

24. $x^2 + y^2$

25. $x + yz$

26. $2 + 3x - y$

27. $\dfrac{y + z - 1}{x}$

Identify the property illustrated by each expression.

28. $8 + (9 + 3) = (8 + 9) + 3$

29. $6 \cdot 8 = 8 \cdot 6$

30. $-6(2 + 4) = -6 \cdot 2 + (-6) \cdot 4$

31. $\dfrac{1}{6}(6) = 1$

32. Find the opposite of -9.

33. Find the reciprocal of $-\dfrac{1}{3}$.

The New Orleans Saints were 22 yards from the goal when the following series of gains and losses occurred.

	Gains and Losses in Yards
First Down	5
Second Down	-10
Third Down	-2
Fourth Down	29

34. During which down did the greatest loss of yardage occur?

35. Was a touchdown scored?

36. The temperature at the Winter Olympics was a frigid 14 degrees below zero in the morning, but by noon it had risen 31 degrees. What was the temperature at noon?

37. A health insurance provider had net incomes of $356 million, $460 million, and -166 million in 3 consecutive years. What was the health insurance provider's total net income for these three years?

38. A stockbroker decided to sell 280 shares of stock, which decreased in value by $1.50 per share yesterday. How much money did she lose?

Equations, Inequalities, and Problem Solving

Much of mathematics relates to deciding which statements are true and which are false. For example, the statement $x + 7 = 15$ is an equation stating that the sum $x + 7$ has the same value as 15. Is this statement true or false? It is false for some values of x and true for just one value of x, namely 8. Our purpose in this chapter is to learn ways of deciding which values make an equation or an inequality true.

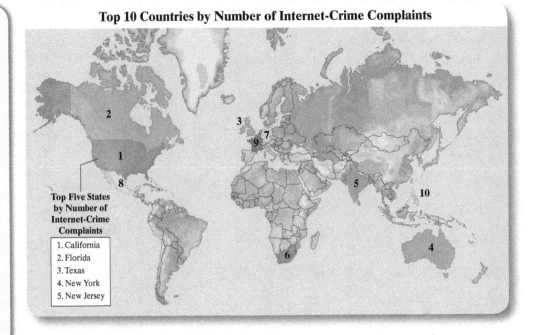

Top 10 Countries by Number of Internet-Crime Complaints

Top Five States by Number of Internet-Crime Complaints

1. California
2. Florida
3. Texas
4. New York
5. New Jersey

Internet Crime

The Internet Crime Complaint Center (IC3) is a joint operation between the FBI and the National White-Collar Crime Center. The IC3 receives and refers criminal complaints occurring on the Internet. Of course, nondelivery of merchandise or payment are the highest reported offenses.

In Section 2.6, Exercises 15 and 16, we analyze a bar graph on the yearly number of complaints received by the IC3.

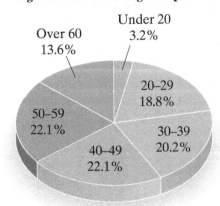

Ages of Persons Filing Complaints

Under 20 3.2%
Over 60 13.6%
20–29 18.8%
50–59 22.1%
30–39 20.2%
40–49 22.1%

2.1   Simplifying Algebraic Expressions

OBJECTIVES

1 Identify Terms, Like Terms, and Unlike Terms.

2 Combine Like Terms.

3 Use the Distributive Property to Remove Parentheses.

4 Write Word Phrases as Algebraic Expressions.

As we explore in this section, an expression such as $3x + 2x$ is not as simple as possible because—even without replacing x by a value—we can perform the indicated addition.

OBJECTIVE

1   Identifying Terms, Like Terms, and Unlike Terms

Before we practice simplifying expressions, some new language of algebra is presented. A **term** is a number or the product of a number and variables raised to powers.

Terms

$$-y, \quad 2x^3, \quad -5, \quad 3xz^2, \quad \frac{2}{y}, \quad 0.8z$$

The **numerical coefficient** (sometimes also simply called the **coefficient**) of a term is the numerical factor. The numerical coefficient of $3x$ is 3. Recall that $3x$ means $3 \cdot x$.

Term	Numerical Coefficient
$3x$	3
$\dfrac{y^3}{5}$	$\dfrac{1}{5}$ since $\dfrac{y^3}{5}$ means $\dfrac{1}{5} \cdot y^3$
$0.7ab^3c^5$	0.7
z	1
$-y$	-1
-5	-5

▶ Helpful Hint

The term $-y$ means $-1y$ and thus has a numerical coefficient of -1.

The term z means $1z$ and thus has a numerical coefficient of 1.

EXAMPLE 1   Identify the numerical coefficient in each term.

a. $-3y$ **b.** $22z^4$ **c.** y **d.** $-x$ **e.** $\dfrac{x}{7}$

Solution

a. The numerical coefficient of $-3y$ is -3.

b. The numerical coefficient of $22z^4$ is 22.

c. The numerical coefficient of y is 1, since y is $1y$.

d. The numerical coefficient of $-x$ is -1, since $-x$ is $-1x$.

e. The numerical coefficient of $\dfrac{x}{7}$ is $\dfrac{1}{7}$, since $\dfrac{x}{7}$ means $\dfrac{1}{7} \cdot x$.

PRACTICE

1   Identify the numerical coefficient in each term.

a. t **b.** $-7x$ **c.** $-\dfrac{w}{5}$ **d.** $43x^4$ **e.** $-b$

Terms with the same variables raised to exactly the same powers are called **like terms.** Terms that aren't like terms are called **unlike terms.**

Like Terms	Unlike Terms	Reason
$3x, 2x$	$5x, 5x^2$	Why? Same variable x but different powers x and x^2
$-6x^2y, 2x^2y, 4x^2y$	$7y, 3z, 8x^2$	Why? Different variables
$2ab^2c^3, ac^3b^2$	$6abc^3, 6ab^2$	Why? Different variables and different powers

> ▶ **Helpful Hint**
>
> In like terms, each variable and its exponent must match exactly, but these factors don't need to be in the same order.
>
> $$2x^2y \text{ and } 3yx^2 \text{ are like terms.}$$

EXAMPLE 2 Determine whether the terms are like or unlike.

a. $2x, 3x^2$　　**b.** $4x^2y, x^2y, -2x^2y$　　**c.** $-2yz, -3zy$　　**d.** $-x^4, x^4$

Solution

a. Unlike terms, since the exponents on x are not the same.

b. Like terms, since each variable and its exponent match.

c. Like terms, since $zy = yz$ by the commutative property.

d. Like terms. ☐

PRACTICE

2　Determine whether the terms are like or unlike.

a. $-4xy, 5yx$　　　　　　　　　　**b.** $5q, -3q^2$

c. $3ab^2, -2ab^2, 43ab^2$　　　　　　**d.** $y^5, \dfrac{y^5}{2}$

OBJECTIVE

2　**Combining Like Terms**

An algebraic expression containing the sum or difference of like terms can be simplified by applying the distributive property. For example, by the distributive property, we rewrite the sum of the like terms $3x + 2x$ as

$$3x + 2x = (3 + 2)x = 5x$$

Also,

$$-y^2 + 5y^2 = -1y^2 + 5y^2 = (-1 + 5)y^2 = 4y^2$$

Simplifying the sum or difference of like terms is called **combining like terms.**

EXAMPLE 3 Simplify each expression by combining like terms.

a. $7x - 3x$　　**b.** $10y^2 + y^2$　　**c.** $8x^2 + 2x - 3x$　　**d.** $9n^2 - 5n^2 + n^2$

Solution

a. $7x - 3x = (7 - 3)x = 4x$

b. $10y^2 + y^2 = 10y^2 + 1y^2 = (10 + 1)y^2 = 11y^2$

c. $8x^2 + 2x - 3x = 8x^2 + (2 - 3)x = 8x^2 - x$

d. $9n^2 - 5n^2 + n^2 = (9 - 5 + 1)n^2 = 5n^2$ ☐

PRACTICE

3　Simplify each expression by combining like terms.

a. $-3y + 11y$　　　　　　　　　　**b.** $4x^2 + x^2$

c. $5x - 3x^2 + 8x^2$　　　　　　　　**d.** $20y^2 + 2y^2 - y^2$

The previous example suggests the following:

Combining Like Terms

To **combine like terms,** add the numerical coefficients and multiply the result by the common variable factors.

EXAMPLE 4   Simplify each expression by combining like terms.

a. $2x + 3x + 5 + 2$ **b.** $-5a - 3 + a + 2$ **c.** $4y - 3y^2$

d. $2.3x + 5x - 6$ **e.** $-\dfrac{1}{2}b + b$

Solution   Use the distributive property to combine like terms.

a. $2x + 3x + 5 + 2 = (2 + 3)x + (5 + 2)$
$$= 5x + 7$$

b. $-5a - 3 + a + 2 = -5a + 1a + (-3 + 2)$
$$= (-5 + 1)a + (-3 + 2)$$
$$= -4a - 1$$

c. $4y - 3y^2$ These two terms cannot be combined because they are unlike terms.

d. $2.3x + 5x - 6 = (2.3 + 5)x - 6$
$$= 7.3x - 6$$

e. $-\dfrac{1}{2}b + b = -\dfrac{1}{2}b + 1b = \left(-\dfrac{1}{2} + 1\right)b = \dfrac{1}{2}b$ □

PRACTICE
4   Use the distributive property to combine like terms.

a. $3y + 8y - 7 + 2$ **b.** $6x - 3 - x - 3$ **c.** $\dfrac{3}{4}t - t$

d. $9y + 3.2y + 10 + 3$ **e.** $5z - 3z^4$

OBJECTIVE
3   **Using the Distributive Property**

Simplifying expressions makes frequent use of the distributive property to also remove parentheses.

It may be helpful to study the examples below.

$$+(3a + 2) = +1(3a + 2) = +1(3a) + (+1)(2) = 3a + 2$$
means

$$-(3a + 2) = -1(3a + 2) = -1(3a) + (-1)(2) = -3a - 2$$
means

EXAMPLE 5   Find each product by using the distributive property to remove parentheses.

a. $5(3x + 2)$ **b.** $-2(y + 0.3z - 1)$ **c.** $-(9x + y - 2z + 6)$

Solution

a. $5(3x + 2) = 5 \cdot 3x + 5 \cdot 2$ Apply the distributive property.
$$= 15x + 10$$ Multiply.

b. $-2(y + 0.3z - 1) = -2(y) + (-2)(0.3z) + (-2)(-1)$ Apply the distributive property.

$$= -2y - 0.6z + 2$$ Multiply.

c. $-(9x + y - 2z + 6) = -1(9x + y - 2z + 6)$ Distribute -1 over each term.

$$= -1(9x) - 1(y) - 1(-2z) - 1(6)$$

$$= -9x - y + 2z - 6$$ □

PRACTICE

5   Find each product by using the distributive property to remove parentheses.

a. $3(2x - 7)$ **b.** $-5(x - 0.5z - 5)$

c. $-(2x - y + z - 2)$

▶ Helpful Hint

If a "$-$" sign precedes parentheses, the sign of each term inside the parentheses is changed when the distributive property is applied to remove parentheses.

Examples:

$$-(2x + 1) = -2x - 1 \qquad -(-5x + y - z) = 5x - y + z$$
$$-(x - 2y) = -x + 2y \qquad -(-3x - 4y - 1) = 3x + 4y + 1$$

When simplifying an expression containing parentheses, we often use the distributive property in both directions—first to remove parentheses and then again to combine any like terms.

EXAMPLE 6   Simplify each expression.

a. $3(2x - 5) + 1$ **b.** $-2(4x + 7) - (3x - 1)$ **c.** $9 + 3(4x - 10)$

Solution

a. $3(2x - 5) + 1 = 6x - 15 + 1$ Apply the distributive property.

$$= 6x - 14$$ Combine like terms.

b. $-2(4x + 7) - (3x - 1) = -8x - 14 - 3x + 1$ Apply the distributive property.

$$= -11x - 13$$ Combine like terms.

▶ Helpful Hint

Don't forget to use the distributive property and multiply before adding or subtracting like terms.

c. $9 + 3(4x - 10) = 9 + 12x - 30$ Apply the distributive property.

$$= -21 + 12x$$ Combine like terms.

$$\text{or } 12x - 21$$ □

PRACTICE

6   Simplify each expression.

a. $4(9x + 1) + 6$ **b.** $-7(2x - 1) - (6 - 3x)$ **c.** $8 - 5(6x + 5)$

EXAMPLE 7   Write the phrase below as an algebraic expression. Then simplify if possible.

$$\text{"Subtract } 4x - 2 \text{ from } 2x - 3.\text{"}$$

Solution   "Subtract $4x - 2$ **from** $2x - 3$" translates to $(2x - 3) - (4x - 2)$. Next, simplify the algebraic expression.

$$(2x - 3) - (4x - 2) = 2x - 3 - 4x + 2$$ Apply the distributive property.

$$= -2x - 1$$ Combine like terms.   □

PRACTICE
7 Write the phrase below as an algebraic expression. Then simplify if possible.

"Subtract $7x - 1$ from $2x + 3$."

OBJECTIVE
4 Writing Word Phrases as Algebraic Expressions

Next, we practice writing word phrases as algebraic expressions.

EXAMPLE 8 Write the following phrases as algebraic expressions and simplify if possible. Let x represent the unknown number.

a. Twice a number, plus 6

b. The difference of a number and 4, divided by 7

c. Five added to triple the sum of a number and 1

d. The sum of twice a number, 3 times the number, and 5 times the number

Solution

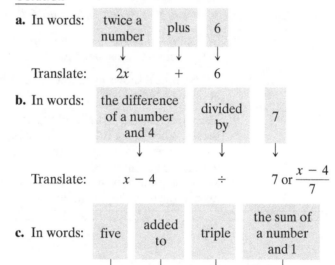

a. In words: twice a number   plus   6

Translate: $2x$ $+$ 6

b. In words: the difference of a number and 4   divided by   7

Translate: $x - 4$ $\div$ 7 or $\dfrac{x - 4}{7}$

c. In words: five   added to   triple   the sum of a number and 1

Translate: 5 $+$ $3\cdot$ $(x + 1)$

Next, we simplify this expression.

$$5 + 3(x + 1) = 5 + 3x + 3 \quad \text{Use the distributive property.}$$
$$= 8 + 3x \quad \text{Combine like terms.}$$

d. The phrase "the sum of" means that we add.

In words: twice a number   added to   3 times the number   added to   5 times the number

Translate: $2x$ $+$ $3x$ $+$ $5x$

Now let's simplify.

$$2x + 3x + 5x = 10x \quad \text{Combine like terms.} \quad \square$$

PRACTICE
8 Write the following phrases as algebraic expressions and simplify if possible. Let x represent the unknown number.

a. Three added to double a number

b. Six subtracted from the sum of 5 and a number

c. Two times the sum of 3 and a number, increased by 4

d. The sum of a number, half the number, and 5 times the number

Vocabulary, Readiness & Video Check

Use the choices below to fill in each blank. Some choices may be used more than once.

like   numerical coefficient   term   distributive

unlike   combine like terms   expression

1. $23y^2 + 10y - 6$ is called a(n) _____ while $23y^2$, $10y$, and -6 are each called a(n) _____.

2. To simplify $x + 4x$, we _____.

3. The term y has an understood _____ of 1.

4. The terms $7z$ and $7y$ are _____ terms and the terms $7z$ and $-z$ are _____ terms.

5. For the term $-\frac{1}{2}xy^2$, the number $-\frac{1}{2}$ is the _____.

6. $5(3x - y)$ equals $15x - 5y$ by the _____ property.

Martin-Gay Interactive Videos

See Video 2.1

Watch the section lecture video and answer the following questions.

OBJECTIVE 1

7. Example 7 shows two terms with exactly the same variables. Why are these terms not considered like terms?

OBJECTIVE 2

8. Example 8 shows us that when combining like terms, we are actually applying what property?

OBJECTIVE 3

9. The expression in Example 11 shows a minus sign before parentheses. When using the distributive property to multiply and remove parentheses, what number are we actually distributing to each term within the parentheses?

OBJECTIVE 4

10. Write the phrase given in Example 14, translate it to an algebraic expression, then simplify it. Why are we able to simplify it?

2.1 Exercise Set

MyMathLab®

Identify the numerical coefficient of each term. See Example 1.

1. $-7y$
2. $3x$
3. x
4. $-y$
5. $17x^2y$
6. $1.2xyz$

Indicate whether the terms in each list are like or unlike. See Example 2.

7. $5y, -y$
8. $-2x^2y, 6xy$
9. $2z, 3z^2$
10. $ab^2, -7ab^2$
11. $8wz, \frac{1}{7}zw$
12. $7.4p^3q^2, 6.2p^3q^2r$

Simplify each expression by combining any like terms. See Examples 3 and 4.

13. $7y + 8y$
14. $3x + 2x$
15. $8w - w + 6w$
16. $c - 7c + 2c$

17. $3b - 5 - 10b - 4$
18. $6g + 5 - 3g - 7$
19. $m - 4m + 2m - 6$
20. $a + 3a - 2 - 7a$
21. $5g - 3 - 5 - 5g$
22. $8p + 4 - 8p - 15$
23. $6.2x - 4 + x - 1.2$
24. $7.9y - 0.7 - y + 0.2$
25. $6x - 5x + x - 3 + 2x$
26. $8h + 13h - 6 + 7h - h$
27. $7x^2 + 8x^2 - 10x^2$
28. $8x^3 + x^3 - 11x^3$
29. $6x + 0.5 - 4.3x - 0.4x + 3$
30. $0.4y - 6.7 + y - 0.3 - 2.6y$

Simplify each expression. First use the distributive property to remove any parentheses. See Examples 5 and 6.

31. $5(y - 4)$

32. $7(r - 3)$

33. $-2(x + 2)$

34. $-4(y + 6)$

35. $7(d - 3) + 10$

36. $9(z + 7) - 15$

37. $-5(2x - 3y + 6)$

38. $-2(4x - 3z - 1)$

39. $-(3x - 2y + 1)$

40. $-(y + 5z - 7)$

41. $5(x + 2) - (3x - 4)$

42. $4(2x - 3) - 2(x + 1)$

Write each of the following as an algebraic expression. Simplify if possible. See Example 7.

43. Add $6x + 7$ to $4x - 10$.

44. Add $3y - 5$ to $y + 16$.

45. Subtract $7x + 1$ from $3x - 8$.

46. Subtract $4x - 7$ from $12 + x$.

47. Subtract $5m - 6$ from $m - 9$.

48. Subtract $m - 3$ from $2m - 6$.

MIXED PRACTICE

Simplify each expression. See Examples 3 through 7.

49. $2k - k - 6$

50. $7c - 8 - c$

51. $-9x + 4x + 18 - 10x$

52. $5y - 14 + 7y - 20y$

53. $-4(3y - 4) + 12y$

54. $-3(2x + 5) - 6x$

55. $3(2x - 5) - 5(x - 4)$

56. $2(6x - 1) - (x - 7)$

57. $-2(3x - 4) + 7x - 6$

58. $8y - 2 - 3(y + 4)$

59. $5k - (3k - 10)$

60. $-11c - (4 - 2c)$

61. Subtract $6x - 1$ from $3x + 4$

62. Subtract $4 + 3y$ from $8 - 5y$

63. $3.4m - 4 - 3.4m - 7$

64. $2.8w - 0.9 - 0.5 - 2.8w$

65. $\frac{1}{3}(7y - 1) + \frac{1}{6}(4y + 7)$

66. $\frac{1}{5}(9y + 2) + \frac{1}{10}(2y - 1)$

67. $2 + 4(6x - 6)$

68. $8 + 4(3x - 4)$

69. $0.5(m + 2) + 0.4m$

70. $0.2(k + 8) - 0.1k$

71. $10 - 3(2x + 3y)$

72. $14 - 11(5m + 3n)$

73. $6(3x - 6) - 2(x + 1) - 17x$

74. $7(2x + 5) - 4(x + 2) - 20x$

75. $\frac{1}{2}(12x - 4) - (x + 5)$

76. $\frac{1}{3}(9x - 6) - (x - 2)$

TRANSLATING

Write each phrase as an algebraic expression and simplify if possible. Let x represent the unknown number. See Examples 7 and 8.

77. Twice a number, decreased by four

78. The difference of a number and two, divided by five

79. Seven added to double a number

80. Eight more than triple a number

81. Three-fourths of a number, increased by twelve

82. Eleven, increased by two-thirds of a number

83. The sum of 5 times a number and -2, added to 7 times a number

84. The sum of 3 times a number and 10, subtracted from 9 times a number

85. Eight times the sum of a number and six

86. Six times the difference of a number and five

87. Double a number, minus the sum of the number and ten

88. Half a number, minus the product of the number and eight

89. The sum of 2, three times a number, -9, and four times a number

90. The sum of twice a number, -1, five times a number, and -12

REVIEW AND PREVIEW

Evaluate the following expressions for the given values. See Section 1.6.

91. If $x = -1$ and $y = 3$, find $y - x^2$.

92. If $g = 0$ and $h = -4$, find $gh - h^2$.

93. If $a = 2$ and $b = -5$, find $a - b^2$.

94. If $x = -3$, find $x^3 - x^2 + 4$.

95. If $y = -5$ and $z = 0$, find $yz - y^2$.

96. If $x = -2$, find $x^3 - x^2 - x$.

CONCEPT EXTENSIONS

△ **97.** Recall that the perimeter of a figure is the total distance around the figure. Given the following rectangle, express the perimeter as an algebraic expression containing the variable x.

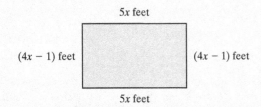

5x feet

$(4x - 1)$ feet $(4x - 1)$ feet

5x feet

△ **98.** Given the following triangle, express its perimeter as an algebraic expression containing the variable x.

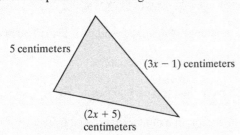

5 centimeters

$(3x - 1)$ centimeters

$(2x + 5)$ centimeters

Given the following two rules, determine whether each scale in Exercises 99 through 102 is balanced.

1 cone balances 1 cube

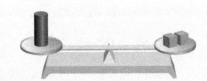

1 cylinder balances 2 cubes

99.

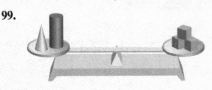

100.

101.

102.

Write each algebraic expression described.

✎ **103.** Write an expression with 4 terms that simplifies to $3x - 4$.

✎ **104.** Write an expression of the form ___ (___ + ___) whose product is $6x + 24$.

105. To convert from feet to inches, we multiply by 12. For example, the number of inches in 2 feet is $12 \cdot 2$ inches. If one board has a length of $(x + 2)$ *feet* and a second board has a length of $(3x - 1)$ *inches,* express their total length in inches as an algebraic expression.

106. The value of 7 nickels is $5 \cdot 7$ cents. Likewise, the value of x nickels is $5x$ cents. If the money box in a drink machine contains x *nickels,* $3x$ *dimes,* and $(30x - 1)$ *quarters,* express their total value in cents as an algebraic expression.

✎ **107.** In your own words, explain how to combine like terms.

✎ **108.** Do like terms always contain the same numerical coefficients? Explain your answer.

For Exercises 109 through 114, see the example below.
Example

Simplify $-3xy + 2x^2y - (2xy - 1)$.

Solution

$$-3xy + 2x^2y - (2xy - 1)$$
$$= -3xy + 2x^2y - 2xy + 1 = -5xy + 2x^2y + 1$$

Simplify each expression.

109. $5b^2c^3 + 8b^3c^2 - 7b^3c^2$

110. $4m^4p^2 + m^4p^2 - 5m^2p^4$

111. $3x - (2x^2 - 6x) + 7x^2$

112. $9y^2 - (6xy^2 - 5y^2) - 8xy^2$

113. $-(2x^2y + 3z) + 3z - 5x^2y$

114. $-(7c^3d - 8c) - 5c - 4c^3d$

2.2 The Addition and Multiplication Properties of Equality

OBJECTIVES

1 Define Linear Equations and Use the Addition Property of Equality to Solve Linear Equations.

2 Use the Multiplication Property of Equality to Solve Linear Equations.

3 Use Both Properties of Equality to Solve Linear Equations.

4 Write Word Phrases as Algebraic Expressions.

OBJECTIVE

1   Defining Linear Equations and Using the Addition Property

Recall from Section 1.4 that an equation is a statement that two expressions have the same value. Also, a value of the variable that makes an equation a true statement is called a solution or root of the equation. The process of finding the solution of an equation is called **solving** the equation for the variable. In this section we concentrate on solving **linear equations** in one variable.

Linear Equation in One Variable

A linear equation in one variable can be written in the form

$$ax + b = c$$

where a, b, and c are real numbers and $a \neq 0$.

Evaluating a linear equation for a given value of the variable, as we did in Section 1.4, can tell us whether that value is a solution, but we can't rely on evaluating an equation as our method of solving it.

Instead, to solve a linear equation in x, we write a series of simpler equations, all *equivalent* to the original equation, so that the final equation has the form

$$x = \textbf{number} \qquad \text{or} \qquad \textbf{number} = x$$

Equivalent equations are equations that have the same solution. This means that the "number" above is the solution to the original equation.

The first property of equality that helps us write simpler equivalent equations is the **addition property of equality.**

Addition Property of Equality

If a, b, and c are real numbers, then

$$a = b \qquad \text{and} \qquad a + c = b + c$$

are equivalent equations.

This property guarantees that adding the same number to both sides of an equation does not change the solution of the equation. Since subtraction is defined in terms of addition, we may also **subtract the same number from both sides** without changing the solution.

A good way to picture a true equation is as a balanced scale. Since it is balanced, each side of the scale weighs the same amount.

If the same weight is added to or subtracted from each side, the scale remains balanced.

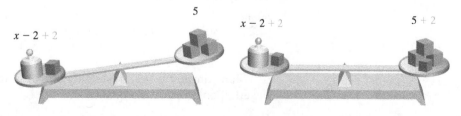

We use the addition property of equality to write equivalent equations until the variable is by itself on one side of the equation, and the equation looks like "x = number" or "number = x."

EXAMPLE 1   Solve $x - 7 = 10$ for x.

Solution   To solve for x, we want x alone on one side of the equation. To do this, we add 7 to both sides of the equation.

$$x - 7 = 10$$
$$x - 7 + 7 = 10 + 7 \quad \text{Add 7 to both sides.}$$
$$x = 17 \qquad \text{Simplify.}$$

The solution of the equation $x = 17$ is obviously 17. Since we are writing equivalent equations, the solution of the equation $x - 7 = 10$ is also 17.

Check: To check, replace x with 17 in the original equation.

$$x - 7 = 10$$
$$17 - 7 \stackrel{?}{=} 10 \quad \text{Replace } x \text{ with 17 in the original equation.}$$
$$10 = 10 \quad \text{True}$$

Since the statement is true, 17 is the solution.

PRACTICE
1   Solve: $x + 3 = -5$ for x.

✓CONCEPT CHECK

Use the addition property to fill in the blanks so that the middle equation simplifies to the last equation.

$$x - 5 = 3$$
$$x - 5 + \underline{} = 3 + \underline{}$$
$$x = 8$$

EXAMPLE 2   Solve $y + 0.6 = -1.0$ for y.

Solution   To get y alone on one side of the equation, subtract 0.6 from both sides of the equation.

$$y + 0.6 = -1.0$$
$$y + 0.6 - 0.6 = -1.0 - 0.6 \quad \text{Subtract 0.6 from both sides.}$$
$$y = -1.6 \qquad \text{Combine like terms.}$$

Check: To check the proposed solution, -1.6, replace y with -1.6 in the original equation.

$$y + 0.6 = -1.0$$
$$-1.6 + 0.6 \stackrel{?}{=} -1.0 \quad \text{Replace } y \text{ with } -1.6 \text{ in the original equation.}$$
$$-1.0 = -1.0 \quad \text{True}$$

The solution is -1.6.

PRACTICE
2   Solve: $y - 0.3 = -2.1$ for y.

Many times, it is best to simplify one or both sides of an equation before applying the addition property of equality.

Answer to Concept Check: 5; 5

EXAMPLE 3 Solve: $2x + 3x - 5 + 7 = 10x + 3 - 6x - 4$

Solution First we simplify both sides of the equation.

$$2x + 3x - 5 + 7 = 10x + 3 - 6x - 4$$
$$5x + 2 = 4x - 1 \qquad \text{Combine like terms on each side of the equation.}$$

Next, we want all terms with a variable on one side of the equation and all numbers on the other side.

$$5x + 2 - 4x = 4x - 1 - 4x \qquad \text{Subtract } 4x \text{ from both sides.}$$
$$x + 2 = -1 \qquad \text{Combine like terms.}$$
$$x + 2 - 2 = -1 - 2 \qquad \text{Subtract 2 from both sides to get } x \text{ alone.}$$
$$x = -3 \qquad \text{Combine like terms.}$$

Check:

$$2x + 3x - 5 + 7 = 10x + 3 - 6x - 4 \qquad \text{Original equation}$$
$$2(-3) + 3(-3) - 5 + 7 \stackrel{?}{=} 10(-3) + 3 - 6(-3) - 4 \qquad \text{Replace } x \text{ with } -3.$$
$$-6 - 9 - 5 + 7 \stackrel{?}{=} -30 + 3 + 18 - 4 \qquad \text{Multiply.}$$
$$-13 = -13 \qquad \text{True}$$

The solution is -3. $\qquad\qquad\qquad\qquad\qquad\qquad\qquad\qquad\qquad\qquad$ □

PRACTICE

3 Solve: $8x - 5x - 3 + 9 = x + x + 3 - 7$

If an equation contains parentheses, we use the distributive property to remove them.

EXAMPLE 4 Solve: $7 = -5(2a - 1) - (-11a + 6)$.

Solution

$$7 = -5(2a - 1) - (-11a + 6)$$
$$7 = -10a + 5 + 11a - 6 \qquad \text{Apply the distributive property.}$$
$$7 = a - 1 \qquad \text{Combine like terms.}$$
$$7 + 1 = a - 1 + 1 \qquad \text{Add 1 to both sides to get } a \text{ alone.}$$
$$8 = a \qquad \text{Combine like terms.}$$

Check to see that 8 is the solution. $\qquad\qquad\qquad\qquad\qquad\qquad\qquad$ □

PRACTICE

4 Solve: $2 = 4(2a - 3) - (7a + 4)$

> ▶ Helpful Hint
> We may solve an equation so that the variable is alone on either side of the equation. For example, $8 = a$ is equivalent to $a = 8$.

When solving equations, we may sometimes encounter an equation such as

$$-x = 5.$$

This equation is not solved for x because x is not isolated. One way to solve this equation for x is to recall that

"$-$" can be read as "the opposite of."

We can read the equation $-x = 5$ then as "the opposite of $x = 5$." If the opposite of x is 5, this means that x is the opposite of 5 or -5.

In summary,

$$-x = 5 \quad \text{and} \quad x = -5$$

are equivalent equations and $x = -5$ is solved for x.

OBJECTIVE

2 Using the Multiplication Property

As useful as the addition property of equality is, it cannot help us solve every type of linear equation in one variable. For example, adding or subtracting a value on both sides of the equation does not help solve

$$\frac{5}{2}x = 15.$$

Instead, we apply another important property of equality, the **multiplication property of equality.**

Multiplication Property of Equality

If $a, b,$ and c are real numbers and $c \neq 0$, then

$$a = b \quad \text{and} \quad ac = bc$$

are equivalent equations.

This property guarantees that multiplying both sides of an equation by the same non-zero number does not change the solution of the equation. Since division is defined in terms of multiplication, we may also **divide both sides of the equation by the same nonzero number** without changing the solution.

EXAMPLE 5   Solve: $\frac{5}{2}x = 15$.

Solution   To get x alone, multiply both sides of the equation by the reciprocal of $\frac{5}{2}$, which is $\frac{2}{5}$.

$$\frac{5}{2}x = 15$$

$$\frac{2}{5} \cdot \frac{5}{2}x = \frac{2}{5} \cdot 15 \qquad \text{Multiply both sides by } \frac{2}{5}.$$

$$\left(\frac{2}{5} \cdot \frac{5}{2}\right)x = \frac{2}{5} \cdot 15 \qquad \text{Apply the associative property.}$$

$$1x = 6 \qquad \text{Simplify.}$$

or

$$x = 6$$

> **Helpful Hint**
> Don't forget to multiply *both* sides by $\frac{2}{5}$.

Check: Replace x with 6 in the original equation.

$$\frac{5}{2}x = 15 \qquad \text{Original equation}$$

$$\frac{5}{2}(6) \stackrel{?}{=} 15 \qquad \text{Replace } x \text{ with 6.}$$

$$15 = 15 \qquad \text{True}$$

The solution is 6.

PRACTICE
5   Solve: $\frac{4}{5}x = 16$

In the equation $\frac{5}{2}x = 15$, $\frac{5}{2}$ is the coefficient of x. When the coefficient of x is a *fraction,* we will get x alone by multiplying by the reciprocal. When the coefficient of x is an integer or a decimal, it is usually more convenient to divide both sides by the coefficient. (Dividing by a number is, of course, the same as multiplying by the reciprocal of the number.)

EXAMPLE 6   Solve: $-3x = 33$

Solution   Recall that $-3x$ means $-3 \cdot x$. To get x alone, we divide both sides by the coefficient of x, that is, -3.

$$-3x = 33$$

$$\frac{-3x}{-3} = \frac{33}{-3} \qquad \text{Divide both sides by } -3.$$

$$1x = -11 \qquad \text{Simplify.}$$

$$x = -11$$

Check:
$$-3x = 33 \qquad \text{Original equation}$$

$$-3(-11) \overset{?}{=} 33 \qquad \text{Replace } x \text{ with } -11.$$

$$33 = 33 \qquad \text{True}$$

The solution is -11.

PRACTICE
6   Solve: $8x = -96$

EXAMPLE 7   Solve: $\frac{y}{7} = 20$

Solution   Recall that $\frac{y}{7} = \frac{1}{7}y$. To get y alone, we multiply both sides of the equation by 7, the reciprocal of $\frac{1}{7}$.

$$\frac{y}{7} = 20$$

$$\frac{1}{7}y = 20$$

$$7 \cdot \frac{1}{7}y = 7 \cdot 20 \qquad \text{Multiply both sides by 7.}$$

$$1y = 140 \qquad \text{Simplify.}$$

$$y = 140$$

Check:
$$\frac{y}{7} = 20 \qquad \text{Original equation}$$

$$\frac{140}{7} \overset{?}{=} 20 \qquad \text{Replace } y \text{ with 140.}$$

$$20 = 20 \qquad \text{True}$$

The solution is 140.

PRACTICE
7   Solve: $\frac{x}{5} = 13$

OBJECTIVE
3   Using Both the Addition and Multiplication Properties
Next, we practice solving equations using both properties.

EXAMPLE 8 Solve: $12a - 8a = 10 + 2a - 13 - 7$

Solution First, simplify both sides of the equation by combining like terms.

$$12a - 8a = 10 + 2a - 13 - 7$$
$$4a = 2a - 10 \qquad \text{Combine like terms.}$$

To get all terms containing a variable on one side, subtract $2a$ from both sides.

$$4a - 2a = 2a - 10 - 2a \qquad \text{Subtract } 2a \text{ from both sides.}$$
$$2a = -10 \qquad \text{Simplify.}$$
$$\frac{2a}{2} = \frac{-10}{2} \qquad \text{Divide both sides by 2.}$$
$$a = -5 \qquad \text{Simplify.}$$

Check: Check by replacing a with -5 in the original equation. The solution is -5. □

PRACTICE
8 Solve: $6b - 11b = 18 + 2b - 6 + 9$

OBJECTIVE
4 Writing Word Phrases as Algebraic Expressions

Next, we practice writing word phrases as algebraic expressions.

EXAMPLE 9

a. The sum of two numbers is 8. If one number is 3, find the other number.

b. The sum of two numbers is 8. If one number is x, write an expression representing the other number.

c. An 8-foot board is cut into two pieces. If one piece is x feet, express the length of the other piece in terms of x.

Solution

a. If the sum of two numbers is 8 and one number is 3, we find the other number by subtracting 3 from 8. The other number is $8 - 3$ or 5.

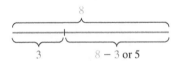

b. If the sum of two numbers is 8 and one number is x, we find the other number by subtracting x from 8. The other number is represented by $8 - x$.

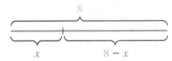

c. If an 8-foot board is cut into two pieces and one piece is x feet, we find the other length by subtracting x from 8. The other piece is $(8 - x)$ feet.

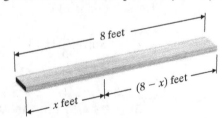

PRACTICE
9

a. The sum of two numbers is 9. If one number is 2, find the other number.

b. The sum of two numbers is 9. If one number is x, write an expression representing the other number.

c. A 9-foot rope is cut into two pieces. If one piece is x feet, express the length of the other piece in terms of x.

EXAMPLE 10   If x is the first of three consecutive integers, express the sum of the three integers in terms of x. Simplify if possible.

Solution   An example of three consecutive integers is

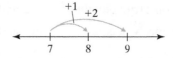

The second consecutive integer is always 1 more than the first, and the third consecutive integer is 2 more than the first. If x is the first of three consecutive integers, the three consecutive integers are

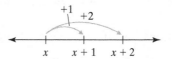

Their sum is

In words: | first integer | $+$ | second integer | $+$ | third integer |

Translate: x $+$ $(x + 1)$ $+$ $(x + 2)$

which simplifies to $3x + 3$.

PRACTICE
10   If x is the first of three consecutive *even* integers, express their sum in terms of x.

Below are examples of consecutive even and odd integers.

Consecutive Even integers: *Consecutive Odd integers:*

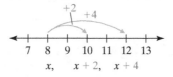   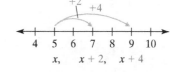

▶ **Helpful Hint**

If x is an odd integer, then $x + 2$ is the next odd integer. This 2 simply means that odd integers are always 2 units from each other. (The same is true for even integers. They are always 2 units from each other.)

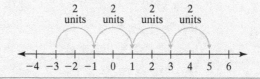

Vocabulary, Readiness & Video Check

Use the choices below to fill in each blank. Some choices will be used more than once.

addition	solving	expression	true	multiplication
equivalent	equation	solution	false	

1. The difference between an equation and an expression is that a(n) _____ contains an equal sign, whereas an _____ does not.

2. _____ equations are equations that have the same solution.

3. A value of the variable that makes the equation a true statement is called a(n) _____ of the equation.

4. The process of finding the solution of an equation is called _____ the equation for the variable.

5. By the _____ property of equality, $x = -2$ and $x + 10 = -2 + 10$ are equivalent equations.

6. By the _____ property of equality, $x = -7$ and $x - 5 = -7 - 5$ are equivalent equations.

7. By the _____ property of equality, $y = \frac{1}{2}$ and $5 \cdot y = 5 \cdot \frac{1}{2}$ are equivalent equations.

8. By the _____ property of equality, $9x = -63$ and $\frac{9x}{9} = \frac{-63}{9}$ are equivalent equations.

9. True or false: The equations $x = \frac{1}{2}$ and $\frac{1}{2} = x$ are equivalent equations. _____

10. True or false: The equations $\frac{z}{4} = 10$ and $4 \cdot \frac{z}{4} = 10$ are equivalent equations. _____

Martin-Gay Interactive Videos

See Video 2.2

Watch the section lecture video and answer the following questions.

OBJECTIVE
1 **11.** Complete this statement based on the lecture given before Example 1. The addition property of equality means that if we have an equation, we can add the same real number to _____ of the equation and have an equivalent equation.

OBJECTIVE
2 **12.** Complete this statement based on the lecture given before Example 4. We can multiply both sides of an equation by _____ nonzero number and have an equivalent equation.

OBJECTIVE
3 **13.** Both the addition and multiplication properties of equality are used to solve Examples 6 and 7. In each of these examples, what property is applied first? What property is applied last? What conclusion, if any, can you make?

OBJECTIVE
4 **14.** Let x be the first of four consecutive integers, as in Example 10. Now express the sum of the second integer and the fourth integer as an algebraic expression containing x.

2.2 Exercise Set   MyMathLab®

Solve each equation. Check each solution. See Examples 1 and 2.

1. $x + 7 = 10$

2. $x + 14 = 25$

3. $x - 2 = -4$

4. $y - 9 = 1$

5. $3 + x = -11$

6. $8 + z = -8$

7. $r - 8.6 = -8.1$

8. $t - 9.2 = -6.8$

9. $8x = 7x - 3$

10. $2x = x - 5$

11. $5b - 0.7 = 6b$

12. $9x + 5.5 = 10x$

13. $7x - 3 = 6x$

14. $18x - 9 = 19x$

Solve each equation. See Examples 3 and 4.

15. $2x + x - 6 = 2x + 5$

16. $7y + 2 = 2y + 4y + 2$

17. $3t - t - 7 = t - 7$

18. $4c + 8 - c = 8 + 2c$

19. $7x + 2x = 8x - 3$

20. $3n + 2n = 7 + 4n$

21. $-2(x + 1) + 3x = 14$

22. $10 = 8(3y - 4) - 23y + 20$

Solve each equation. See Example 6.

23. $-5x = 20$

24. $-7x = -49$

25. $3x = 0$ **26.** $-2x = 0$

27. $-x = -12$ **28.** $-y = 8$

29. $3x + 2x = 50$ **30.** $-y + 4y = 33$

Solve each equation. See Examples 5 and 7.

31. $\dfrac{2}{3}x = -8$ **32.** $\dfrac{3}{4}n = -15$

33. $\dfrac{1}{6}d = \dfrac{1}{2}$ **34.** $\dfrac{1}{8}v = \dfrac{1}{4}$

35. $\dfrac{a}{-2} = 1$ **36.** $\dfrac{d}{15} = 2$

37. $\dfrac{k}{7} = 0$ **38.** $\dfrac{f}{-5} = 0$

39. In your own words, explain the addition property of equality.

40. In your own words, explain the multiplication property of equality.

MIXED PRACTICE

Solve each equation. Check each solution. See Examples 1 through 8.

41. $2x - 4 = 16$ **42.** $3x - 1 = 26$

43. $-x + 2 = 22$ **44.** $-x + 4 = -24$

45. $6a + 3 = 3$ **46.** $8t + 5 = 5$

47. $6x + 10 = -20$ **48.** $-10y + 15 = 5$

49. $5 - 0.3k = 5$ **50.** $2 + 0.4p = 2$

51. $-2x + \dfrac{1}{2} = \dfrac{7}{2}$ **52.** $-3n - \dfrac{1}{3} = \dfrac{8}{3}$

53. $\dfrac{x}{3} + 2 = -5$ **54.** $\dfrac{b}{4} - 1 = -7$

55. $10 = 2x - 1$ **56.** $12 = 3j - 4$

57. $6z - 8 - z + 3 = 0$ **58.** $4a + 1 + a - 11 = 0$

59. $10 - 3x - 6 - 9x = 7$ **60.** $12x + 30 + 8x - 6 = 10$

61. $\dfrac{5}{6}x = 10$ **62.** $-\dfrac{3}{4}x = 9$

63. $1 = 0.3x - 0.5x - 5$ **64.** $19 = 0.4x - 0.9x - 6$

65. $z - 5z = 7z - 9 - z$ **66.** $t - 6t = -13 + t - 3t$

67. $0.4x - 0.6x - 5 = 1$ **68.** $0.1x - 0.6x - 6 = 19$

69. $6 - 2x + 8 = 10$

70. $-5 - 6y + 6 = 19$

71. $-3a + 6 + 5a = 7a - 8a$

72. $4b - 8 - b = 10b - 3b$

73. $20 = -3(2x + 1) + 7x$

74. $-3 = -5(4x + 3) + 21x$

See Example 9.

75. Two numbers have a sum of 20. If one number is p, express the other number in terms of p.

76. Two numbers have a sum of 13. If one number is y, express the other number in terms of y.

77. A 10-foot board is cut into two pieces. If one piece is x feet long, express the other length in terms of x.

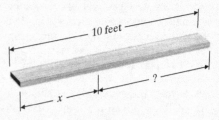

78. A 5-foot piece of string is cut into two pieces. If one piece is x feet long, express the other length in terms of x.

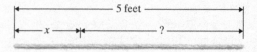

79. Two angles are *supplementary* if their sum is 180°. If one angle measures $x°$, express the measure of its supplement in terms of x.

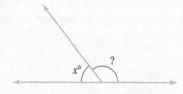

80. Two angles are *complementary* if their sum is 90°. If one angle measures $x°$, express the measure of its complement in terms of x.

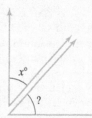

81. In a mayoral election, April Catarella received 284 more votes than Charles Pecot. If Charles received n votes, how many votes did April receive?

82. The length of the top of a computer desk is $1\dfrac{1}{2}$ feet longer than its width. If its width measures m feet, express its length as an algebraic expression in m.

83. The Verrazano-Narrows Bridge in New York City is the longest suspension bridge in North America. The Golden Gate Bridge in San Francisco is 60 feet shorter than the Verrazano-Narrows Bridge. If the length of the Verrazano-Narrows Bridge is m feet, express the length of the Golden Gate Bridge as an algebraic expression in m. (*Source: World Almanac, 2000*).

84. The longest interstate highway in the U.S. is I-90, which connects Seattle, Washington, and Boston, Massachusetts. The second longest interstate highway, I-80 (connecting San Francisco, California, and Teaneck, New Jersey), is 178.5 miles shorter than I-90. If the length of I-80 is m miles, express the length of I-90 as an algebraic expression in m. (*Source:* U.S. Department of Transportation–Federal Highway Administration)

85. In a recent year, the number of graduate students at the University of Texas at Austin was approximately 28,000 fewer than the number of undergraduate students. If the number of undergraduate students was n, how many graduate students attend UT Austin? (*Source:* University of Texas at Austin)

86. The Missouri River is the longest river in the United States. The Mississippi River is 200 miles shorter than the Missouri River. If the length of the Missouri River is r miles, express the length of the Mississippi River as an algebraic expression in r. (*Source:* U.S. Geological Survey)

87. The area of the Sahara Desert in Africa is 7 times the area of the Gobi Desert in Asia. If the area of the Gobi Desert is x square miles, express the area of the Sahara Desert as an algebraic expression in x.

88. The largest meteorite in the world is the Hoba West located in Namibia. Its weight is 3 times the weight of the Armanty meteorite located in Outer Mongolia. If the weight of the Armanty meteorite is y kilograms, express the weight of the Hoba West meteorite as an algebraic expression in y.

Write each algebraic expression described. Simplify if possible. See Example 10.

89. If x represents the first of two consecutive odd integers, express the sum of the two integers in terms of x.

90. If x is the first of four consecutive even integers, write their sum as an algebraic expression in x.

91. If x is the first of four consecutive integers, express the sum of the first integer and the third integer as an algebraic expression containing the variable x.

92. If x is the first of two consecutive integers, express the sum of 20 and the second consecutive integer as an algebraic expression containing the variable x.

93. Classrooms on one side of the science building are all numbered with consecutive even integers. If the first room on this side of the building is numbered x, write an expression in x for the sum of five classroom numbers in a row. Then simplify this expression.

94. Two sides of a quadrilateral have the same length, x, while the other two sides have the same length, both being the next consecutive odd integer. Write the sum of these lengths. Then simplify this expression.

REVIEW AND PREVIEW

Simplify each expression. See Section 2.1.

95. $5x + 2(x - 6)$ **96.** $-7y + 2y - 3(y + 1)$

97. $-(x - 1) + x$ **98.** $-(3a - 3) + 2a - 6$

Insert $<$, $>$, or $=$ in the appropriate space to make each statement true. See Sections 1.2 and 1.7.

99. $(-3)^2$ -3^2 **100.** $(-2)^4$ -2^4

101. $(-2)^3$ -2^3 **102.** $(-4)^3$ -4^3

CONCEPT EXTENSIONS

103. The sum of the angles of a triangle is 180°. If one angle of a triangle measures $x°$ and a second angle measures $(2x + 7)°$, express the measure of the third angle in terms of x. Simplify the expression.

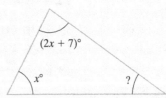

104. A quadrilateral is a four-sided figure like the one shown below whose angle sum is 360°. If one angle measures $x°$, a second angle measures $3x°$, and a third angle measures $5x°$, express the measure of the fourth angle in terms of x. Simplify the expression.

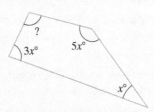

105. Write two terms whose sum is $-3x$.

106. Write four terms whose sum is $2y - 6$.

Use the addition property to fill in each blank so that the middle equation simplifies to the last equation. See the Concept Check in this section.

107.
$$x - 4 = -9$$
$$x - 4 + (\quad) = -9 + (\quad)$$
$$x = -5$$

108.
$$a + 9 = 15$$
$$a + 9 + (\quad) = 15 + (\quad)$$
$$a = 6$$

Fill in the blanks with numbers of your choice so that each equation has the given solution. Note: Each blank may be replaced with a different number.

109. _____ $+ x =$ _____; Solution: -3

110. $x -$ _____ $=$ _____; Solution: -10

111. Let $x = 1$ and then $x = 2$ in the equation $x + 5 = x + 6$. Is either number a solution? How many solutions do you think this equation has? Explain your answer.

112. Let $x = 1$ and then $x = 2$ in the equation $x + 3 = x + 3$. Is either number a solution? How many solutions do you think this equation has? Explain your answer.

Fill in the blank with a number so that each equation has the given solution.

113. $6x =$ _____; solution: -8

114. _____ $x = 10$; solution: $\dfrac{1}{2}$

115. A licensed nurse practitioner is instructed to give a patient 2100 milligrams of an antibiotic over a period of 36 hours. If the antibiotic is to be given every 4 hours starting immediately, how much antibiotic should be given in each dose? To answer this question, solve the equation $9x = 2100$.

116. Suppose you are a pharmacist and a customer asks you the following question. His child is to receive 13.5 milliliters of a nausea medicine over a period of 54 hours. If the nausea medicine is to be administered every 6 hours starting immediately, how much medicine should be given in each dose?

Use a calculator to determine whether the given value is a solution of the given equation.

117. $8.13 + 5.85y = 20.05y - 8.91$; $y = 1.2$

118. $3(a + 4.6) = 5a + 2.5$; $a = 6.3$

Solve each equation.

119. $-3.6x = 10.62$

120. $4.95y = -31.185$

121. $7x - 5.06 = -4.92$

122. $0.06y + 2.63 = 2.5562$

2.3 │ Solving Linear Equations ▸

OBJECTIVES

1 Apply a General Strategy for Solving a Linear Equation. ▸

2 Solve Equations Containing Fractions. ▸

3 Solve Equations Containing Decimals. ▸

4 Recognize Identities and Equations with No Solution. ▸

OBJECTIVE

1   Apply a General Strategy for Solving a Linear Equation ▸

We now present a general strategy for solving linear equations. One new piece of strategy is a suggestion to "clear an equation of fractions" as a first step. Doing so makes the equation less tedious, since operating on integers is usually more convenient than operating on fractions.

Solving Linear Equations in One Variable

Step 1. Multiply on both sides by the LCD to clear the equation of fractions if they occur.

Step 2. Use the distributive property to remove parentheses if they occur.

Step 3. Simplify each side of the equation by combining like terms.

Step 4. Get all variable terms on one side and all numbers on the other side by using the addition property of equality.

Step 5. Get the variable alone by using the multiplication property of equality.

Step 6. Check the solution by substituting it into the original equation.

EXAMPLE 1   Solve: $4(2x - 3) + 7 = 3x + 5$

Solution   There are no fractions, so we begin with Step 2.

$$4(2x - 3) + 7 = 3x + 5$$

Step 2.	$8x - 12 + 7 = 3x + 5$	Apply the distributive property.
Step 3.	$8x - 5 = 3x + 5$	Combine like terms.

Step 4. Get all variable terms on the same side of the equation by subtracting $3x$ from both sides, then adding 5 to both sides.

$8x - 5 - 3x = 3x + 5 - 3x$	Subtract $3x$ from both sides.
$5x - 5 = 5$	Simplify.
$5x - 5 + 5 = 5 + 5$	Add 5 to both sides.
$5x = 10$	Simplify.

Step 5. Use the multiplication property of equality to get x alone.

$\dfrac{5x}{5} = \dfrac{10}{5}$	Divide both sides by 5.
$x = 2$	Simplify.

Step 6. Check.

> ▶ **Helpful Hint**
> When checking solutions, remember to use the original written equation.

$4(2x - 3) + 7 = 3x + 5$	Original equation
$4[2(2) - 3] + 7 \stackrel{?}{=} 3(2) + 5$	Replace x with 2.
$4(4 - 3) + 7 \stackrel{?}{=} 6 + 5$	
$4(1) + 7 \stackrel{?}{=} 11$	
$4 + 7 \stackrel{?}{=} 11$	
$11 = 11$	True

The solution is 2 or the solution set is $\{2\}$.

PRACTICE
1   Solve: $2(4a - 9) + 3 = 5a - 6$

EXAMPLE 2   Solve: $8(2 - t) = -5t$

Solution   First, we apply the distributive property.

$$8(2 - t) = -5t$$

Step 2.	$16 - 8t = -5t$	Use the distributive property.
Step 4.	$16 - 8t + 8t = -5t + 8t$	To get variable terms on one side, add $8t$ to both sides.
	$16 = 3t$	Combine like terms.
Step 5.	$\dfrac{16}{3} = \dfrac{3t}{3}$	Divide both sides by 3.
	$\dfrac{16}{3} = t$	Simplify.

Step 6. Check.

$8(2 - t) = -5t$	Original equation
$8\left(2 - \dfrac{16}{3}\right) \stackrel{?}{=} -5\left(\dfrac{16}{3}\right)$	Replace t with $\dfrac{16}{3}$.
$8\left(\dfrac{6}{3} - \dfrac{16}{3}\right) \stackrel{?}{=} -\dfrac{80}{3}$	The LCD is 3.

$$8\left(-\frac{10}{3}\right) \stackrel{?}{=} -\frac{80}{3} \quad \text{Subtract fractions.}$$

$$-\frac{80}{3} = -\frac{80}{3} \quad \text{True}$$

The solution is $\frac{16}{3}$.

PRACTICE
2   Solve: $7(x - 3) = -6x$

OBJECTIVE
2   Solving Equations Containing Fractions

If an equation contains fractions, we can clear the equation of fractions by multiplying both sides by the LCD of all denominators. By doing this, we avoid working with time-consuming fractions.

EXAMPLE 3   Solve: $\frac{x}{2} - 1 = \frac{2}{3}x - 3$

Solution   We begin by clearing fractions. To do this, we multiply both sides of the equation by the LCD of 2 and 3, which is 6.

$$\frac{x}{2} - 1 = \frac{2}{3}x - 3$$

Step 1. $6\left(\dfrac{x}{2} - 1\right) = 6\left(\dfrac{2}{3}x - 3\right)$ Multiply both sides by the LCD, 6.

Step 2. $6\left(\dfrac{x}{2}\right) - 6(1) = 6\left(\dfrac{2}{3}x\right) - 6(3)$ Apply the distributive property.

> **Helpful Hint**
> Don't forget to multiply *each* term by the LCD.

$$3x - 6 = 4x - 18 \quad \text{Simplify.}$$

There are no longer grouping symbols and no like terms on either side of the equation, so we continue with Step 4.

$$3x - 6 = 4x - 18$$

Step 4. $3x - 6 - 3x = 4x - 18 - 3x$ To get variable terms on one side, subtract $3x$ from both sides.

$$-6 = x - 18 \quad \text{Simplify.}$$

$$-6 + 18 = x - 18 + 18 \quad \text{Add 18 to both sides.}$$

$$12 = x \quad \text{Simplify.}$$

Step 5. The variable is now alone, so there is no need to apply the multiplication property of equality.

Step 6. Check.

$$\frac{x}{2} - 1 = \frac{2}{3}x - 3 \quad \text{Original equation}$$

$$\frac{12}{2} - 1 \stackrel{?}{=} \frac{2}{3} \cdot 12 - 3 \quad \text{Replace } x \text{ with 12.}$$

$$6 - 1 \stackrel{?}{=} 8 - 3 \quad \text{Simplify.}$$

$$5 = 5 \quad \text{True}$$

The solution is 12.

PRACTICE
3   Solve: $\frac{3}{5}x - 2 = \frac{2}{3}x - 1$

EXAMPLE 4   Solve: $\dfrac{2(a + 3)}{3} = 6a + 2$

Solution   We clear the equation of fractions first.

$$\dfrac{2(a + 3)}{3} = 6a + 2$$

Step 1. $3 \cdot \dfrac{2(a + 3)}{3} = 3(6a + 2)$ Clear the fraction by multiplying both sides by the LCD, 3.

$$2(a + 3) = 3(6a + 2)$$

Step 2.   Next, we use the distributive property and remove parentheses.

$$2a + 6 = 18a + 6$$ Apply the distributive property.

Step 4. $2a + 6 - 6 = 18a + 6 - 6$ Subtract 6 from both sides.

$$2a = 18a$$

$$2a - 18a = 18a - 18a$$ Subtract 18a from both sides.

$$-16a = 0$$

Step 5. $\dfrac{-16a}{-16} = \dfrac{0}{-16}$ Divide both sides by −16.

$$a = 0$$ Write the fraction in simplest form.

Step 6.   To check, replace a with 0 in the original equation. The solution is 0.   □

PRACTICE
4   Solve: $\dfrac{4(y + 3)}{3} = 5y - 7$

....

▶ **Helpful Hint**
Remember: When solving an equation, it makes no difference on which side of the equation variable terms lie. Just make sure that constant terms lie on the other side.

OBJECTIVE
3   **Solving Equations Containing Decimals**

When solving a problem about money, you may need to solve an equation containing decimals. If you choose, you may multiply to clear the equation of decimals.

EXAMPLE 5   Solve: $0.25x + 0.10(x - 3) = 0.05(22)$

Solution   First we clear this equation of decimals by multiplying both sides of the equation by 100. Recall that multiplying a decimal number by 100 has the effect of moving the decimal point 2 places to the right.

$$0.25x + 0.10(x - 3) = 0.05(22)$$

▶ **Helpful Hint**
By the distributive property, 0.10 is multiplied by x and −3. Thus to multiply each term here by 100, we only need to multiply 0.10 by 100.

Step 1. $0.25x + 0.10(x - 3) = 0.05(22)$ Multiply both sides by 100.

$$25x + 10(x - 3) = 5(22)$$

Step 2. $25x + 10x - 30 = 110$ Apply the distributive property.

Step 3. $35x - 30 = 110$ Combine like terms.

Step 4. $35x - 30 + 30 = 110 + 30$ Add 30 to both sides.

$$35x = 140$$ Combine like terms.

Step 5.
$$\frac{35x}{35} = \frac{140}{35}$$ Divide both sides by 35.
$$x = 4$$

Step 6. To check, replace x with 4 in the original equation. The solution is 4. ☐

PRACTICE
5   Solve: $0.35x + 0.09(x + 4) = 0.03(12)$

OBJECTIVE
4   **Recognizing Identities and Equations with No Solution**

So far, each equation that we have solved has had a single solution. However, not every equation in one variable has a single solution. Some equations have no solution, while others have an infinite number of solutions. For example,

$$x + 5 = x + 7$$

has no solution since no matter which **real number** we replace x with, the equation is false.

real number $+ 5 =$ same real number $+ 7$ **FALSE**

On the other hand,

$$x + 6 = x + 6$$

has infinitely many solutions since x can be replaced by any real number and the equation is always true.

real number $+ 6 =$ same real number $+ 6$ **TRUE**

The equation $x + 6 = x + 6$ is called an **identity.** The next two examples illustrate special equations like these.

EXAMPLE 6   Solve: $-2(x - 5) + 10 = -3(x + 2) + x$
Solution

$$
\begin{aligned}
-2(x - 5) + 10 &= -3(x + 2) + x \\
-2x + 10 + 10 &= -3x - 6 + x \qquad \text{Apply the distributive property on both sides.} \\
-2x + 20 &= -2x - 6 \qquad \text{Combine like terms.} \\
-2x + 20 + 2x &= -2x - 6 + 2x \qquad \text{Add } 2x \text{ to both sides.} \\
20 &= -6 \qquad \text{Combine like terms.}
\end{aligned}
$$

The final equation contains no variable terms, and there is no value for x that makes $20 = -6$ a true equation. We conclude that there is **no solution** to this equation. In set notation, we can indicate that there is no solution with the empty set, $\{\ \}$, or use the empty set or null set symbol, $\varnothing$. In this chapter, we will simply write *no solution*. ☐

PRACTICE
6   Solve: $4(x + 4) - x = 2(x + 11) + x$

EXAMPLE 7   Solve: $3(x - 4) = 3x - 12$
Solution

$$
\begin{aligned}
3(x - 4) &= 3x - 12 \\
3x - 12 &= 3x - 12 \qquad \text{Apply the distributive property.}
\end{aligned}
$$

The left side of the equation is now identical to the right side. Every real number may be substituted for x and a true statement will result. We arrive at the same conclusion if we continue.

$$3x - 12 = 3x - 12$$
$$3x - 12 + 12 = 3x - 12 + 12 \quad \text{Add 12 to both sides.}$$
$$3x = 3x \quad \text{Combine like terms.}$$
$$3x - 3x = 3x - 3x \quad \text{Subtract } 3x \text{ from both sides.}$$
$$0 = 0$$

Again, one side of the equation is identical to the other side. Thus, $3(x - 4) = 3x - 12$ is an **identity** and **all real numbers** are solutions. In set notation, this is $\{\text{all real numbers}\}$.

PRACTICE
7 Solve: $12x - 18 = 9(x - 2) + 3x$

 CONCEPT CHECK

Suppose you have simplified several equations and obtain the following results. What can you conclude about the solutions to the original equation?

a. $7 = 7$ **b.** $x = 0$ **c.** $7 = -4$

Graphing Calculator Explorations

Checking Equations

We can use a calculator to check possible solutions of equations. To do this, replace the variable by the possible solution and evaluate both sides of the equation separately.

Equation: $3x - 4 = 2(x + 6)$ *Solution:* $x = 16$
$$3x - 4 = 2(x + 6) \quad \text{Original equation}$$
$$3(16) - 4 \overset{?}{=} 2(16 + 6) \quad \text{Replace } x \text{ with 16.}$$

Now evaluate each side with your calculator.

Evaluate left side:

$\boxed{3}\ \boxed{\times}\ \boxed{16}\ \boxed{-}\ \boxed{4}\ \boxed{=}$ or $\boxed{\text{ENTER}}$ Display: $\boxed{44}$ or $\boxed{\begin{matrix} 3*16 - 4 \\ \quad 44 \end{matrix}}$

Evaluate right side:

$\boxed{2}\ \boxed{(}\ \boxed{16}\ \boxed{+}\ \boxed{6}\ \boxed{)}\ \boxed{=}$ or $\boxed{\text{ENTER}}$ Display: $\boxed{44}$ or $\boxed{\begin{matrix} 2(16 + 6) \\ \quad 44 \end{matrix}}$

Since the left side equals the right side, the solution checks.

Use a calculator to check the possible solutions to each equation.

1. $2x = 48 + 6x;\quad x = -12$ **2.** $-3x - 7 = 3x - 1;\quad x = -1$

3. $5x - 2.6 = 2(x + 0.8);\quad x = 4.4$ **4.** $-1.6x - 3.9 = -6.9x - 25.6;\quad x = 5$

5. $\dfrac{564x}{4} = 200x - 11(649);\quad x = 121$ **6.** $20(x - 39) = 5x - 432;\quad x = 23.2$

Answers to Concept Check:
a. Every real number is a solution.
b. The solution is 0.
c. There is no solution.

Vocabulary, Readiness & Video Check

Throughout algebra, it is important to be able to identify equations and expressions.

Remember,
- an equation contains an equal sign and
- an expression does not.

Also,
- we solve equations and
- we simplify or perform operations on expressions.

Identify each as an equation or an expression.

1. $x = -7$ _____

2. $x - 7$ _____

3. $4y - 6 + 9y + 1$ _____

4. $4y - 6 = 9y + 1$ _____

5. $\dfrac{1}{x} - \dfrac{x-1}{8}$ _____

6. $\dfrac{1}{x} - \dfrac{x-1}{8} = 6$ _____

7. $0.1x + 9 = 0.2x$ _____

8. $0.1x^2 + 9y - 0.2x^2$ _____

Martin-Gay Interactive Videos

See Video 2.3 🍎

Watch the section lecture video and answer the following questions.

OBJECTIVE 1

9. The general strategy for solving linear equations in one variable is discussed after Example 1. How many properties are mentioned in this strategy and what are they?

OBJECTIVE 2

10. In the first step for solving Example 2, both sides of the equation are being multiplied by the LCD. Why is the distributive property mentioned?

OBJECTIVE 3

11. In Example 3, why is the number of decimal places in each term of the equation important?

OBJECTIVE 4

12. Complete each statement based on Examples 4 and 5.

When solving an equation and all variable terms subtract out:

a. If you have a true statement, then the equation has _____ solution(s).

b. If you have a false statement, then the equation has _____ solution (s).

2.3 Exercise Set MyMathLab®

Solve each equation. See Examples 1 and 2.

1. $-4y + 10 = -2(3y + 1)$

2. $-3x + 1 = -2(4x + 2)$

3. $15x - 8 = 10 + 9x$

4. $15x - 5 = 7 + 12x$

5. $-2(3x - 4) = 2x$

6. $-(5x - 10) = 5x$

⊙ 7. $5(2x - 1) - 2(3x) = 1$

8. $3(2 - 5x) + 4(6x) = 12$

9. $-6(x - 3) - 26 = -8$

10. $-4(n - 4) - 23 = -7$

11. $8 - 2(a + 1) = 9 + a$

12. $5 - 6(2 + b) = b - 14$

13. $4x + 3 = -3 + 2x + 14$

14. $6y - 8 = -6 + 3y + 13$

15. $-2y - 10 = 5y + 18$

16. $-7n + 5 = 8n - 10$

Solve each equation. See Examples 3 through 5.

17. $\dfrac{2}{3}x + \dfrac{4}{3} = -\dfrac{2}{3}$

18. $\dfrac{4}{5}x - \dfrac{8}{5} = -\dfrac{16}{5}$

19. $\dfrac{3}{4}x - \dfrac{1}{2} = 1$

20. $\dfrac{2}{9}x - \dfrac{1}{3} = 1$

⊙ 21. $0.50x + 0.15(70) = 35.5$

22. $0.40x + 0.06(30) = 9.8$

23. $\dfrac{2(x + 1)}{4} = 3x - 2$

24. $\dfrac{3(y + 3)}{5} = 2y + 6$

25. $x + \dfrac{7}{6} = 2x - \dfrac{7}{6}$

26. $\dfrac{5}{2}x - 1 = x + \dfrac{1}{4}$

27. $0.12(y - 6) + 0.06y = 0.08y - 0.70$

28. $0.60(z - 300) + 0.05z = 0.70z - 205$

Solve each equation. See Examples 6 and 7.

29. $4(3x + 2) = 12x + 8$

30. $14x + 7 = 7(2x + 1)$

31. $\dfrac{x}{4} + 1 = \dfrac{x}{4}$

32. $\dfrac{x}{3} - 2 = \dfrac{x}{3}$

33. $3x - 7 = 3(x + 1)$

34. $2(x - 5) = 2x + 10$

35. $-2(6x - 5) + 4 = -12x + 14$

36. $-5(4y - 3) + 2 = -20y + 17$

MIXED PRACTICE

Solve. See Examples 1 through 7.

37. $\dfrac{6(3 - z)}{5} = -z$

38. $\dfrac{4(5 - w)}{3} = -w$

39. $-3(2t - 5) + 2t = 5t - 4$

40. $-(4a - 7) - 5a = 10 + a$

41. $5y + 2(y - 6) = 4(y + 1) - 2$

42. $9x + 3(x - 4) = 10(x - 5) + 7$

43. $\dfrac{3(x - 5)}{2} = \dfrac{2(x + 5)}{3}$

44. $\dfrac{5(x - 1)}{4} = \dfrac{3(x + 1)}{2}$

45. $0.7x - 2.3 = 0.5$

46. $0.9x - 4.1 = 0.4$

▶ **47.** $5x - 5 = 2(x + 1) + 3x - 7$

48. $3(2x - 1) + 5 = 6x + 2$

49. $4(2n + 1) = 3(6n + 3) + 1$

50. $4(4y + 2) = 2(1 + 6y) + 8$

51. $x + \dfrac{5}{4} = \dfrac{3}{4}x$

52. $\dfrac{7}{8}x + \dfrac{1}{4} = \dfrac{3}{4}x$ ▶ **53.** $\dfrac{x}{2} - 1 = \dfrac{x}{5} + 2$

54. $\dfrac{x}{5} - 7 = \dfrac{x}{3} - 5$

▶ **55.** $2(x + 3) - 5 = 5x - 3(1 + x)$

56. $4(2 + x) + 1 = 7x - 3(x - 2)$

57. $0.06 - 0.01(x + 1) = -0.02(2 - x)$

58. $-0.01(5x + 4) = 0.04 - 0.01(x + 4)$

59. $\dfrac{9}{2} + \dfrac{5}{2}y = 2y - 4$

60. $3 - \dfrac{1}{2}x = 5x - 8$

61. $-2y - 10 = 5y + 18$

62. $7n + 5 = 10n - 10$

63. $0.6x - 0.1 = 0.5x + 0.2$

64. $0.2x - 0.1 = 0.6x - 2.1$

65. $0.02(6t - 3) = 0.12(t - 2) + 0.18$

66. $0.03(2m + 7) = 0.06(5 + m) - 0.09$

TRANSLATING

Write each phrase as an algebraic expression. Use x for the unknown number. See Section 2.1.

67. A number subtracted from -8

68. Three times a number

69. The sum of -3 and twice a number

70. The difference of 8 and twice a number

71. The product of 9 and the sum of a number and 20

72. The quotient of -12 and the difference of a number and 3

See Section 2.1.

73. A plot of land is in the shape of a triangle. If one side is x meters, a second side is $(2x - 3)$ meters, and a third side is $(3x - 5)$ meters, express the perimeter of the lot as a simplified expression in x.

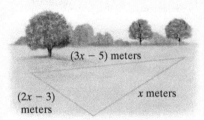

See Section 2.2.

74. A portion of a board has length x feet. The other part has length $(7x - 9)$ feet. Express the total length of the board as a simplified expression in x.

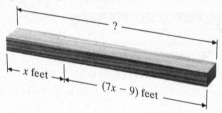

CONCEPT EXTENSIONS

See the Concept Check in this section.

75. a. Solve: $x + 3 = x + 3$

    b. If you simplify an equation and get $0 = 0$, what can you conclude about the solution(s) of the original equation?

    c. On your own, construct an equation for which every real number is a solution.

76. a. Solve: $x + 3 = x + 5$

    b. If you simplify an equation and get $3 = 5$, what can you conclude about the solution(s) of the original equation?

    c. On your own, construct an equation that has no solution.

For Exercises 77 through 82, match each equation in the first column with its solution in the second column. Items in the second column may be used more than once.

77. $5x + 1 = 5x + 1$

78. $3x + 1 = 3x + 2$

79. $2x - 6x - 10 = -4x + 3 - 10$

80. $x - 11x - 3 = -10x - 1 - 2$

81. $9x - 20 = 8x - 20$

82. $-x + 15 = x + 15$

A. all real numbers

B. no solution

C. 0

83. Explain the difference between simplifying an expression and solving an equation.

84. On your own, write an expression and then an equation. Label each.

For Exercises 85 and 86, **a.** *Write an equation for perimeter.* **b.** *Solve the equation in part (a).* **c.** *Find the length of each side.*

85. The perimeter of a geometric figure is the sum of the lengths of its sides. The perimeter of the following pentagon (five-sided figure) is 28 centimeters.

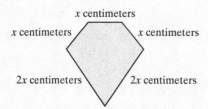

x centimeters

x centimeters x centimeters

$2x$ centimeters $2x$ centimeters

86. The perimeter of the following triangle is 35 meters.

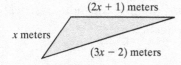

$(2x + 1)$ meters

x meters

$(3x - 2)$ meters

Fill in the blanks with numbers of your choice so that each equation has the given solution. Note: Each blank may be replaced by a different number.

87. $x + \underline{\quad} = 2x - \underline{\quad}$; solution: 9

88. $-5x - \underline{\quad} = \underline{\quad}$; solution: 2

Solve.

89. $1000(7x - 10) = 50(412 + 100x)$

90. $1000(x + 40) = 100(16 + 7x)$

91. $0.035x + 5.112 = 0.010x + 5.107$

92. $0.127x - 2.685 = 0.027x - 2.38$

For Exercises 93 through 96, see the example below.

Example

Solve: $t(t + 4) = t^2 - 2t + 6$.

Solution
$$t(t + 4) = t^2 - 2t + 6$$
$$t^2 + 4t = t^2 - 2t + 6$$
$$t^2 + 4t - t^2 = t^2 - 2t + 6 - t^2$$
$$4t = -2t + 6$$
$$4t + 2t = -2t + 6 + 2t$$
$$6t = 6$$
$$t = 1$$

Solve each equation.

93. $x(x - 3) = x^2 + 5x + 7$

94. $t^2 - 6t = t(8 + t)$

95. $2z(z + 6) = 2z^2 + 12z - 8$

96. $y^2 - 4y + 10 = y(y - 5)$

Integrated Review   SOLVING LINEAR EQUATIONS

Sections 2.1–2.3

Solve. Feel free to use the steps given in Section 2.3.

1. $x - 10 = -4$

2. $y + 14 = -3$

3. $9y = 108$

4. $-3x = 78$

5. $-6x + 7 = 25$

6. $5y - 42 = -47$

7. $\frac{2}{3}x = 9$

8. $\frac{4}{5}z = 10$

9. $\frac{r}{-4} = -2$

10. $\frac{y}{-8} = 8$

11. $6 - 2x + 8 = 10$

12. $-5 - 6y + 6 = 19$

13. $2x - 7 = 2x - 27$

14. $3 + 8y = 8y - 2$

15. $-3a + 6 + 5a = 7a - 8a$

16. $4b - 8 - b = 10b - 3b$

17. $-\frac{2}{3}x = \frac{5}{9}$

18. $-\frac{3}{8}y = -\frac{1}{16}$

19. $10 = -6n + 16$

20. $-5 = -2m + 7$

21. $3(5c - 1) - 2 = 13c + 3$

22. $4(3t + 4) - 20 = 3 + 5t$

23. $\frac{2(z + 3)}{3} = 5 - z$

24. $\frac{3(w + 2)}{4} = 2w + 3$

25. $-2(2x - 5) = -3x + 7 - x + 3$

26. $-4(5x - 2) = -12x + 4 - 8x + 4$

27. $0.02(6t - 3) = 0.04(t - 2) + 0.02$

28. $0.03(m + 7) = 0.02(5 - m) + 0.03$

29. $-3y = \dfrac{4(y-1)}{5}$ **30.** $-4x = \dfrac{5(1-x)}{6}$ **35.** $\dfrac{1}{10}(3x - 7) = \dfrac{3}{10}x + 5$

31. $\dfrac{5}{3}x - \dfrac{7}{3} = x$ **32.** $\dfrac{7}{5}n + \dfrac{3}{5} = -n$ **36.** $\dfrac{1}{7}(2x - 5) = \dfrac{2}{7}x + 1$

33. $9(3x - 1) = -4 + 49$

34. $12(2x + 1) = -6 + 66$

37. $5 + 2(3x - 6) = -4(6x - 7)$

38. $3 + 5(2x - 4) = -7(5x + 2)$

2.4   An Introduction to Problem Solving

OBJECTIVES

Apply the steps for problem solving as we

1 Solve Problems Involving Direct Translations.

2 Solve Problems Involving Relationships Among Unknown Quantities.

3 Solve Problems Involving Consecutive Integers.

OBJECTIVE
1   **Solving Direct Translation Problems**

In previous sections, we practiced writing word phrases and sentences as algebraic expressions and equations to help prepare for problem solving. We now use these translations to help write equations that model a problem. The problem-solving steps given next may be helpful.

General Strategy for Problem Solving

1. UNDERSTAND the problem. During this step, become comfortable with the problem. Some ways of doing this are to:

    Read and reread the problem.

    Choose a variable to represent the unknown.

    Construct a drawing whenever possible.

    Propose a solution and check. Pay careful attention to how you check your proposed solution. This will help when writing an equation to model the problem.

2. TRANSLATE the problem into an equation.

3. SOLVE the equation.

4. INTERPRET the results: *Check* the proposed solution in the stated problem and state your conclusion.

Much of problem solving involves a direct translation from a sentence to an equation.

EXAMPLE 1   **Finding an Unknown Number**

Twice a number, added to seven, is the same as three subtracted from the number. Find the number.

Solution   Translate the sentence into an equation and solve.

In words:	twice a number	added to	seven	is the same as	three subtracted from the number
	↓	↓	↓	↓	↓
Translate:	$2x$	$+$	7	$=$	$x - 3$

> ▶ Helpful Hint
> Order matters when subtracting (and dividing), so be especially careful with these translations.

To solve, begin by subtracting x from both sides to get all variable terms on one side.

$$2x + 7 = x - 3$$

$2x + 7 - x = x - 3 - x$ Subtract x from both sides.

$x + 7 = -3$ Combine like terms.

$x + 7 - 7 = -3 - 7$ Subtract 7 from both sides.

$x = -10$ Combine like terms.

Check the solution in the problem as it was originally stated. To do so, replace "number" in the sentence with -10. Twice "-10" added to 7 is the same as 3 subtracted from "-10."

$$2(-10) + 7 = -10 - 3$$
$$-13 = -13$$

The unknown number is -10.

PRACTICE

1   Three times a number, minus 6, is the same as two times a number, plus 3. Find the number.

▶ **Helpful Hint**

When checking solutions, go back to the original stated problem, rather than to your equation, in case errors have been made in translating to an equation.

EXAMPLE 2   **Finding an Unknown Number**

Twice the sum of a number and 4 is the same as four times the number, decreased by 12. Find the number.

Solution

1. UNDERSTAND. Read and reread the problem. If we let

$$x = \text{the unknown number, then}$$

"the sum of a number and 4" translates to "$x + 4$" and "four times the number" translates to "$4x$."

2. TRANSLATE.

twice	the sum of a number and 4	is the same as	four times the number	decreased by	12
↓	↓	↓	↓	↓	↓
2	$(x + 4)$	=	$4x$	−	12

3. SOLVE.

$$2(x + 4) = 4x - 12$$
$$2x + 8 = 4x - 12 \qquad \text{Apply the distributive property.}$$
$$2x + 8 - 4x = 4x - 12 - 4x \quad \text{Subtract } 4x \text{ from both sides.}$$
$$-2x + 8 = -12$$
$$-2x + 8 - 8 = -12 - 8 \qquad \text{Subtract 8 from both sides.}$$
$$-2x = -20$$
$$\frac{-2x}{-2} = \frac{-20}{-2} \qquad \text{Divide both sides by } -2.$$
$$x = 10$$

4. INTERPRET.

Check: Check this solution in the problem as it was originally stated. To do so, replace "number" with 10. Twice the sum of "10" and 4 is 28, which is the same as 4 times "10" decreased by 12.

State: The number is 10.

PRACTICE

2   Three times a number, decreased by 4, is the same as double the difference of the number and 1.

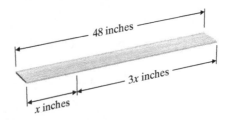

OBJECTIVE

2 **Solving Problems Involving Relationships Among Unknown Quantities** ▶

The next three examples have to do with relationships among unknown quantities.

EXAMPLE 3 **Finding the Length of a Board**

Balsa wood sticks are commonly used for building models (for example, bridge models). A 48-inch balsa wood stick is to be cut into two pieces so that the longer piece is 3 times the shorter. Find the length of each piece.

Solution

1. UNDERSTAND the problem. To do so, read and reread the problem. You may also want to propose a solution. For example, if 10 inches represents the length of the shorter piece, then $3(10) = 30$ inches is the length of the longer piece, since it is 3 times the length of the shorter piece. This guess gives a total stick length of 10 inches + 30 inches = 40 inches, too short. However, the purpose of proposing a solution is not to guess correctly but to help understand the problem better and how to model it.

   Since the length of the longer piece is given in terms of the length of the shorter piece, let's let

   x = length of shorter piece; then

   $3x$ = length of longer piece

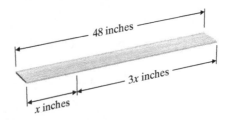

2. TRANSLATE the problem. First, we write the equation in words.

length of shorter piece	added to	length of longer piece	equals	total length of stick
↓	↓	↓	↓	↓
x	+	$3x$	=	48

3. SOLVE.

$$x + 3x = 48$$
$$4x = 48 \quad \text{Combine like terms.}$$
$$\frac{4x}{4} = \frac{48}{4} \quad \text{Divide both sides by 4.}$$
$$x = 12$$

4. INTERPRET.

Check: Check the solution in the stated problem. If the shorter piece of stick is 12 inches, the longer piece is $3 \cdot (12 \text{ inches}) = 36$ inches, and the sum of the two pieces is 12 inches + 36 inches = 48 inches.

State: The shorter piece of balsa wood is 12 inches, and the longer piece of balsa wood is 36 inches.

▶ Helpful Hint
Make sure that units are included in your answer, if appropriate.

PRACTICE

3 A 45-inch board is to be cut into two pieces so that the longer piece is 4 times the shorter. Find the length of each piece.

EXAMPLE 4   **Finding the Number of Republican and Democratic Representatives**

The 112th Congress began on January 3, 2011, and had a total of 435 Democrat and Republican representatives. There were 49 fewer Democratic representatives than Republican. Find the number of representatives from each party. (*Source:* Wikipedia.com)

Solution:

1. **UNDERSTAND** the problem. Read and reread the problem. Let's suppose that there were 200 Republican representatives. Since there were 49 fewer Democrats than Republicans, there must have been $200 - 49 = 151$ Democrats. The total number of Republicans and Democrats was then $200 + 151 = 351$. This is incorrect since the total should be 435, but we now have a better understanding of the problem.

In general, if we let

$$x = \text{number of Republicans, then}$$
$$x - 49 = \text{number of Democrats}$$

2. **TRANSLATE** the problem. First, we write the equation in words.

number of Republicans	added to	number of Democrats	equals	435
↓	↓	↓	↓	↓
x	$+$	$(x - 49)$	$=$	435

3. **SOLVE.**

$$x + (x - 49) = 435$$
$$2x - 49 = 435 \qquad \text{Combine like terms.}$$
$$2x - 49 + 49 = 435 + 49 \qquad \text{Add 49 to both sides.}$$
$$2x = 484$$
$$\frac{2x}{2} = \frac{484}{2} \qquad \text{Divide both sides by 2.}$$
$$x = 242$$

4. **INTERPRET.**

Check: If there were 242 Republican representatives, then there were $242 - 49 = 193$ Democratic representatives. The total number of representatives was then $242 + 193 = 435$. The results check.

State: There were 242 Republican and 193 Democratic representatives at the beginning of the 112th Congress.   □

PRACTICE

4   In 2011, there were 9 fewer Democratic State Governors than Republican State Governors. Find the number of State Governors from each party. Rhode Island had an independent governor, so use a total of 49, representing the other 49 states. (*Source:* National Conference of State Legislatures).

 EXAMPLE 5   **Finding Angle Measures**

If the two walls of the Vietnam Veterans Memorial in Washington, D.C., were connected, an isosceles triangle would be formed. The measure of the third angle is 97.5° more than the measure of either of the other two equal angles. Find the measure of the third angle. (*Source:* National Park Service)

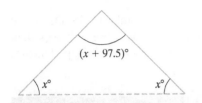

Solution

1. UNDERSTAND. Read and reread the problem. We then draw a diagram (recall that an isosceles triangle has two angles with the same measure) and let

$$x = \text{degree measure of one angle}$$
$$x = \text{degree measure of the second equal angle}$$
$$x + 97.5 = \text{degree measure of the third angle}$$

2. TRANSLATE. Recall that the sum of the measures of the angles of a triangle equals 180.

measure of first angle		measure of second angle		measure of third angle		equals		180
↓		↓		↓		↓		↓
x	+	x	+	$(x + 97.5)$		=		180

3. SOLVE.

$$x + x + (x + 97.5) = 180$$

$$3x + 97.5 = 180 \qquad \text{Combine like terms.}$$

$$3x + 97.5 - 97.5 = 180 - 97.5 \quad \text{Subtract 97.5 from both sides.}$$

$$3x = 82.5$$

$$\frac{3x}{3} = \frac{82.5}{3} \qquad \text{Divide both sides by 3.}$$

$$x = 27.5$$

4. INTERPRET.

Check: If $x = 27.5$, then the measure of the third angle is $x + 97.5 = 125$. The sum of the angles is then $27.5 + 27.5 + 125 = 180$, the correct sum.

State: The third angle measures 125°.*

PRACTICE

5   The second angle of a triangle measures three times as large as the first. If the third angle measures 55° more than the first, find the measures of all three angles.

OBJECTIVE

3   Solving Consecutive Integer Problems

The next example has to do with consecutive integers. Recall what we have learned thus far about these integers.

	Example	*General Representation*
Consecutive Integers	11, 12, 13 +1 +1	Let x be an integer. x, $x + 1$, $x + 2$ +1 +1
Consecutive Even Integers	38, 40, 42 +2 +2	Let x be an even integer. x, $x + 2$, $x + 4$ +2 +2
Consecutive Odd Integers	57, 59, 61 +2 +2	Let x be an odd integer. x, $x + 2$, $x + 4$ +2 +2

*The two walls actually meet at an angle of 125 degrees 12 minutes. The measurement of 97.5° given in the problem is an approximation.

EXAMPLE 6   Some states have a single area code for the entire state. Two such states have area codes that are consecutive odd integers. If the sum of these integers is 1208, find the two area codes. (*Source:* North American Numbering Plan Administration)

Solution:

1. UNDERSTAND. Read and reread the problem. If we let

$$x = \text{the first odd integer, then}$$
$$x + 2 = \text{the next odd integer}$$

> **▶ Helpful Hint**
> Remember, the 2 here means that odd integers are 2 units apart, for example, the odd integers 13 and 13 + 2 = 15.

2. TRANSLATE.

first odd integer	the sum of	next odd integer	is	1208
↓	↓	↓	↓	↓
x	$+$	$(x + 2)$	$=$	1208

3. SOLVE.

$$x + x + 2 = 1208$$
$$2x + 2 = 1208$$
$$2x + 2 - 2 = 1208 - 2$$
$$2x = 1206$$
$$\frac{2x}{2} = \frac{1206}{2}$$
$$x = 603$$

4. INTERPRET.

Check: If $x = 603$, then the next odd integer $x + 2 = 603 + 2 = 605$. Notice their sum, $603 + 605 = 1208$, as needed.

State: The area codes are 603 and 605.

Note: New Hampshire's area code is 603 and South Dakota's area code is 605.

PRACTICE
6   The sum of three consecutive even integers is 144. Find the integers.

Vocabulary, Readiness & Video Check

Fill in the table.

1.	A number: → x	Double the number:	→ Double the number, decreased by 31:
2.	A number: → x	Three times the number:	→ Three times the number, increased by 17:
3.	A number: → x	The sum of the number and 5:	→ Twice the sum of the number and 5:
4.	A number: → x	The difference of the number and 11:	→ Seven times the difference of a number and 11:
5.	A number: → y	The difference of 20 and the number:	→ The difference of 20 and the number, divided by 3:
6.	A number: → y	The sum of −10 and the number:	→ The sum of −10 and the number, divided by 9:

Martin-Gay Interactive Videos

See Video 2.4

Watch the section lecture video and answer the following questions.

OBJECTIVE 1

7. At the end of Example 1, where are you told is the best place to check the solution of an application problem?

OBJECTIVE 2

8. The solution of the equation for Example 3 is $x = 43$. Why is this not the solution to the application?

OBJECTIVE 3

9. What are two things that should be checked to make sure the solution of Example 4 is correct?

2.4 Exercise Set   MyMathLab®

TRANSLATING

Write each of the following as an equation. Then solve. See Examples 1 and 2.

1. The sum of six times a number, and 1, is equal to five times the number. Find the number.

2. The difference of three times a number, and 1, is the same as twice the number. Find the number.

3. Three times a number, minus 6, is equal to two times the number, plus 8. Find the number.

4. The sum of 4 times a number, and −2, is equal to the sum of 5 times the number, and −2. Find the number.

5. Twice the difference of a number and 8 is equal to three times the sum of the number and 3. Find the number.

6. Five times the sum of a number and −1 is the same as 6 times the difference of the number and 5. Find the number.

7. Twice the sum of −2 and a number is the same as the number decreased by $\frac{1}{2}$. Find the number.

8. If the difference of a number and four is doubled, the result is $\frac{1}{4}$ less than the number. Find the number.

Solve. For Exercises 9 and 10, the solutions have been started for you. See Examples 3 through 5.

9. A 25-inch piece of steel is cut into three pieces so that the second piece is twice as long as the first piece, and the third piece is one inch more than five times the length of the first piece. Find the lengths of the pieces.

Start the solution:

1. UNDERSTAND the problem. Reread it as many times as needed.

2. TRANSLATE into an equation. (Fill in the blanks below.)

total length of steel	equals	length of first piece	plus	length of second piece	plus	length of third piece
↓	↓	↓	↓	↓	↓	↓
25	=	___	+	___	+	___

Finish with:

3. SOLVE and   **4.** INTERPRET

10. A 46-foot piece of rope is cut into three pieces so that the second piece is three times as long as the first piece, and the third piece is two feet more than seven times the length of the first piece. Find the lengths of the pieces.

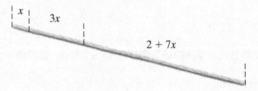

Start the solution:

1. UNDERSTAND the problem. Reread it as many times as needed.

2. TRANSLATE into an equation. (Fill in the blanks below.)

total length of rope	equals	length of first piece	plus	length of second piece	plus	length of third piece
↓	↓	↓	↓	↓	↓	↓
46	=	___	+	___	+	___

Finish with:

3. SOLVE and   **4.** INTERPRET

11. A 40-inch board is to be cut into three pieces so that the second piece is twice as long as the first piece, and the third piece is 5 times as long as the first piece. If x represents the length of the first piece, find the lengths of all three pieces.

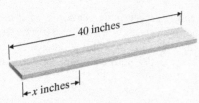

12. A 21-foot beam is to be cut into three pieces so that the second and the third piece are each 3 times the length of the first piece. If x represents the length of the shorter piece, find the lengths of all three pieces.

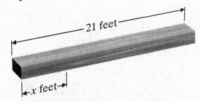

For Exercises 13 and 14, use each table to find the value of x. Then write a sentence to explain, in words, the meaning and the value of x. (Source: IHS Screen Digest)

13. The fastest growing type of movie screen in 2010 was 3D.

Type of Screen	Number of Screens
3D	x
Non-3D	23,873 more than x
Total screens	39,547

14. The majority of movie screens in the United States in 2010 were located at sites with five or more screens.

Type of Site	Number of Screens
Smaller (1–4 screens)	x
Larger (5 or more screens)	22,857 more than x
Total screens	39,547

15. The flag of Equatorial Guinea contains an isosceles triangle. (Recall that an isosceles triangle contains two angles with the same measure.) If the measure of the third angle of the triangle is 30° more than twice the measure of either of the other two angles, find the measure of each angle of the triangle. (*Hint:* Recall that the sum of the measures of the angles of a triangle is 180°.)

16. The flag of Brazil contains a parallelogram. One angle of the parallelogram is 15° less than twice the measure of the angle next to it. Find the measure of each angle of the parallelogram. (*Hint:* Recall that opposite angles of a parallelogram have the same measure and that the sum of the measures of the angles is 360°.)

Solve. See Example 6. For Exercises 17 through 24, fill in the table. Most of the first row has been completed for you.

	First Integer →	Next Integers	→	Indicated Sum
17. Three consecutive integers:	Integer: x	$x + 1$ $x + 2$		Sum of the three consecutive integers, simplified:
18. Three consecutive integers:	Integer: x			Sum of the second and third consecutive integers, simplified:
19. Three consecutive even integers:	Even integer: x			Sum of the first and third even consecutive integers, simplified:
20. Three consecutive odd integers:	Odd integer: x			Sum of the three consecutive odd integers, simplified:
21. Four consecutive integers:	Integer: x			Sum of the four consecutive integers, simplified:
22. Four consecutive integers:	Integer: x			Sum of the first and fourth consecutive integers, simplified:
23. Three consecutive odd integers:	Odd integer: x			Sum of the second and third consecutive odd integers, simplified:
24. Three consecutive even integers:	Even integer: x			Sum of the three consecutive even integers, simplified:

25. The left and right page numbers of an open book are two consecutive integers whose sum is 469. Find these page numbers.

26. The room numbers of two adjacent classrooms are two consecutive even numbers. If their sum is 654, find the classroom numbers.

27. To make an international telephone call, you need the code for the country you are calling. The codes for Belgium, France, and Spain are three consecutive integers whose sum is 99. Find the code for each country. (*Source: The World Almanac and Book of Facts*, 2007)

28. To make an international telephone call, you need the code for the country you are calling. The codes for Mali Republic, Côte d'Ivoire, and Niger are three consecutive odd integers whose sum is 675. Find the code for each country.

MIXED PRACTICE

Solve. See Examples 1 through 6.

29. The area of the Sahara Desert is 7 times the area of the Gobi Desert. If the sum of their areas is 4,000,000 square miles, find the area of each desert.

30. The largest meteorite in the world is the Hoba West, located in Namibia. Its weight is 3 times the weight of the Armanty meteorite, located in Outer Mongolia. If the sum of their weights is 88 tons, find the weight of each.

31. A 17-foot piece of string is cut into two pieces so that the longer piece is 2 feet longer than twice the length of the shorter piece. Find the lengths of both pieces.

32. A 25-foot wire is to be cut so that the longer piece is one foot longer than 5 times the length of the shorter piece. Find the length of each piece.

33. Five times a number, subtracted from ten, is triple the number. Find the number.

34. Nine is equal to ten subtracted from double a number. Find the number.

35. The greatest producer of diamonds in carats is Botswana. This country produces about four times the amount produced in Angola. If the total produced in both countries is 40,000,000 carats, find the amount produced in each country. (*Source: Diamond Facts.*)

36. Beetles have the greatest number of different species. There are twenty times the number of beetle species as grasshopper species, and the total number of species for both is 420,000. Find the number of species for each type of insect.

37. The measures of the angles of a triangle are 3 consecutive even integers. Find the measure of each angle.

38. A quadrilateral is a polygon with 4 sides. The sum of the measures of the 4 angles in a quadrilateral is 360°. If the measures of the angles of a quadrilateral are consecutive odd integers, find the measures.

39. For the 2010 Winter Olympics, the total number of medals won by athletes from each of the countries of South Korea, Russia, and Austria are three consecutive integers whose sum is 45. Find the number of medals for each country.

40. The code to unlock a student's combination lock happens to be three consecutive odd integers whose sum is 51. Find the integers.

41. If the sum of a number and five is tripled, the result is one less than twice the number. Find the number.

42. Twice the sum of a number and six equals three times the sum of the number and four. Find the number.

43. Two angles are supplementary if their sum is 180°. The larger angle measures eight degrees more than three times the measure of a smaller angle. If x represents the measure of the smaller angle and these two angles are supplementary, find the measure of each angle.

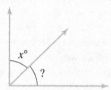

44. Two angles are complementary if their sum is 90°. The larger angle measures three degrees less than twice the measure of a smaller angle. If x represents the measure of the smaller angle and these two angles are complementary, find the measure of each angle.

45. If the quotient of a number and 4 is added to $\frac{1}{2}$, the result is $\frac{3}{4}$. Find the number.

46. The sum of $\frac{1}{5}$ and twice a number is equal to $\frac{4}{5}$ subtracted from three times the number. Find the number.

47. The sum of $\frac{2}{3}$ and four times a number is equal to $\frac{5}{6}$ subtracted from five times the number. Find the number.

48. If $\frac{3}{4}$ is added to three times a number, the result is $\frac{1}{2}$ subtracted from twice the number. Find the number.

49. Currently, the two fastest trains are the Japanese Maglev and the French TGV. The sum of their fastest speeds is 718.2 miles per hour. If the speed of the Maglev is 3.8 mph faster than the speed of the TGV, find the speeds of each.

50. The Pentagon is the world's largest office building in terms of floor space. It has three times the amount of floor space as the Empire State Building. If the total floor space for these two buildings is approximately 8700 thousand square feet, find the floor space of each building.

51. One-third of a number is five-sixths. Find the number.

52. Seven-eighths of a number is one-half. Find the number.

53. The number of counties in California and the number of counties in Montana are consecutive even integers whose sum is 114. If California has more counties than Montana, how many counties does each state have? (*Source: The World Almanac and Book of Facts*)

54. A student is building a bookcase with stepped shelves for her dorm room. She buys a 48-inch board and wants to cut the board into three pieces with lengths equal to three consecutive even integers. Find the three board lengths.

55. A geodesic dome, based on the design by Buckminster Fuller, is composed of two types of triangular panels. One of these is an isosceles triangle. In one geodesic dome, the measure of the third angle is 76.5° more than the measure of either of the two equal angles. Find the measure of the third angle. (*Source:* Buckminster Fuller Institute)

56. The measures of the angles of a particular triangle are such that the second and third angles are each four times larger than the smallest angle. Find the measures of the angles of this triangle.

57. A 30-foot piece of siding is cut into three pieces so that the second piece is four times as long as the first piece and the third piece is five times as long as the first piece. If x represents the length of the first piece, find the lengths of all three pieces.

58. A 48-foot-long piece of cable wire is to be cut into three pieces so that the second piece is five times as long as the first piece and the third piece is six times as long as the first piece. If x represents the length of the first piece, find the lengths of all three pieces.

The graph below shows the best-selling albums of all time. Use this graph for Exercises 59 through 64.

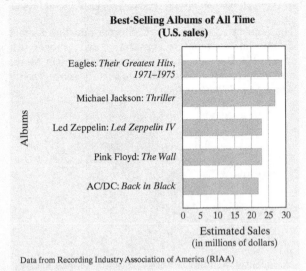

Best-Selling Albums of All Time
(U.S. sales)

Data from Recording Industry Association of America (RIAA)

(*Note:* These numbers are before the death of Michael Jackson.)

59. Which album is the best-selling album of all time?

60. Which albums had total sales between $20 million and $25 million?

61. *Thriller* and *The Wall* had sales worth a total of $50 million. *Thriller* brought in $4 million more than *The Wall*. Find the amount of sales that each album brought in.

62. Eagles: *Their Greatest Hits, 1971–1975*, and AC/DC: *Back in Black* had sales worth $51 million. Eagles: *Their Greatest Hits, 1971–1975*, sold $7 million more than AC/DC: *Back in Black*. Find the amount of sales for each album.

Compare the lengths of the bars in the graph with your results for the exercises below. Are your answers reasonable?

63. Exercise 61   **64.** Exercise 62

REVIEW AND PREVIEW

Evaluate each expression for the given values. See Section 1.4.

65. $2W + 2L$; $W = 7$ and $L = 10$

66. $\frac{1}{2}Bh$; $B = 14$ and $h = 22$

67. πr^2; $r = 15$ **68.** $r \cdot t$; $r = 15$ and $t = 2$

CONCEPT EXTENSIONS

69. A golden rectangle is a rectangle whose length is approximately 1.6 times its width. The early Greeks thought that a rectangle with these dimensions was the most pleasing to the eye, and examples of the golden rectangle are found in many early works of art. For example, the Parthenon in Athens contains many examples of golden rectangles.

Mike Hallahan would like to plant a rectangular garden in the shape of a golden rectangle. If he has 78 feet of fencing available, find the dimensions of the garden.

70. Dr. Dorothy Smith gave the students in her geometry class at the University of New Orleans the following question. Is it possible to construct a triangle such that the second angle of the triangle has a measure that is twice the measure of the first angle and the measure of the third angle is 5 times the measure of the first? If so, find the measure of each angle. (*Hint:* Recall that the sum of the measures of the angles of a triangle is 180°.)

71. Only male crickets chirp. They chirp at different rates depending on their species and the temperature of their environment. Suppose a certain species is currently chirping at a rate of 90 chirps per minute. At this rate, how many chirps occur in one hour? In one 24-hour day? In one year?

72. The human eye blinks once every 5 seconds on average. How many times does the average eye blink in one hour? In one 16-hour day while awake? In one year while awake?

73. In your own words, explain why a solution of a word problem should be checked using the original wording of the problem and not the equation written from the wording.

74. Give an example of how you recently solved a problem using mathematics.

Recall from Exercise 69 that a golden rectangle is a rectangle whose length is approximately 1.6 times its width.

75. It is thought that for about 75% of adults, a rectangle in the shape of the golden rectangle is the most pleasing to the eye. Draw three rectangles, one in the shape of the golden rectangle, and poll your class. Do the results agree with the percentage given above?

76. Examples of golden rectangles can be found today in architecture and manufacturing packaging. Find an example of a golden rectangle in your home. A few suggestions: the front face of a book, the floor of a room, the front of a box of food.

For Exercises 77 and 78, measure the dimensions of each rectangle and decide which one best approximates the shape of a golden rectangle.

77.

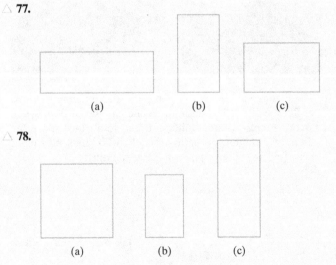

(a)   (b)   (c)

78.

(a)   (b)   (c)

2.5   Formulas and Problem Solving

OBJECTIVES

1 Use Formulas to Solve Problems.

2 Solve a Formula or Equation for One of Its Variables.

OBJECTIVE

1   Using Formulas to Solve Problems

An equation that describes a known relationship among quantities, such as distance, time, volume, weight, and money, is called a **formula.** These quantities are represented by letters and are thus variables of the formula. Here are some common formulas and their meanings.

Formulas	*Their Meanings*
$A = lw$	Area of a rectangle = length · width
$I = PRT$	Simple interest = principal · rate · time
$P = a + b + c$	Perimeter of a triangle = side a + side b + side c
$d = rt$	distance = rate · time
$V = lwh$	Volume of a rectangular solid = length · width · height
$F = \left(\dfrac{9}{5}\right)C + 32$ or $F = 1.8C + 32$	degrees Fahrenheit = $\left(\dfrac{9}{5}\right)$ · degrees Celsius + 32

Formulas are valuable tools because they allow us to calculate measurements as long as we know certain other measurements. For example, if we know we traveled a distance of 100 miles at a rate of 40 miles per hour, we can replace the variables d and r in the formula $d = rt$ and find our time, t.

$$d = rt \qquad \text{Formula.}$$
$$100 = 40t \qquad \text{Replace } d \text{ with 100 and } r \text{ with 40.}$$

This is a linear equation in one variable, t. To solve for t, divide both sides of the equation by 40.

$$\frac{100}{40} = \frac{40t}{40} \qquad \text{Divide both sides by 40.}$$
$$\frac{5}{2} = t \qquad \text{Simplify.}$$

The time traveled is $\dfrac{5}{2}$ hours, or $2\dfrac{1}{2}$ hours, or 2.5 hours.

In this section, we solve problems that can be modeled by known formulas. We use the same problem-solving steps that were introduced in the previous section. These steps have been slightly revised to include formulas.

EXAMPLE 1   Finding Time Given Rate and Distance

A glacier is a giant mass of rocks and ice that flows downhill like a river. Portage Glacier in Alaska is about 6 miles, or 31,680 *feet,* long and moves 400 *feet* per year. Icebergs are created when the front end of the glacier flows into Portage Lake. How long does it take for ice at the head (beginning) of the glacier to reach the lake?

Solution

1. UNDERSTAND. Read and reread the problem. The appropriate formula needed to solve this problem is the distance formula, $d = rt$. To become familiar with this formula, let's find the distance that ice traveling at a rate of 400 feet per year travels in 100 years. To do so, we let time t be 100 years and rate r be the given 400 feet per year and substitute these values into the formula $d = rt$. We then have that distance $d = 400(100) = 40{,}000$ feet. Since we are interested in finding how long it takes ice to travel 31,680 feet, we now know that it is less than 100 years.

Since we are using the formula $d = rt$, we let

t = the time in years for ice to reach the lake

r = rate or speed of ice

d = distance from beginning of glacier to lake

2. TRANSLATE. To translate to an equation, we use the formula $d = rt$ and let distance $d = 31{,}680$ feet and rate $r = 400$ feet per year.

$$d = r \cdot t$$
$$31{,}680 = 400 \cdot t \qquad \text{Let } d = 31{,}680 \text{ and } r = 400.$$

3. SOLVE. Solve the equation for t. To solve for t, divide both sides by 400.

$$\frac{31{,}680}{400} = \frac{400 \cdot t}{400} \qquad \text{Divide both sides by 400.}$$

$$79.2 = t \qquad \text{Simplify.}$$

4. INTERPRET.

Check: To check, substitute 79.2 for t and 400 for r in the distance formula and check to see that the distance is 31,680 feet.

State: It takes 79.2 years for the ice at the head of Portage Glacier to reach the lake. □

Helpful Hint
Don't forget to include units if appropriate.

PRACTICE
1 The Stromboli Volcano, in Italy, began erupting in 2002 after a dormant period of over 17 years. In 2007, a volcanologist measured the lava flow to be moving at 5 meters/second. If the path the lava follows to the sea is 580 meters long, how long does it take the lava to reach the sea? *(Source: Thorsten Boeckel and CNN)*

⚠ **EXAMPLE 2** Calculating the Length of a Garden

Charles Pecot can afford enough fencing to enclose a rectangular garden with a perimeter of 140 feet. If the width of his garden must be 30 feet, find the length.

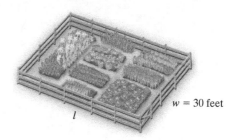

w = 30 feet

l

Solution

1. UNDERSTAND. Read and reread the problem. The formula needed to solve this problem is the formula for the perimeter of a rectangle, $P = 2l + 2w$. Before continuing, let's become familiar with this formula.

   l = the length of the rectangular garden
   w = the width of the rectangular garden
   P = perimeter of the garden

2. TRANSLATE. To translate to an equation, we use the formula $P = 2l + 2w$ and let perimeter $P = 140$ feet and width $w = 30$ feet.

$$P = 2l + 2w$$
$$\downarrow \qquad \downarrow$$
$$140 = 2l + 2(30) \quad \text{Let } P = 140 \text{ and } w = 30.$$

3. SOLVE.

$$140 = 2l + 2(30)$$
$$140 = 2l + 60 \qquad \text{Multiply } 2(30).$$
$$140 - 60 = 2l + 60 - 60 \quad \text{Subtract 60 from both sides.}$$
$$80 = 2l \qquad \text{Combine like terms.}$$
$$40 = l \qquad \text{Divide both sides by 2.}$$

4. INTERPRET.

Check: Substitute 40 for l and 30 for w in the perimeter formula and check to see that the perimeter is 140 feet.

State: The length of the rectangular garden is 40 feet. ☐

PRACTICE
2 Evelyn Gryk fenced in part of her backyard for a dog run. The dog run was 40 feet in length and used 98 feet of fencing. Find the width of the dog run.

EXAMPLE 3 Finding an Equivalent Temperature

The average minimum temperature for July in Shanghai, China, is 77° Fahrenheit. Find the equivalent temperature in degrees Celsius.

Solution

1. UNDERSTAND. Read and reread the problem. A formula that can be used to solve this problem is the formula for converting degrees Celsius to degrees Fahrenheit, $F = \dfrac{9}{5}C + 32$. Before continuing, become familiar with this formula. Using this formula, we let

$$C = \text{temperature in degrees Celsius, and}$$
$$F = \text{temperature in degrees Fahrenheit.}$$

2. TRANSLATE. To translate to an equation, we use the formula $F = \frac{9}{5}C + 32$ and let degrees Fahrenheit $F = 77$.

Formula: $\quad F = \frac{9}{5}C + 32$

Substitute: $\quad 77 = \frac{9}{5}C + 32 \quad$ Let $F = 77$.

3. SOLVE.

$$77 = \frac{9}{5}C + 32$$

$$77 - 32 = \frac{9}{5}C + 32 - 32 \quad \text{Subtract 32 from both sides.}$$

$$45 = \frac{9}{5}C \quad \text{Combine like terms.}$$

$$\frac{5}{9} \cdot 45 = \frac{5}{9} \cdot \frac{9}{5}C \quad \text{Multiply both sides by } \frac{5}{9}.$$

$$25 = C \quad \text{Simplify.}$$

4. INTERPRET.

Check: To check, replace C with 25 and F with 77 in the formula and see that a true statement results.

State: Thus, $77°$ Fahrenheit is equivalent to $25°$ Celsius.

Note: There is a formula for directly converting degrees Fahrenheit to degrees Celsius. It is $C = \frac{5}{9}(F - 32)$, as we shall see in Example 8. □

PRACTICE
3 The average minimum temperature for July in Sydney, Australia, is $8°$ Celsius. Find the equivalent temperature in degrees Fahrenheit.

In the next example, we again use the formula for perimeter of a rectangle as in Example 2. In Example 2, we knew the width of the rectangle. In this example, both the length and width are unknown.

⚠ **EXAMPLE 4** **Finding Road Sign Dimensions**

The length of a rectangular road sign is 2 feet less than three times its width. Find the dimensions if the perimeter is 28 feet.

Solution

1. UNDERSTAND. Read and reread the problem. Recall that the formula for the perimeter of a rectangle is $P = 2l + 2w$. Draw a rectangle and guess the solution. If the width of the rectangular sign is 5 feet, its length is 2 feet less than 3 times the width or $3(5 \text{ feet}) - 2 \text{ feet} = 13 \text{ feet}$. The perimeter P of the rectangle is then $2(13 \text{ feet}) + 2(5 \text{ feet}) = 36 \text{ feet}$, too much. We now know that the width is less than 5 feet.

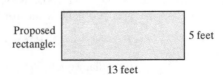

Proposed rectangle:

5 feet

13 feet

Let

w = the width of the rectangular sign; then
$3w - 2$ = the length of the sign.

w

$3w - 2$

Draw a rectangle and label it with the assigned variables.

2. TRANSLATE.

Formula: $P = 2l + 2w$ or

Substitute: $28 = 2(3w - 2) + 2w$.

3. SOLVE.

$28 = 2(3w - 2) + 2w$

$28 = 6w - 4 + 2w$ Apply the distributive property.

$28 = 8w - 4$

$28 + 4 = 8w - 4 + 4$ Add 4 to both sides.

$32 = 8w$

$\dfrac{32}{8} = \dfrac{8w}{8}$ Divide both sides by 8.

$4 = w$

4. INTERPRET.

Check: If the width of the sign is 4 feet, the length of the sign is 3(4 feet) − 2 feet = 10 feet. This gives a perimeter of $P = 2(4 \text{ feet}) + 2(10 \text{ feet}) = 28 \text{ feet}$, the correct perimeter.

State: The width of the sign is 4 feet, and the length of the sign is 10 feet.   □

PRACTICE

4   The new street signs along Route 114 have a length that is 3 inches more than 5 times the width. Find the dimensions of the signs if the perimeter of the signs is 66 inches.

OBJECTIVE

2   Solving a Formula for One of Its Variables

We say that the formula

$$F = \frac{9}{5}C + 32$$

is solved for F because F is alone on one side of the equation, and the other side of the equation contains no F's. Suppose that we need to convert many Fahrenheit temperatures to equivalent degrees Celsius. In this case, it is easier to perform this task by solving the formula $F = \dfrac{9}{5}C + 32$ for C. (See Example 8.) For this reason, it is important to be able to solve an equation for any one of its specified variables. For example, the formula $d = rt$ is solved for d in terms of r and t. We can also solve $d = rt$ for t in terms of d and r. To solve for t, divide both sides of the equation by r.

$d = rt$

$\dfrac{d}{r} = \dfrac{rt}{r}$ Divide both sides by r.

$\dfrac{d}{r} = t$ Simplify.

To solve a formula or an equation for a specified variable, we use the same steps as for solving a linear equation. These steps are listed next.

Solving Equations for a Specified Variable

Step 1. Multiply on both sides to clear the equation of fractions if they occur.

Step 2. Use the distributive property to remove parentheses if they occur.

Step 3. Simplify each side of the equation by combining like terms.

Step 4. Get all terms containing the specified variable on one side and all other terms on the other side by using the addition property of equality.

Step 5. Get the specified variable alone by using the multiplication property of equality.

 EXAMPLE 5 Solve $V = lwh$ for l.

Solution This formula is used to find the volume of a box. To solve for l, divide both sides by wh.

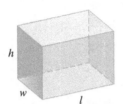

$$V = lwh$$

$$\frac{V}{wh} = \frac{lwh}{wh} \quad \text{Divide both sides by } wh.$$

$$\frac{V}{wh} = l \quad \text{Simplify.}$$

Since we have l alone on one side of the equation, we have solved for l in terms of V, w, and h. Remember that it does not matter on which side of the equation we isolate the variable. □

PRACTICE
5 Solve $I = Prt$ for r.

EXAMPLE 6 Solve $y = mx + b$ for x.

Solution The term containing the variable we are solving for, mx, is on the right side of the equation. Get mx alone by subtracting b from both sides.

$$y = mx + b$$

$$y - b = mx + b - b \quad \text{Subtract } b \text{ from both sides.}$$

$$y - b = mx \quad \text{Combine like terms.}$$

Next, solve for x by dividing both sides by m.

$$\frac{y - b}{m} = \frac{mx}{m}$$

$$\frac{y - b}{m} = x \quad \text{Simplify.} \quad □$$

PRACTICE
6 Solve $H = 5as + 10a$ for s.

✓CONCEPT CHECK

Solve:

a. ⬤ = ▢ − ▢ for ▢

b. ⬤ = ▢ · △ − ▢ for ▢

△ **EXAMPLE 7** Solve $P = 2l + 2w$ for w.

Solution This formula relates the perimeter of a rectangle to its length and width. Find the term containing the variable w. To get this term, $2w$, alone subtract $2l$ from both sides.

l

w

> ▶ **Helpful Hint**
>
> The 2's may *not* be divided out here. Although 2 is a factor of the denominator, 2 is *not* a factor of the numerator since it is not a factor of both terms in the numerator.

$$P = 2l + 2w$$

$$P - 2l = 2l + 2w - 2l \quad \text{Subtract } 2l \text{ from both sides.}$$

$$P - 2l = 2w \quad \text{Combine like terms.}$$

$$\frac{P - 2l}{2} = \frac{2w}{2} \quad \text{Divide both sides by 2.}$$

$$\frac{P - 2l}{2} = w \quad \text{Simplify.} \qquad \square$$

PRACTICE
7   Solve $N = F + d(n - 1)$ for d.

....

The next example has an equation containing a fraction. We will first clear the equation of fractions and then solve for the specified variable.

EXAMPLE 8   Solve $F = \frac{9}{5}C + 32$ for C.

Solution

$$F = \frac{9}{5}C + 32$$

$$5(F) = 5\left(\frac{9}{5}C + 32\right) \quad \text{Clear the fraction by multiplying both sides by the LCD.}$$

$$5F = 9C + 160 \quad \text{Distribute the 5.}$$

$$5F - 160 = 9C + 160 - 160 \quad \text{To get the term containing the variable } C \text{ alone, subtract 160 from both sides.}$$

$$5F - 160 = 9C \quad \text{Combine like terms.}$$

$$\frac{5F - 160}{9} = \frac{9C}{9} \quad \text{Divide both sides by 9.}$$

$$\frac{5F - 160}{9} = C \quad \text{Simplify.}$$

Note: An equivalent way to write this formula is $C = \frac{5}{9}(F - 32)$. $\square$

PRACTICE
8   Solve $A = \frac{1}{2}a(b + B)$ for B.

....

Vocabulary, Readiness & Video Check

Martin-Gay Interactive Videos

See Video 2.5

Watch the section lecture video and answer the following questions.

OBJECTIVE
1
1. Complete this statement based on the lecture given before ⊞ Example 1. A formula is an equation that describes known _____ among quantities.

OBJECTIVE
1
2. In ⊞ Example 2, how are the units for the solution determined?

OBJECTIVE
2
3. During ⊞ Example 4, why is the equation $5x = 30$?

2.5   Exercise Set

MyMathLab®

Substitute the given values into each given formula and solve for the unknown variable. If necessary, round to one decimal place. See Examples 1 through 4.

1. $A = bh$; $A = 45, b = 15$ (Area of a parallelogram)

2. $d = rt$; $d = 195, t = 3$ (Distance formula)

3. $S = 4lw + 2wh$; $S = 102, l = 7, w = 3$ (Surface area of a special rectangular box)

4. $V = lwh$; $l = 14, w = 8, h = 3$ (Volume of a rectangular box)

5. $A = \frac{1}{2}h(B + b)$; $A = 180, B = 11, b = 7$ (Area of a trapezoid)

6. $A = \frac{1}{2}h(B + b)$; $A = 60, B = 7, b = 3$ (Area of a trapezoid)

7. $P = a + b + c$; $P = 30, a = 8, b = 10$ (Perimeter of a triangle)

8. $V = \frac{1}{3}Ah$; $V = 45, h = 5$ (Volume of a pyramid)

9. $C = 2\pi r$; $C = 15.7$ (use the approximation 3.14 or a calculator approximation for π) (Circumference of a circle)

10. $A = \pi r^2$; $r = 4.5$ (use the approximation 3.14 or a calculator approximation for π) (Area of a circle)

11. $I = PRT$; $I = 3750, P = 25,000, R = 0.05$ (Simple interest formula)

12. $I = PRT$; $I = 1,056,000, R = 0.055, T = 6$ (Simple interest formula)

13. $V = \frac{1}{3}\pi r^2 h$; $V = 565.2, r = 6$ (use a calculator approximation for π) (Volume of a cone)

14. $V = \frac{4}{3}\pi r^3$; $r = 3$ (use a calculator approximation for π) (Volume of a sphere)

Solve each formula for the specified variable. See Examples 5 through 8.

15. $f = 5gh$ for h

16. $A = \pi ab$ for b

17. $V = lwh$ for w

18. $T = mnr$ for n

19. $3x + y = 7$ for y

20. $-x + y = 13$ for y

21. $A = P + PRT$ for R

22. $A = P + PRT$ for T

23. $V = \frac{1}{3}Ah$ for A

24. $D = \frac{1}{4}fk$ for k

25. $P = a + b + c$ for a

26. $PR = x + y + z + w$ for z

27. $S = 2\pi rh + 2\pi r^2$ for h

28. $S = 4lw + 2wh$ for h

Solve. For Exercises 29 and 30, the solutions have been started for you. See Examples 1 through 4.

29. The iconic NASDAQ sign in New York's Times Square has a width of 84 feet and an area of 10,080 square feet. Find the height (or length) of the sign. (*Source:* livedesignonline.com)

Start the solution:

1. UNDERSTAND the problem. Reread it as many times as needed.

2. TRANSLATE into an equation. (Fill in the blanks below.)

Area	=	length	times	width
↓	↓	↓	↓	↓
____	=	x	·	____

Finish with:

3. SOLVE and   4. INTERPRET

30. The world's largest sign for Coca-Cola is located in Arica, Chile. The rectangular sign has a length of 400 feet and an area of 52,400 square feet. Find the width of the sign. (*Source:* Fabulous Facts about Coca-Cola, Atlanta, GA)

Start the solution:

1. UNDERSTAND the problem. Reread it as many times as needed.

2. TRANSLATE into an equation. (Fill in the blanks below.)

Area	=	length	times	width
↓	↓	↓	↓	↓
____	=	____	·	x

Finish with:

3. SOLVE and   4. INTERPRET

31. For the purpose of purchasing new baseboard and carpet,

a. Find the area and perimeter of the room below (neglecting doors).

b. Identify whether baseboard has to do with area or perimeter and the same with carpet.

11.5 ft   9 ft

32. For the purpose of purchasing lumber for a new fence and seed to plant grass,

   a. Find the area and perimeter of the yard below.

   b. Identify whether a fence has to do with area or perimeter and the same with grass seed.

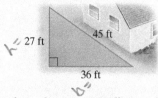

27 ft   45 ft   36 ft

33. A frame shop charges according to both the amount of framing needed to surround the picture and the amount of glass needed to cover the picture.

   a. Find the area and perimeter of the trapezoid-shaped framed picture below.

   b. Identify whether the amount of framing has to do with perimeter or area and the same with the amount of glass.

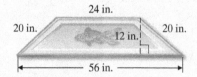

24 in.

20 in.   12 in.   20 in.

56 in.

34. A decorator is painting and placing a border completely around the parallelogram-shaped wall.

   a. Find the area and perimeter of the wall below.

   b. Identify whether the border has to do with perimeter or area and the same with paint.

7 ft   11.7 ft   9.3 ft

35. Convert Nome, Alaska's 14°F high temperature to Celsius.

36. Convert Paris, France's low temperature of −5°C to Fahrenheit.

37. An architect designs a rectangular flower garden such that the width is exactly two-thirds of the length. If 260 feet of antique picket fencing are to be used to enclose the garden, find the dimensions of the garden.

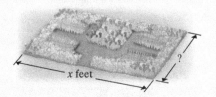

x feet

38. If the length of a rectangular parking lot is 10 meters less than twice its width, and the perimeter is 400 meters, find the length of the parking lot.

x meters

39. A flower bed is in the shape of a triangle with one side twice the length of the shortest side, and the third side is 30 feet more than the length of the shortest side. Find the dimensions if the perimeter is 102 feet.

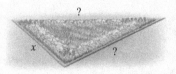

?

x   ?

40. The perimeter of a yield sign in the shape of an isosceles triangle is 22 feet. If the shortest side is 2 feet less than the other two sides, find the length of the shortest side. (*Hint:* An isosceles triangle has two sides the same length.)

?

YIELD

x feet   x feet

41. The Cat is a high-speed catamaran auto ferry that operates between Bar Harbor, Maine, and Yarmouth, Nova Scotia. The Cat can make the 138-mile trip in about $2\frac{1}{2}$ hours. Find the catamaran speed for this trip. (*Source:* Bay Ferries)

42. A family is planning their vacation to Disney World. They will drive from a small town outside New Orleans, Louisiana, to Orlando, Florida, a distance of 700 miles. They plan to average a rate of 55 mph. How long will this trip take?

△ **43.** Piranha fish require 1.5 cubic feet of water per fish to maintain a healthy environment. Find the maximum number of piranhas you could put in a tank measuring 8 feet by 3 feet by 6 feet.

6 feet

3 feet   8 feet

△ **44.** Find the maximum number of goldfish you can put in a cylindrical tank whose diameter is 8 meters and whose height is 3 meters if each goldfish needs 2 cubic meters of water.

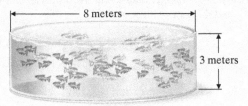

8 meters

3 meters

Dolbear's Law states the relationship between the rate at which Snowy Tree crickets chirp and the air temperature of their environment. The formula is

$$T = 50 + \frac{N - 40}{4}, \text{ where } \begin{array}{l} T = \text{temperature in degrees Fahrenheit and} \\ N = \text{number of chirps per minute} \end{array}$$

45. If $N = 86$, find the temperature in degrees Fahrenheit, T.

46. If $N = 94$, find the temperature in degrees Fahrenheit, T.

47. If $T = 55°F$, find the number of chirps per minute.

48. If $T = 65°F$, find the number of chirps per minute.

Use the results of Exercises 45–48 to complete each sentence with "increases" or "decreases."

49. As the number of cricket chirps per minute increases, the air temperature of their environment _____ .

50. As the air temperature of their environment decreases, the number of cricket chirps per minute _____ .

△ **51.** A lawn is in the shape of a trapezoid with a height of 60 feet and bases of 70 feet and 130 feet. How many whole bags of fertilizer must be purchased to cover the lawn if each bag covers 4000 square feet?

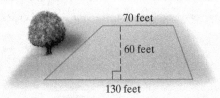

70 feet

60 feet

130 feet

△ **52.** If the area of a right-triangularly shaped sail is 20 square feet and its base is 5 feet, find the height of the sail.

?

5 feet

△ **53.** Maria's Pizza sells one 16-inch cheese pizza or two 10-inch cheese pizzas for $9.99. Determine which size gives more pizza.

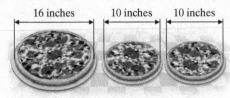

16 inches   10 inches   10 inches

△ **54.** Find how much rope is needed to wrap around the earth at the equator if the radius of the earth is 4000 miles. (*Hint:* Use 3.14 for π and the formula for circumference.)

△ **55.** The perimeter of a geometric figure is the sum of the lengths of its sides. If the perimeter of the following pentagon (five-sided figure) is 48 meters, find the length of each side.

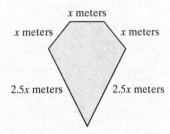

x meters

x meters x meters

2.5x meters   2.5x meters

△ **56.** The perimeter of the following triangle is 82 feet. Find the length of each side.

$(2x - 8)$ feet

x feet

$(3x - 12)$ feet

57. The Hawaiian volcano Kilauea is one of the world's most active volcanoes and has had continuous eruptive activity since 1983. Erupting lava flows through a tube system about 11 kilometers to the sea. Assume a lava flow speed of 0.5 kilometer per hour and calculate how long it takes to reach the sea.

58. The world's largest pink ribbon, the sign of the fight against breast cancer, was erected out of pink Post-it® notes on a billboard in New York City in October 2004. If the area of the rectangular billboard covered by the ribbon was approximately 3990 square feet, and the width of the billboard was approximately 57 feet, what was the height of this billboard?

△ **59.** The perimeter of an equilateral triangle is 7 inches more than the perimeter of a square, and the side of the triangle is 5 inches longer than the side of the square. Find the side of the triangle. (*Hint:* An equilateral triangle has three sides the same length.)

△ **60.** A square animal pen and a pen shaped like an equilateral triangle have equal perimeters. Find the length of the sides of each pen if the sides of the triangular pen are fifteen less than twice a side of the square pen.

61. Find how long it takes a person to drive 135 miles on I-10 if she merges onto I-10 at 10 a.m. and drives nonstop with her cruise control set on 60 mph.

62. Beaumont, Texas, is about 150 miles from Toledo Bend. If Leo Miller leaves Beaumont at 4 a.m. and averages 45 mph, when should he arrive at Toledo Bend?

△ **63.** The longest runway at Los Angeles International Airport has the shape of a rectangle and an area of 1,813,500 square feet. This runway is 150 feet wide. How long is the runway? (*Source:* Los Angeles World Airports)

64. Normal room temperature is about 78°F. Convert this temperature to Celsius.

65. The highest temperature ever recorded in Europe was 122°F in Seville, Spain, in August 1881. Convert this record high temperature to Celsius. (*Source:* National Climatic Data Center)

66. The lowest temperature ever recorded in Oceania was −10°C at the Haleakala Summit in Maui, Hawaii, in January 1961. Convert this record low temperature to Fahrenheit. (*Source:* National Climatic Data Center)

67. The average temperature on the planet Mercury is 167°C. Convert this temperature to degrees Fahrenheit. (*Source:* National Space Science Data Center)

68. The average temperature on the planet Jupiter is −227°F. Convert this temperature to degrees Celsius. Round to the nearest degree. (*Source:* National Space Science Data Center)

△ **69.** The Hoberman Sphere is a toy ball that expands and contracts. When it is completely closed, it has a diameter of 9.5 inches. Find the volume of the Hoberman Sphere when it is

completely closed. Use 3.14 for π. Round to the nearest whole cubic inch. (*Hint:* Volume of a sphere $= \frac{4}{3}\pi r^3$. *Source:* Hoberman Designs, Inc.)

70. When the Hoberman Sphere (see Exercise 69) is completely expanded, its diameter is 30 inches. Find the volume of the Hoberman Sphere when it is completely expanded. Use 3.14 for π. (*Source:* Hoberman Designs, Inc.)

REVIEW AND PREVIEW

Write each percent as a decimal. See Appendix B.2.

71. 32%   **72.** 8%

73. 200%   **74.** 0.5%

Write each decimal as a percent. See Appendix B.2.

75. 0.17   **76.** 0.03

77. 7.2   **78.** 5

CONCEPT EXTENSIONS

△ **79.** The formula $V = lwh$ is used to find the volume of a box. If the length of a box is doubled, the width is doubled, and the height is doubled, how does this affect the volume? Explain your answer.

△ **80.** The formula $A = bh$ is used to find the area of a parallelogram. If the base of a parallelogram is doubled and its height is doubled, how does this affect the area? Explain your answer.

81. Use the Dolbear's Law formula for Exercises 45–48 and calculate when the number of cricket chirps per minute is the same as the temperature in degrees Fahrenheit. (*Hint:* Replace T with N and solve for N or replace N with T and solve for T.)

82. Find the temperature at which the Celsius measurement and the Fahrenheit measurement are the same number.

Solve.

83. $N = R + \dfrac{V}{G}$ for V (Urban forestry: tree plantings per year)

84. $B = \dfrac{F}{P - V}$ for V (Business: break-even point)

Solve. See the Concept Check in this section.

85. ⬛ − ⬤ · ⬛ = ▲ for ⬤

86. ⬢ · ⬛ + ▲ = ⬤ for ⬛

87. The distance from the sun to the earth is approximately 93,000,000 miles. If light travels at a rate of 186,000 miles per second, how long does it take light from the sun to reach us?

88. Light travels at a rate of 186,000 miles per second. If our moon is 238,860 miles from the earth, how long does it take light from the moon to reach us? (Round to the nearest tenth of a second.)

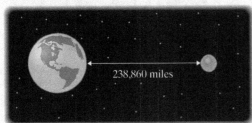

238,860 miles

89. A glacier is a giant mass of rocks and ice that flows downhill like a river. Exit Glacier, near Seward, Alaska, moves at a rate of 20 inches a day. Find the distance in feet the glacier moves in a year. (Assume 365 days a year. Round to 2 decimal places.)

90. Flying fish do not *actually* fly, but glide. They have been known to travel a distance of 1300 feet at a rate of 20 miles per hour. How many seconds does it take to travel this distance? (*Hint:* First convert miles per hour to feet per second. Recall that 1 mile = 5280 feet. Round to the nearest tenth of a second.)

91. A Japanese "bullet" train set a new world record for train speed at 581 kilometers per hour during a manned test run on the Yamanashi Maglev Test Line in 2003. The Yamanashi Maglev Test Line is 42.8 kilometers long. How many *minutes* would a test run on the Yamanashi Line last at this record-setting speed? Round to the nearest hundredth of a minute. (*Source:* Japan Railways Central Co.)

92. The Boeing X-51 is an unmanned demonstration aircraft for hypersonic flight testing. In May 2010, it successfully completed a free flight at about 3800 mph. Neglecting altitude, if the circumference of Earth is approximately 25,000 miles, how long would it take for the X-51 to travel around Earth? Give your answer in hours and minutes rounded to the nearest whole minute.

93. In the United States, a notable hang glider flight was a 303-mile, $8\frac{1}{2}$-hour flight from New Mexico to Kansas. What was the average rate during this flight?

94. Stalactites join stalagmites to form columns. A column found at Natural Bridge Caverns near San Antonio, Texas, rises 15 feet and has a *diameter* of only 2 inches. Find the volume of this column in cubic inches. (*Hint:* Use the formula for volume of a cylinder and use a calculator approximation for π. Round to the nearest tenth of an inch.)

2.6 Percent and Mixture Problem Solving

OBJECTIVES

1 Solve Percent Equations.

2 Solve Discount and Mark-up Problems.

3 Solve Percent Increase and Percent Decrease Problems.

4 Solve Mixture Problems.

This section is devoted to solving problems in the categories listed. The same problem-solving steps used in previous sections are also followed in this section. They are listed below for review.

General Strategy for Problem Solving

1. UNDERSTAND the problem. During this step, become comfortable with the problem. Some ways of doing this are as follows:

   Read and reread the problem.

   Choose a variable to represent the unknown.

   Construct a drawing whenever possible.

   Propose a solution and check. Pay careful attention to how you check your proposed solution. This will help writing an equation to model the problem.

2. TRANSLATE the problem into an equation.

3. SOLVE the equation.

4. INTERPRET the results: *Check* the proposed solution in the stated problem and *state* your conclusion.

^{OBJECTIVE}
1   Solving Percent Equations

Many of today's statistics are given in terms of percent: a basketball player's free throw percent, current interest rates, stock market trends, and nutrition labeling, just to name a few. In this section, we first explore percent, percent equations, and applications involving percents. See Appendix B.2 if a further review of percents is needed.

EXAMPLE 1   The number 63 is what percent of 72?

Solution

1. UNDERSTAND. Read and reread the problem. Next, let's suppose that the percent is 80%. To check, we find 80% of 72.

$$80\% \text{ of } 72 = 0.80(72) = 57.6$$

This is close but not 63. At this point, though, we have a better understanding of the problem, we know the correct answer is close to and greater than 80%, and we know how to check our proposed solution later.

Let x = the unknown percent.

2. TRANSLATE. Recall that "is" means "equals" and "of" signifies multiplying. Let's translate the sentence directly.

the number 63	is	what percent	of	72
↓	↓	↓	↓	↓
63	=	x	·	72

3. SOLVE.

$$63 = 72x$$
$$0.875 = x \qquad \text{Divide both sides by 72.}$$
$$87.5\% = x \qquad \text{Write as a percent.}$$

4. INTERPRET.

Check: Verify that 87.5% of 72 is 63.

State: The number 63 is 87.5% of 72.

^{PRACTICE}
1   The number 35 is what percent of 56?

EXAMPLE 2   The number 120 is 15% of what number?

Solution

1. UNDERSTAND. Read and reread the problem.

Let x = the unknown number.

2. TRANSLATE.

the number 120	is	15%	of	what number
↓	↓	↓	↓	↓
120	=	15%	·	x

3. SOLVE.

$$120 = 0.15x \quad \text{Write 15\% as 0.15.}$$
$$800 = x \quad \text{Divide both sides by 0.15.}$$

4. INTERPRET.

Check: Check the proposed solution by finding 15% of 800 and verifying that the result is 120.

State: Thus, 120 is 15% of 800.

PRACTICE
2 The number 198 is 55% of what number?

> **Helpful Hint**
> The percents in a circle graph should have a sum of 100%.

The next example contains a circle graph. This particular circle graph shows percents of pets owned in the United States. Since the circle graph represents all pets owned in the United States, the percents should add to 100%.

EXAMPLE 3 The circle graph below shows the breakdown of total pets owned in the United States. Use this graph to answer the questions.

Pets Owned in the United States

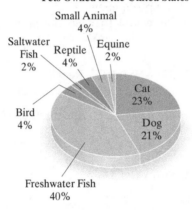

Data from American Pet Products Association's Industry Statistics and Trends results

a. What percent of pets owned in the United States are cats or dogs?

b. What percent of pets owned in the United States are not birds?

c. Currently, 377.41 million pets are owned in the United States. How many of these would be cats? (Round to the nearest tenth of a million.)

Solution

a. From the circle graph, we see that 23% of pets owned are cats and 21% are dogs; thus,

$$23\% + 21\% = 44\%.$$

44% of pets owned are cats or dogs.

b. The circle graph percents have a sum of 100%; thus, the percent of pets owned in the United States that are not birds is

$$100\% - 4\% = 96\%.$$

c. To find the number of cats owned, we find

$$23\% \text{ of } 377.41 = 0.23(377.41)$$
$$= 86.8043$$
$$\approx 86.8 \quad \text{Rounded to the nearest tenth of a million.}$$

Thus, about 86.8 million cats are owned in the United States.

PRACTICE
3 Use the Example 3 circle graph to answer each question.

a. What percent of pets owned in the United States are freshwater fish or saltwater fish?

b. What percent of pets owned in the United States are not equines (horses, ponies, etc.)?

c. Currently, 377.41 million pets are owned in the United States. How many of these would be dogs? (Round to the nearest tenth of a million.)

OBJECTIVE

2   **Solving Discount and Mark-up Problems**

The next example has to do with discounting the price of a cell phone.

EXAMPLE 4   Cell Phones Unlimited recently reduced the price of a $140 phone by 20%. What are the discount and the new price?

Solution

1. UNDERSTAND. Read and reread the problem. Make sure you understand the meaning of the word *discount*. Discount is the amount of money by which the cost of an item has been decreased. To find the discount, we simply find 20% of $140. In other words, we have the formulas,

$$\text{discount} = \text{percent} \cdot \text{original price} \quad \text{Then}$$
$$\text{new price} = \text{original price} - \text{discount}$$

2, 3. TRANSLATE and SOLVE.

$$
\begin{aligned}
\text{discount} = \quad &\text{percent} \quad \cdot \quad \text{original price} \\
&\quad\downarrow \qquad\qquad\quad \downarrow \\
= \quad &20\% \quad\cdot\quad \$140 \\
= \quad &0.20 \quad\cdot\quad \$140 \\
= \quad &\$28
\end{aligned}
$$

Thus, the discount in price is $28.

$$
\begin{aligned}
\text{new price} \quad = \quad &\text{original price} \quad - \quad \text{discount} \\
&\quad\downarrow \qquad\qquad\qquad \downarrow \\
= \quad &\$140 \quad\quad - \quad \$28 \\
= \$112
\end{aligned}
$$

4. INTERPRET.

Check: Check your calculations in the formulas; see also whether our results are reasonable. They are.

State: The discount in price is $28, and the new price is $112.

PRACTICE

4   A used treadmill, originally purchased for $480, was sold at a garage sale at a discount of 85% of the original price. What were the discount and the new price?

A concept similar to discount is mark-up. What is the difference between the two? A discount is subtracted from the original price while a mark-up is added to the original price. For mark-ups,

$$\text{mark-up} = \text{percent} \cdot \text{original price}$$
$$\text{new price} = \text{original price} + \text{mark-up}$$

▶ Helpful Hint
Discounts are subtracted from the original price, while mark-ups are added.

Mark-up exercises can be found in Exercise Set 2.6 in the form of calculating tips.

OBJECTIVE

3 Solving Percent Increase and Percent Decrease Problems

Percent increase or percent decrease is a common way to describe how some measurement has increased or decreased. For example, crime increased by 8%, teachers received a 5.5% increase in salary, or a company decreased its number of employees by 10%. The next example is a review of percent increase.

EXAMPLE 5 Calculating the Percent Increase of Attending College

The tuition and fees cost of attending a public four-year college rose from $4020 in 1996 to $7610 in 2011. Find the percent increase. Round to the nearest tenth of a percent. (*Source:* The College Board)

Solution

1. UNDERSTAND. Read and reread the problem. Notice that the new tuition, $7610, is almost double the old tuition of $4020. Because of that, we know that the percent increase is close to 100%. To see this, let's guess that the percent increase is 100%. To check, we find 100% of $4020 to find the *increase* in cost. Then we add this increase to $4020 to find the *new cost*. In other words, 100%($4020) = 1.00($4020) = $4020, the *increase* in cost. The *new cost* would be old cost + increase = $4020 + $4020 = $8040, close to the actual new cost of $7610. We now know that the increase is close to, but less than, 100% and we know how to check our proposed solution.

   Let $x = $ the percent increase.

2. TRANSLATE. First, find the **increase** and then the **percent increase.** The increase in cost is found by:

In words:	increase	=	new cost	−	old cost	or
Translate:	increase	=	$7610	−	$4020	
		=	$3590			

   Next, find the percent increase. The percent increase or percent decrease is always a percent of the original number or, in this case, the old cost.

In words:	increase	is	what percent	of	old cost
Translate:	$3590	=	x	·	$4020

3. SOLVE.

   $$3590 = 4020x$$
   $$0.893 \approx x \qquad \text{Divide both sides by 4020 and round to 3 decimal places.}$$
   $$89.3\% \approx x \qquad \text{Write as a percent.}$$

4. INTERPRET.

   Check: Check the proposed solution

   State: The percent increase in cost is approximately 89.3%.

PRACTICE

5 The tuition and fees cost of attending a public two-year college rose from $1900 in 1996 to $2710 in 2011. Find the percent increase. Round to the nearest tenth of a percent. (*Source:* The College Board)

Percent decrease is found using a method similar to that in Example 5. First find the decrease, then determine what percent of the original or first amount is that decrease.

Read the next example carefully. For Example 5, we were asked to find percent increase. In Example 6, we are given the percent increase and asked to find the number before the increase.

EXAMPLE 6 Most of the movie screens globally project analog film, but the number of cinemas using digital is increasing. Find the number of digital screens worldwide last year if, after a 122% increase, the number this year is 36,208. Round to the nearest whole number. (*Source:* Motion Picture Association of America)

Solution

1. **UNDERSTAND.** Read and reread the problem. Let's guess a solution and see how we would check our guess. If the number of digital screens worldwide last year was 20,000, we would see if 20,000 plus the increase is 36,208; that is,

$$20,000 + 122\%(20,000) = 20,000 + 1.22(20,000) = 2.22(20,000) = 44,400$$

Since 44,400 is too large, we know that our guess of 20,000 is too large. We also have a better understanding of the problem. Let

$$x = \text{number of digital screens last year}$$

2. **TRANSLATE.** To translate an equation, we remember that

In words:	number of digital screens last year	plus	increase	equals	number of digital screens this year
	↓	↓	↓	↓	↓
Translate:	x	$+$	$1.22x$	$=$	$36{,}208$

3. **SOLVE.**

$$2.22x = 36{,}208 \quad \text{Add like terms.}$$

$$x = \frac{36{,}208}{2.22}$$

$$x \approx 16{,}310$$

4. **INTERPRET.**

Check: Recall that x represents the number of digital screens worldwide last year. If this number is approximately 16,310, let's see if 16,310 plus the increase is close to 36,208. (We use the word *close* since 16,310 is rounded.)

$$16{,}310 + 122\%(16{,}310) = 16{,}310 + 1.22(16{,}310) = 2.22(16{,}310) = 36{,}208.2$$

which is close to 36,208.

State: There were approximately 16,310 digital screens worldwide last year. □

PRACTICE

6 The fastest-growing sector of digital theater screens is 3D. Find the number of digital 3D screens in the United States and Canada last year if after a 138% increase, the number this year is 8459. Round to the nearest whole. (*Source:* MPAA)

OBJECTIVE

4 Solving Mixture Problems

Mixture problems involve two or more quantities being combined to form a new mixture. These applications range from Dow Chemical's need to form a chemical mixture of a required strength to Planter's Peanut Company's need to find the correct mixture of peanuts and cashews, given taste and price constraints.

EXAMPLE 7 Calculating Percent for a Lab Experiment

A chemist working on his doctoral degree at Massachusetts Institute of Technology needs 12 liters of a 50% acid solution for a lab experiment. The stockroom has only 40% and 70% solutions. How much of each solution should be mixed together to form 12 liters of a 50% solution?

Solution:

1. UNDERSTAND. First, read and reread the problem a few times. Next, guess a solution. Suppose that we need 7 liters of the 40% solution. Then we need $12 - 7 = 5$ liters of the 70% solution. To see if this is indeed the solution, find the amount of pure acid in 7 liters of the 40% solution, in 5 liters of the 70% solution, and in 12 liters of a 50% solution, the required amount and strength.

number of liters	×	acid strength	=	amount of pure acid
7 liters	×	40%		7(0.40) or 2.8 liters
5 liters	×	70%		5(0.70) or 3.5 liters
12 liters	×	50%		12(0.50) or 6 liters

Since 2.8 liters + 3.5 liters = 6.3 liters and not 6, our guess is incorrect, but we have gained some valuable insight into how to model and check this problem.

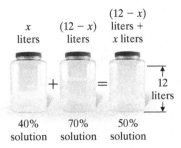

x liters $(12 - x)$ liters $(12 - x)$ liters $+$ x liters

40% solution   70% solution   50% solution

12 liters

Let
$$x = \text{number of liters of 40\% solution; then}$$
$$12 - x = \text{number of liters of 70\% solution.}$$

2. TRANSLATE. To help us translate to an equation, the following table summarizes the information given. Recall that the amount of acid in each solution is found by multiplying the acid strength of each solution by the number of liters.

	No. of Liters	·	Acid Strength	=	Amount of Acid
40% Solution	x		40%		$0.40x$
70% Solution	$12 - x$		70%		$0.70(12 - x)$
50% Solution Needed	12		50%		$0.50(12)$

The amount of acid in the final solution is the sum of the amounts of acid in the two beginning solutions.

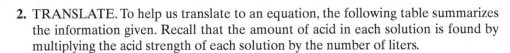

In words: acid in 40% solution $+$ acid in 70% solution $=$ acid in 50% mixture

Translate: $0.40x$ $+$ $0.70(12 - x)$ $=$ $0.50(12)$

3. SOLVE.

$$0.40x + 0.70(12 - x) = 0.50(12)$$
$$0.4x + 8.4 - 0.7x = 6 \qquad \text{Apply the distributive property.}$$
$$-0.3x + 8.4 = 6 \qquad \text{Combine like terms.}$$
$$-0.3x = -2.4 \qquad \text{Subtract 8.4 from both sides.}$$
$$x = 8 \qquad \text{Divide both sides by } -0.3.$$

4. INTERPRET.

Check: To check, recall how we checked our guess.

State: If 8 liters of the 40% solution are mixed with $12 - 8$ or 4 liters of the 70% solution, the result is 12 liters of a 50% solution.

PRACTICE

7   Hamida Barash was responsible for refilling the eye wash stations in the chemistry lab. She needed 6 liters of 3% strength eyewash to refill the dispensers. The supply room only had 2% and 5% eyewash in stock. How much of each solution should she mix to produce the needed 3% strength eyewash?

Vocabulary, Readiness & Video Check

Tell whether the percent labels in the circle graphs are correct.

1.
25% 40% 25%

2.
30% 30% 30%

3.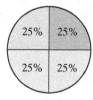
25% 25% 25% 25%

4.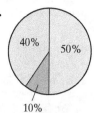
40% 50% 10%

Martin-Gay Interactive Videos

See Video 2.6

Watch the section lecture video and answer the following questions.

OBJECTIVE 1

5. Answer these questions based on how Example 2 was translated to an equation.
   a. What does "is" translate to?
   b. What does "of" translate to?
   c. How do you write a percent as an equivalent decimal?

OBJECTIVE 2

6. At the end of ⊞ Example 3 you are told that the process for finding discount is *almost* the same as finding mark-up.
   a. How is discount similar?
   b. How does discount differ?

OBJECTIVE 3

7. According to ⊞ Example 4, what amount must you find before you can find a percent increase in price? How do you find this amount?

OBJECTIVE 4

8. The following problem is worded like ⊞ Example 6 in the video, but using different quantities.

   How much of an alloy that is 10% copper should be mixed with 400 ounces of an alloy that is 30% copper in order to get an alloy that is 20% copper? Fill in the table and set up an equation that could be used to solve for the unknowns (do not actually solve). Use ⊞ Example 6 in the video as a model for your work.

Alloy	Ounces	Copper Strength	Amount of Copper

2.6   Exercise Set   MyMathLab®

Find each number described. For Exercises 1 and 2, the solutions have been started for you. See Examples 1 and 2.

1. What number is 16% of 70?

   Start the solution:

   1. UNDERSTAND the problem. Reread it as many times as needed.
   2. TRANSLATE into an equation. (Fill in the blanks below.)

What number	is	16%	of	70
↓	↓	↓	↓	↓
x	___	0.16	___	70

   Finish with:
   3. SOLVE and **4.** INTERPRET

2. What number is 88% of 1000?

   Start the solution:

   1. UNDERSTAND the problem. Reread it as many times as needed.
   2. TRANSLATE into an equation. (Fill in the blanks below.)

What number	is	88%	of	1000
↓	↓	↓	↓	↓
x	___	0.88	___	1000

   Finish with:
   3. SOLVE and **4.** INTERPRET

3. The number 28.6 is what percent of 52?

4. The number 87.2 is what percent of 436?

5. The number 45 is 25% of what number?

6. The number 126 is 35% of what number?

The circle graph below shows the number of minutes that adults spend on their home phone each day. Use this graph for Exercises 7 through 10. See Example 3.

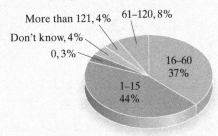

Data from Bruskin/Goldring Research for Sony Electronics

7. What percent of adults spend more than 121 minutes on the phone each day?

8. What percent of adults spend no time on the phone each day?

9. Florence is a town in Alabama whose adult population is approximately 27,000. How many of these adults might you expect to talk 16–60 minutes on the phone each day?

10. Columbus is a town in Indiana whose adult population is approximately 29,250. How many of these adults might you expect to talk 61–120 minutes on the phone each day?

Solve. If needed, round answers to the nearest cent. See Example 4.

11. A used automobile dealership recently reduced the price of a used compact car by 8%. If the price of the car before discount was $18,500, find the discount and the new price.

12. A music store is advertising a 25%-off sale on all new releases. Find the discount and the sale price of a newly released CD that regularly sells for $12.50.

13. A birthday celebration meal is $40.50 including tax. Find the total cost if a 15% tip is added to the given cost.

14. A retirement dinner for two is $65.40 including tax. Find the total cost if a 20% tip is added to the given cost.

Solve. See Example 5.

Use the graph below for Exercises 15 and 16.

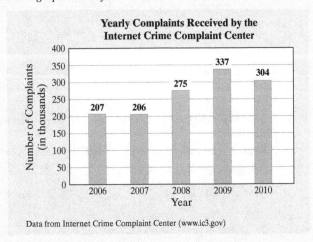

Data from Internet Crime Complaint Center (www.ic3.gov)

15. The number of Internet-crime complaints decreased from 2009 to 2010. Find the percent decrease. Round to the nearest tenth of a percent.

16. The number of Internet-crime complaints decreased from 2006 to 2007. Find the percent decrease. Round to the nearest tenth of a percent.

17. By decreasing each dimension by 1 unit, the area of a rectangle decreased from 40 square feet (on the left) to 28 square feet (on the right). Find the percent decrease in area.

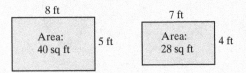

18. By decreasing the length of the side by one unit, the area of a square decreased from 100 square meters to 81 square meters. Find the percent decrease in area.

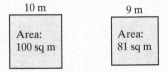

Solve. See Example 6.

19. Find the original price of a pair of shoes if the sale price is $78 after a 25% discount.

20. Find the original price of a popular pair of shoes if the increased price is $80 after a 25% increase.

21. Find last year's salary if, after a 4% pay raise, this year's salary is $44,200.

22. Find last year's salary if after a 3% pay raise, this year's salary is $55,620.

Solve. For each exercise, a table is given for you to complete and use to write an equation that models the situation. See Example 7.

23. How much pure acid should be mixed with 2 gallons of a 40% acid solution in order to get a 70% acid solution?

	Number of Gallons	·	Acid Strength	=	Amount of Acid
Pure Acid			100%		
40% Acid Solution					
70% Acid Solution Needed					

24. How many cubic centimeters (cc) of a 25% antibiotic solution should be added to 10 cubic centimeters of a 60% antibiotic solution to get a 30% antibiotic solution?

	Number of Cubic cm	·	Antibiotic Strength	=	Amount of Antibiotic
25% Antibiotic Solution					
60% Antibiotic Solution					
30% Antibiotic Solution Needed					

25. Community Coffee Company wants a new flavor of Cajun coffee. How many pounds of coffee worth $7 a pound should be added to 14 pounds of coffee worth $4 a pound to get a mixture worth $5 a pound?

	Number of Pounds	·	Cost per pound	= Value
$7 per lb Coffee				
$4 per lb Coffee				
$5 per lb Coffee Wanted				

26. Planter's Peanut Company wants to mix 20 pounds of peanuts worth $3 a pound with cashews worth $5 a pound in order to make an experimental mix worth $3.50 a pound. How many pounds of cashews should be added to the peanuts?

	Number of Pounds	·	Cost per pound	= Value
$3 per lb Peanuts				
$5 per lb Cashews				
$3.50 per lb Mixture Wanted				

MIXED PRACTICE

Solve. If needed, round money amounts to two decimal places and all other amounts to one decimal place. See Examples 1 through 7.

27. Find 23% of 20.   **28.** Find 140% of 86.

29. The number 40 is 80% of what number?

30. The number 56.25 is 45% of what number?

31. The number 144 is what percent of 480?

32. The number 42 is what percent of 35?

The graph below is the result of a survey of U.S. citizens who have made an online purchase in the past 3 months. Use this graph for Exercises 33 through 36.

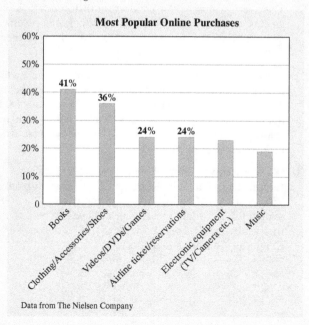

Most Popular Online Purchases

Data from The Nielsen Company

33. Estimate the percent of online purchases in the category of electronic equipment.

34. Estimate the percent of online purchases in the category of music.

35. Suppose a city has 220,500 people who regularly make online purchases. How many of these people might we predict purchased books online?

36. Suppose a community has 50,000 people who regularly make online purchases. How many of these people might we predict purchased airline tickets online?

For Exercises 37 and 38, fill in the percent column in each table. Each table contains a worked-out example.

37.

Top Cranberry-Producing States Forecast in 2010 (in millions of pounds)		
	Millions of Pounds	Percent of Total (rounded to nearest percent)
Wisconsin	435	
Oregon	39	
Massachusetts	195	
Washington	14	
New Jersey	53	Example: $\frac{53}{736} \approx 7\%$
Total	736	

Data from National Agricultural Statistics Service

38.

Kraft Foods Number of Manufacturing Facilities		
Region	Volume (in pounds)	Percent of Total (round to nearest percent)
U.S.	46	
Canada	11	
Western Europe	59	Example: $\frac{59}{223} \approx 26\%$
Central & Eastern Europe, Middle East and Africa	50	
Latin America	20	
Asia Pacific	37	
Total	223	

Data from Kraft Foods Inc.

39. Nordstrom advertised a 25%-off sale. If a London Fog coat originally sold for $256, find the decrease in price and the sale price.

40. A gasoline station decreased the price of a $0.95 cola by 15%. Find the decrease in price and the new price.

41. Although the consumption of washed leaf lettuce is increasing, the consumption of head lettuce is decreasing. The head lettuce consumption per capita in 2000 was 23.5 pounds, and in 2010 the consumption dropped to 17.1 pounds. Find the percent decrease. Round to the nearest tenth of a percent. (*Source:* USDA)

42. Iceberg lettuce is grown and shipped to stores for about 40 cents a head, and consumers purchase it for about 86 cents a head. Find the percent increase. (*Source: Statistical Abstract of the United States*)

43. The number of registered vehicles on the road in the United States is constantly increasing. In 2009, there were approximately 246 million registered vehicles. This represents a 3% increase over 2002. How many registered vehicles were there in the United States in 2002? Round to the nearest million. (*Source:* Federal Highway Administration)

44. A student at the University of New Orleans makes money by buying and selling used cars. Charles bought a used car and later sold it for a 20% profit. If he sold it for $4680, how much did Charles pay for the car?

45. By doubling each dimension, the area of a parallelogram increased from 36 square centimeters to 144 square centimeters. Find the percent increase in area.

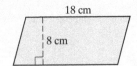

9 cm   4 cm

18 cm   8 cm

46. By doubling each dimension, the area of a triangle increased from 6 square miles to 24 square miles. Find the percent increase in area.

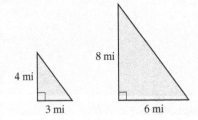

4 mi   3 mi   8 mi   6 mi

47. How much of an alloy that is 20% copper should be mixed with 200 ounces of an alloy that is 50% copper to get an alloy that is 30% copper?

48. How much water should be added to 30 gallons of a solution that is 70% antifreeze to get a mixture that is 60% antifreeze?

49. The number of farms in the United States is decreasing. In 1940, there were approximately 6.3 million farms, while in 2009 there were only 2.1 million farms. Find the percent decrease in the number of farms. Round to the nearest tenth of a percent.

50. During the 1982–1983 term, the Supreme Court made 151 decisions, while during the 2007–2008 term, they made only 72. Find the percent decrease in number of decisions. Round to the nearest tenth of a percent.

51. A company recently downsized its number of employees by 35%. If there are still 78 employees, how many employees were there prior to the layoffs?

52. The average number of children born to each U.S. woman has decreased by 44% since 1920. If this average is now 1.9, find the average in 1920. Round to the nearest tenth.

53. A recent survey showed that 42% of recent college graduates named flexible hours as their most desired employment benefit. In a graduating class of 860 college students, how many would you expect to rank flexible hours as their top priority in job benefits? (Round to the nearest whole.) (*Source:* JobTrak.com)

54. A recent survey showed that 64% of U.S. colleges have Internet access in their classrooms. There are approximately 9800 post-secondary institutions in the United States. How many of these would you expect to have Internet access in their classrooms? (*Source:* Market Data Retrieval, National Center for Education Statistics)

55. A new self-tanning lotion for everyday use is to be sold. First, an experimental lotion mixture is made by mixing 800 ounces of everyday moisturizing lotion worth $0.30 an ounce with self-tanning lotion worth $3 per ounce. If the experimental lotion is to cost $1.20 per ounce, how many ounces of the self-tanning lotion should be in the mixture?

56. The owner of a local chocolate shop wants to develop a new trail mix. How many pounds of chocolate-covered peanuts worth $5 a pound should be mixed with 10 pounds of granola bites worth $2 a pound to get a mixture worth $3 per pound?

57. Scoville units are used to measure the hotness of a pepper. Measuring 577 thousand Scoville units, the "Red Savina" habañero pepper was known as the hottest chili pepper. That has recently changed with the discovery of the Naga Jolokia pepper from India. It measures 48% hotter than the habañero. Find the measure of the Naga Jolokia pepper. Round to the nearest thousand units.

58. As of this writing, the women's record for throwing a disc (like a heavy Frisbee) was set by Valarie Jenkins of the United States in 2008. Her throw was 148.00 meters. The men's world record was set by Christian Sandstrom of Sweden in 2002. His throw was 68.9% farther than Valarie's. Find the distance of his throw. Round to the nearest meter. (*Source: World Flying Disc Federation*)

REVIEW AND PREVIEW

Place $<$, $>$, or $=$ in the appropriate space to make each a true statement. See Sections 1.2, 1.3, and 1.5.

59. -5 ___ -7

60. $\dfrac{12}{3}$ ___ 2^2

61. $|-5|$ ___ $-(-5)$

62. -3^3 ___ $(-3)^3$

63. $(-3)^2$ ___ -3^2

64. $|-2|$ ___ $-|-2|$

CONCEPT EXTENSIONS

65. Is it possible to mix a 10% acid solution and a 40% acid solution to obtain a 60% acid solution? Why or why not?

66. Must the percents in a circle graph have a sum of 100%? Why or why not?

67. A trail mix is made by combining peanuts worth $3 a pound, raisins worth $2 a pound, and M&M's worth $4 a pound. Would it make good business sense to sell the trail mix for $1.98 a pound? Why or why not?

68. a. Can an item be marked up by more than 100%? Why or why not?

  b. Can an item be discounted by more than 100%? Why or why not?

Standardized nutrition labels like the one below have been displayed on food items since 1994. The percent column on the right shows the percent of daily values (based on a 2000-calorie diet) shown at the bottom of the label. For example, a serving of this food contains 4 grams of total fat when the recommended daily fat based on a 2000-calorie diet is less than 65 grams of fat. This means that $\dfrac{4}{65}$ or approximately 6% (as shown) of your daily recommended fat is taken in by eating a serving of this food. Use this nutrition label to answer Exercises 69 through 71.

Nutrition Facts

Serving Size   18 Crackers (31g)
Servings Per Container   About 9

Amount Per Serving

Calories 130	Calories from Fat 35

	% Daily Value*
Total Fat 4g	**6%**
Saturated Fat 0.5g	**3%**
Polyunsaturated Fat 0g	
Monounsaturated Fat 1.5g	
Cholesterol 0mg	**0%**
Sodium 230mg	*x*
Total Carbohydrate 23g	*y*
Dietary Fiber 2g	**8%**
Sugars 3g	
Protein 2g	

Vitamin A 0%	•	Vitamin C 0%
Calcium 2%	•	Iron 6%

* Percent Daily Values are based on a 2,000 calorie diet. Your daily values may be higher or lower depending on your calorie needs.

		Calories	2,000	2,500
Total Fat	Less than		65g	80g
Sat. Fat	Less than		20g	25g
Cholesterol	Less than		300mg	300mg
Sodium	Less than		2400mg	2400mg
Total Carbohydrate			300g	375g
Dietary Fiber			25g	30g

69. Based on a 2000-calorie diet, what percent of daily value of sodium is contained in a serving of this food? In other words, find *x* in the label. (Round to the nearest tenth of a percent.)

70. Based on a 2000-calorie diet, what percent of daily value of total carbohydrate is contained in a serving of this food? In other words, find *y* in the label. (Round to the nearest tenth of a percent.)

71. Notice on the nutrition label that one serving of this food contains 130 calories and 35 of these calories are from fat. Find the percent of calories from fat. (Round to the nearest tenth of a percent.) It is recommended that no more than 30% of calorie intake come from fat. Does this food satisfy this recommendation?

Use the nutrition label below to answer Exercises 72 through 74.

NUTRITIONAL INFORMATION PER SERVING

Serving Size: 9.8 oz	Servings Per Container: 1
Calories 280	Polyunsaturated Fat 1g
Protein 12g	Saturated Fat 3g
Carbohydrate 45g	Cholesterol 20mg
Fat .6g	Sodium 520mg
Percent of Calories from Fat....?	Potassium 220mg

72. If fat contains approximately 9 calories per gram, find the percent of calories from fat in one serving of this food. (Round to the nearest tenth of a percent.)

73. If protein contains approximately 4 calories per gram, find the percent of calories from protein from one serving of this food. (Round to the nearest tenth of a percent.)

74. Find a food that contains more than 30% of its calories per serving from fat. Analyze the nutrition label and verify that the percents shown are correct.

2.7 Further Problem Solving

OBJECTIVES

1 Solve Problems Involving Distance.

2 Solve Problems Involving Money.

3 Solve Problems Involving Interest

This section is devoted to solving problems in the categories listed. The same problem-solving steps used in previous sections are also followed in this section. They are listed below for review.

General Strategy for Problem Solving

1. **UNDERSTAND** the problem. During this step, become comfortable with the problem. Some ways of doing this are to:

   Read and reread the problem.

   Choose a variable to represent the unknown.

   Construct a drawing whenever possible.

   Propose a solution and check. Pay careful attention to how you check your proposed solution. This will help writing an equation to model the problem.

2. **TRANSLATE** the problem into an equation.

3. **SOLVE** the equation.

4. **INTERPRET** the results: *Check* the proposed solution in the stated problem and *state* your conclusion.

OBJECTIVE

1 Solving Distance Problems

Our first example involves distance. For a review of the distance formula, $d = r \cdot t$, see Section 2.5, Example 1, and the table before the example.

EXAMPLE 1 **Finding Time Given Rate and Distance**

Marie Antonio, a bicycling enthusiast, rode her 21-speed at an average speed of 18 miles per hour on level roads and then slowed down to an average of 10 mph on the hilly roads of the trip. If she covered a distance of 98 miles, how long did the entire trip take if traveling the level roads took the same time as traveling the hilly roads?

Solution

1. **UNDERSTAND** the problem. To do so, read and reread the problem. The formula $d = r \cdot t$ is needed. At this time, let's guess a solution. Suppose that she spent 2 hours traveling on the level roads. This means that she also spent 2 hours traveling on the hilly roads, since the times spent were the same. What is her total distance? Her distance on the level road is rate $\cdot$ time $= 18(2) = 36$ miles. Her distance on the hilly roads is rate $\cdot$ time $= 10(2) = 20$ miles. This gives a total distance of 36 miles + 20 miles = 56 miles, not the correct distance of 98 miles. Remember that the purpose of guessing a solution is not to guess correctly (although this may happen) but to help understand the problem better and how to model it with an equation. We are looking for the length of the entire trip, so we begin by letting

   $x =$ the time spent on level roads.

   Because the same amount of time is spent on hilly roads, then also

   $x =$ the time spent on hilly roads.

2. **TRANSLATE.** To help us translate to an equation, we now summarize the information from the problem on the following chart. Fill in the rates given and the variables used to represent the times and use the formula $d = r \cdot t$ to fill in the distance column.

	Rate	$\cdot$ Time	= Distance
Level	18	x	$18x$
Hilly	10	x	$10x$

Since the entire trip covered 98 miles, we have that

In words: total distance   =   level distance   +   hilly distance

Translate: 98   =   18x   +   10x

3. SOLVE.

$$98 = 28x \qquad \text{Add like terms.}$$

$$\frac{98}{28} = \frac{28x}{28} \qquad \text{Divide both sides by 28.}$$

$$3.5 = x$$

4. INTERPRET the results.

Check: Recall that x represents the time spent on the level portion of the trip and the time spent on the hilly portion. If Marie rides for 3.5 hours at 18 mph, her distance is $18(3.5) = 63$ miles. If Marie rides for 3.5 hours at 10 mph, her distance is $10(3.5) = 35$ miles. The total distance is 63 miles + 35 miles = 98 miles, the required distance.

State: The time of the entire trip is then 3.5 hours + 3.5 hours or 7 hours.   ☐

PRACTICE

1   Sat Tranh took a short hike with his friends up Mt. Wachusett. They hiked uphill at a steady pace of 1.5 miles per hour and downhill at a rate of 4 miles per hour. If the time to climb the mountain took an hour more than the time to hike down, how long was the entire hike?

EXAMPLE 2   **Finding Train Speeds**

The Kansas City Southern Railway operates in 10 states and Mexico. Suppose two trains leave Neosho, Missouri, at the same time. One travels north and the other travels south at a speed that is 15 miles per hour faster. In 2 hours, the trains are 230 miles apart. Find the speed of each train.

Neosho

Kansas City Southern Railway

Solution

1. UNDERSTAND the problem. Read and reread the problem. Guess a solution and check. Let's let

$$x = \text{speed of train traveling north}$$

Because the train traveling south is 15 mph faster, we have

$$x + 15 = \text{speed of train traveling south}$$

2. TRANSLATE. Just as for Example 1, let's summarize our information on a chart. Use the formula $d = r \cdot t$ to fill in the distance column.

	r	$\cdot$	t	$=$	d
North Train	x		2		$2x$
South Train	$x + 15$		2		$2(x + 15)$

Since the total distance between the trains is 230 miles, we have

In words: north train distance   +   south train distance   =   total distance

Translate: 2x   +   2(x + 15)   =   230

3. SOLVE.

$$2x + 2x + 30 = 230 \quad \text{Use the distributive property.}$$

$$4x + 30 = 230 \quad \text{Combine like terms.}$$

$$4x = 200 \quad \text{Subtract 30 from both sides.}$$

$$\frac{4x}{4} = \frac{200}{4} \quad \text{Divide both sides by 4.}$$

$$x = 50 \quad \text{Simplify.}$$

4. INTERPRET the results.

Check: Recall that x is the speed of the train traveling north, or 50 mph. In 2 hours, this train travels a distance of $2(50) = 100$ miles. The speed of the train traveling south is $x + 15$ or $50 + 15 = 65$ mph. In 2 hours, this train travels $2(65) = 130$ miles. The total distance of the trains is 100 miles $+ 130$ miles $= 230$ miles, the required distance.

State: The northbound train's speed is 50 mph and the southbound train's speed is 65 mph.   □

PRACTICE
2   The Kansas City Southern Railway has a station in Mexico City, Mexico. Suppose two trains leave Mexico City at the same time. One travels east and the other west at a speed that is 10 mph slower. In 1.5 hours, the trains are 171 miles apart. Find the speed of each train.

OBJECTIVE
2   Solving Money Problems

The next example has to do with finding an unknown number of a certain denomination of coin or bill. These problems are extremely useful in that they help you understand the difference between the number of coins or bills and the total value of the money.

For example, suppose there are seven $5-bills. The *number* of $5-bills is 7 and the *total value* of the money is $5(7) = $35.

Study the table below for more examples.

Denomination of Coin or Bill	*Number of Coins or Bills*	*Value of Coins or Bills*
20-dollar bills	17	$20(17) = $340
nickels	31	$0.05(31) = $1.55
quarters	x	$0.25(x) = $0.25x

EXAMPLE 3   **Finding Numbers of Denominations**

Part of the proceeds from a local talent show was $2420 worth of $10 and $20 bills. If there were 37 more $20 bills than $10 bills, find the number of each denomination.

Solution

1. UNDERSTAND the problem. To do so, read and reread the problem. If you'd like, let's guess a solution. Suppose that there are 25 $10 bills. Since there are 37 more $20 bills, we have $25 + 37 = 62$ $20 bills. The total amount of money is $10(25) + $20(62) = 1490, below the given amount of $2420. Remember that our purpose for guessing is to help us understand the problem better.

We are looking for the number of each denomination, so we let

$$x = \text{number of \$10 bills}$$

There are 37 more $20 bills, so

$$x + 37 = \text{number of \$20 bills}$$

2. TRANSLATE. To help us translate to an equation, study the table below.

Denomination	Number of Bills	Value of Bills (in dollars)
$10 bills	x	$10x$
$20 bills	$x + 37$	$20(x + 37)$

Since the total value of these bills is $2420, we have

In words: value of $10 bills   plus   value of $20 bills   is   2420

Translate: $10x$ $+$ $20(x + 37)$ $=$ 2420

3. SOLVE:

$$10x + 20x + 740 = 2420 \quad \text{Use the distributive property.}$$
$$30x + 740 = 2420 \quad \text{Add like terms.}$$
$$30x = 1680 \quad \text{Subtract 740 from both sides.}$$
$$\frac{30x}{30} = \frac{1680}{30} \quad \text{Divide both sides by 30.}$$
$$x = 56$$

4. INTERPRET the results.

Check: Since x represents the number of $10 bills, we have 56 $10 bills and 56 + 37, or 93 $20 bills. The total amount of these bills is $10(56) + $20(93) = $2420, the correct total.

State: There are 56 $10 bills and 93 $20 bills. □

PRACTICE

3   A stack of $5 and $20 bills was counted by the treasurer of an organization. The total value of the money was $1710 and there were 47 more $5 bills than $20 bills. Find the number of each type of bill.

OBJECTIVE

3   **Solving Interest Problems**

The next example is an investment problem. For a review of the simple interest formula, $I = PRT$, see the table at the beginning of Section 2.5 and Exercises 11 and 12 in that exercise set.

EXAMPLE 4   **Finding the Investment Amount**

Rajiv Puri invested part of his $20,000 inheritance in a mutual funds account that pays 7% simple interest yearly and the rest in a certificate of deposit that pays 9% simple interest yearly. At the end of one year, Rajiv's investments earned $1550. Find the amount he invested at each rate.

Solution

1. UNDERSTAND. Read and reread the problem. Next, guess a solution. Suppose that Rajiv invested $8000 in the 7% fund and the rest, $12,000, in the fund paying 9%. To check, find his interest after one year. Recall the formula $I = PRT$, so the interest from the 7% fund = $8000(0.07)(1) = $560. The interest from the 9% fund = $12,000(0.09)(1) = $1080. The sum of the interests is $560 + $1080 = $1640. Our guess is incorrect, since the sum of the interests is not $1550, but we now have a better understanding of the problem.

Let

$$x = \text{amount of money in the account paying 7\%.}$$

The rest of the money is $20,000 less x or

$$20,000 - x = \text{amount of money in the account paying 9\%.}$$

2. TRANSLATE. We apply the simple interest formula $I = PRT$ and organize our information in the following chart. Since there are two rates of interest and two amounts invested, we apply the formula twice.

	Principal ·	*Rate*	· *Time* =	*Interest*
7% Fund	x	0.07	1	$x(0.07)(1)$ or $0.07x$
9% Fund	$20{,}000 - x$	0.09	1	$(20{,}000 - x)(0.09)(1)$ or $0.09(20{,}000 - x)$
Total	20,000			1550

The total interest earned, $1550, is the sum of the interest earned at 7% and the interest earned at 9%.

In words: interest at 7%   +   interest at 9%   =   total interest

Translate: $0.07x$ + $0.09(20{,}000 - x)$ =   1550

3. SOLVE.

$$0.07x + 0.09(20{,}000 - x) = 1550$$
$$0.07x + 1800 - 0.09x = 1550 \quad \text{Apply the distributive property.}$$
$$1800 - 0.02x = 1550 \quad \text{Combine like terms.}$$
$$-0.02x = -250 \quad \text{Subtract 1800 from both sides.}$$
$$x = 12{,}500 \quad \text{Divide both sides by } -0.02.$$

4. INTERPRET.

Check: If $x = 12{,}500$, then $20{,}000 - x = 20{,}000 - 12{,}500$ or 7500. These solutions are reasonable, since their sum is $20,000 as required. The annual interest on $12,500 at 7% is $875; the annual interest on $7500 at 9% is $675, and $875 + $675 = $1550.

State: The amount invested at 7% was $12,500. The amount invested at 9% was $7500. □

PRACTICE

4   Suzanne Scarpulla invested $30,000, part of it in a high-risk venture that yielded 11.5% per year and the rest in a secure mutual fund paying interest of 6% per year. At the end of one year, Suzanne's investments earned $2790. Find the amount she invested at each rate.

Vocabulary, Readiness & Video Check

Martin-Gay Interactive Videos

See Video 2.7

Watch the section lecture video and answer the following questions.

OBJECTIVE
1

1. The following problem is worded like 🖿 Example 1 but using different quantities.

How long will it take a bus traveling at 55 miles per hour to overtake a car traveling at 50 mph if the car had a 3 hour head start? Fill in the table and set up an equation that could be used to solve for the unknown (do not actually solve). Use 🖿 Example 1 in the video as a model for your work.

	r ·	t =	d
bus			
car			

OBJECTIVE
2

2. In the lecture before 🖿 Example 3, what important point are you told to remember when working with applications that have to do with money?

OBJECTIVE
3

3. The following problem is worded like Example 4 in the video, but using different quantities.

How can $36,000 be invested, part at 6% annual simple interest and the remainder at 4% annual simple interest, so that the annual simple interest earned by the two accounts is equal? Fill in the table and set up an equation that could be used to solve for the unknowns (do not actually solve). Use Example 4 in the video as a model for your work.

P	·	R	·	T	=	I

2.7   Exercise Set

MyMathLab®

Solve. See Examples 1 and 2.

1. A jet plane traveling at 500 mph overtakes a propeller plane traveling at 200 mph that had a 2-hour head start. How far from the starting point are the planes?

2. How long will it take a bus traveling at 60 miles per hour to overtake a car traveling at 40 mph if the car had a 1.5-hour head start?

3. A bus traveled on a level road for 3 hours at an average speed 20 miles per hour faster than it traveled on a winding road. The time spent on the winding road was 4 hours. Find the average speed on the level road if the entire trip was 305 miles.

4. The Jones family drove to Disneyland at 50 miles per hour and returned on the same route at 40 mph. Find the distance to Disneyland if the total driving time was 7.2 hours.

Complete the table. The first and sixth rows have been completed for you. See Example 3.

		Number of Coins or Bills	Value of Coins or Bills (in dollars)
	pennies	x	$0.01x$
5.	dimes	y	
6.	quarters	z	
7.	nickels	$(x + 7)$	
8.	half-dollars	$(20 - z)$	
	$5 bills	$9x$	$5(9x)$
9.	$20 bills	$4y$	
10.	$100 bills	$97z$	
11.	$50 bills	$(35 - x)$	
12.	$10 bills	$(15 - y)$	

13. Part of the proceeds from a garage sale was $280 worth of $5 and $10 bills. If there were 20 more $5 bills than $10 bills, find the number of each denomination.

	Number of Bills	Value of Bills
$5 bills		
$10 bills		
Total		

14. A bank teller is counting $20- and $50-dollar bills. If there are six times as many $20 bills as $50 bills and the total amount of money is $3910, find the number of each denomination.

	Number of Bills	Value of Bills
$20 bills		
$50 bills		
Total		

Solve. See Example 4.

15. Zoya Lon invested part of her $25,000 advance at 8% annual simple interest and the rest at 9% annual simple interest. If her total yearly interest from both accounts was $2135, find the amount invested at each rate.

16. Karen Waugtal invested some money at 9% annual simple interest and $250 more than that amount at 10% annual simple interest. If her total yearly interest was $101, how much was invested at each rate?

17. Sam Mathius invested part of his $10,000 bonus in a fund that paid an 11% profit and invested the rest in stock that suffered a 4% loss. Find the amount of each investment if his overall net profit was $650.

18. Bruce Blossum invested a sum of money at 10% annual simple interest and invested twice that amount at 12% annual simple interest. If his total yearly income from both investments was $2890, how much was invested at each rate?

19. The Concordia Theatre contains 500 seats, and the ticket prices for a recent play were $43 for adults and $28 for children. For one sold-out matinee, if the total proceeds were $16,805, how many of each type of ticket were sold?

20. A zoo in Oklahoma charged $22 for adults and $15 for children. During a summer day, 732 zoo tickets were sold, and the total receipts were $12,912. How many child and how many adult tickets were sold?

MIXED PRACTICE

21. Two cars leave Richmond, Virginia, at the same time after visiting the nearby Richmond International Speedway. The cars travel in opposite directions, one traveling north at 56 mph and one traveling south at 47 mph. When will the two cars be 206 miles apart?

22. Two cars leave Las Vegas, Nevada, at the same time after visiting the Las Vegas Motor Speedway. The cars travel in opposite directions, one traveling northeast at 65 mph and one traveling southwest at 41 mph. When will the two cars be 530 miles apart?

▶ 23. How can $54,000 be invested, part at 8% annual simple interest and the remainder at 10% annual simple interest, so that the interest earned by the two accounts will be equal?

24. Ms. Mills invested her $20,000 bonus in two accounts. She took a 4% loss on one investment and made a 12% profit on another investment but ended up breaking even. How much was invested in each account?

25. Alan and Dave Schaferkötter leave from the same point driving in opposite directions, Alan driving at 55 miles per hour and Dave at 65 mph. Alan has a one-hour head start. How long will they be able to talk on their car phones if the phones have a 250-mile range?

26. Kathleen and Cade Williams leave simultaneously from the same point, hiking in opposite directions, Kathleen walking at 4 miles per hour and Cade at 5 mph. How long can they talk on their walkie-talkies if the walkie-talkies have a 20-mile radius?

27. Suppose two trains leave Corpus Christi, Texas, at the same time, traveling in opposite directions. One train travels 10 mph faster than the other. In 2.5 hours, the trains are 205 miles apart. Find the speed of each train.

28. Suppose two trains leave Edmonton, Canada, at the same time, traveling in opposite directions. One train travels 8 mph faster than the other. In 1.5 hours, the trains are 162 miles apart. Find the speed of each train.

29. A youth organization collected nickels and dimes for a charity drive. By the end of the 1-day drive, the youth had collected $56.35. If there were three times as many dimes as nickels, how many of each type of coin was collected?

30. A collection of dimes and quarters is retrieved from a soft drink machine. There are five times as many dimes as quarters and the total value of the coins is $27.75. Find the number of dimes and the number of quarters.

31. A truck and a van leave the same location at the same time and travel in opposite directions. The truck's speed is 52 mph and the van's speed is 63 mph. When will the truck and the van be 460 miles apart?

32. Two cars leave the same location at the same time and travel in opposite directions. One car's speed is 65 mph and the other car's speed is 45 mph. When will the two cars be 330 miles apart?

33. Two cars leave Pecos, Texas, at the same time and both travel east on Interstate 20. The first car's speed is 70 mph and the second car's speed is 58 mph. When will the cars be 30 miles apart?

34. Two cars leave Savannah, Georgia, at the same time and both travel north on Interstate 95. The first car's speed is 40 mph and the second car's speed is 50 mph. When will the cars be 20 miles apart?

35. If $3000 is invested at 6% annual simple interest, how much should be invested at 9% annual simple interest so that the total yearly income from both investments is $585?

36. Trudy Waterbury, a financial planner, invested a certain amount of money at 9% annual simple interest, twice that amount at 10% annual simple interest, and three times that amount at 11% annual simple interest. Find the amount invested at each rate if her total yearly income from the investments was $2790.

▶ 37. Two hikers are 11 miles apart and walking toward each other. They meet in 2 hours. Find the rate of each hiker if one hiker walks 1.1 mph faster than the other.

38. Nedra and Latonya Dominguez are 12 miles apart hiking toward each other. How long will it take them to meet if Nedra walks at 3 mph and Latonya walks 1 mph faster?

39. Mark Martin can row upstream at 5 mph and downstream at 11 mph. If Mark starts rowing upstream until he gets tired and then rows downstream to his starting point, how far did Mark row if the entire trip took 4 hours?

40. On a 255-mile trip, Gary Alessandrini traveled at an average speed of 70 mph, got a speeding ticket, and then traveled at 60 mph for the remainder of the trip. If the entire trip took 4.5 hours and the speeding ticket stop took 30 minutes, how long did Gary speed before getting stopped?

REVIEW AND PREVIEW

Perform the indicated operations. See Sections 1.5 and 1.6.

41. $3 + (-7)$

42. $(-2) + (-8)$

43. $\dfrac{3}{4} - \dfrac{3}{16}$

44. $-11 + 2.9$

45. $-5 - (-1)$

46. $-12 - 3$

CONCEPT EXTENSIONS

47. A stack of $20, $50, and $100 bills was retrieved as part of an FBI investigation. There were 46 more $50 bills than $100 bills. Also, the number of $20 bills was 7 times the number of $100 bills. If the total value of the money was $9550, find the number of each type of bill.

48. A man places his pocket change in a jar every day. The jar is full and his children have counted the change. The total value is $44.86. Let x represent the number of quarters and use the information below to find the number of each type of coin.

There are: 136 more dimes than quarters

8 times as many nickels as quarters

32 more than 16 times as many pennies as quarters

To "break even" in a manufacturing business, revenue R (income) **must equal** *the cost C of production, or R = C.*

49. The cost C to produce x number of skateboards is given by $C = 100 + 20x$. The skateboards are sold wholesale for $24 each, so revenue R is given by $R = 24x$. Find how many skateboards the manufacturer needs to produce and sell to break even. (*Hint:* Set the expression for R equal to the expression for C, then solve for x.)

50. The revenue R from selling x number of computer boards is given by $R = 60x$, and the cost C of producing them is given by $C = 50x + 5000$. Find how many boards must be sold to break even. Find how much money is needed to produce the break-even number of boards.

51. The cost C of producing x number of paperback books is given by $C = 4.50x + 2400$. Income R from these books is given by $R = 7.50x$. Find how many books should be produced and sold to break even.

52. Find the break-even quantity for a company that makes x number of computer monitors at a cost C given by $C = 875 + 70x$ and receives revenue R given by $R = 105x$.

53. Exercises 49 through 52 involve finding the break-even point for manufacturing. Discuss what happens if a company makes and sells fewer products than the break-even point. Discuss what happens if more products than the break-even point are made and sold.

2.8 Solving Linear Inequalities

OBJECTIVES

1. Define Linear Inequality in One Variable, Graph Solution Sets on a Number Line, and Use Interval Notation.

2. Solve Linear Inequalities.

3. Solve Compound Inequalities.

4. Solve Inequality Applications.

OBJECTIVE

1 Graphing Solution Sets to Linear Inequalities and Using Interval Notation

In Chapter 1, we reviewed these inequality symbols and their meanings:

$<$ means "is less than" $\leq$ means "is less than or equal to"
$>$ means "is greater than" $\geq$ means "is greater than or equal to"

Equations	*Inequalities*
$x = 3$	$x \leq 3$
$5n - 6 = 14$	$5n - 6 < 14$
$12 = 7 - 3y$	$12 \geq 7 - 3y$
$\dfrac{x}{4} - 6 = 1$	$\dfrac{x}{4} - 6 > 1$

A linear inequality is similar to a linear equation except that the equality symbol is replaced with an inequality symbol.

> **Linear Inequality in One Variable**
>
> A **linear inequality in one variable** is an inequality that can be written in the form
>
> $$ax + b < c$$
>
> where a, b, and c are real numbers and a is not 0.

This definition and all other definitions, properties, and steps in this section also hold true for the inequality symbols $>$, $\geq$, and $\leq$.

A **solution of an inequality** is a value of the variable that makes the inequality a true statement. The solution set is the set of all solutions. For the inequality $x < 3$, replacing x with any number less than 3, that is, to the left of 3 on a number line, makes the resulting inequality true. This means that any number less than 3 is a solution of the inequality $x < 3$.

Since there are infinitely many such numbers, we cannot list all the solutions of the inequality. We *can* use set notation and write

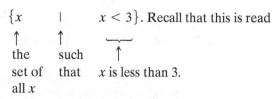

$\{x$ | $x < 3\}$. Recall that this is read

the such ⌣
set of that x is less than 3.
all x

We can also picture the solutions on a number line. If we use open/closed-circle notation, the graph of $\{x \mid x < 3\}$ looks like the following.

In this text, a convenient notation, called **interval notation,** will be used to write solution sets of inequalities. To help us understand this notation, a different graphing notation will be used. Instead of an open circle, we use a parenthesis; instead of a closed circle, we use a bracket. With this new notation, the graph of $\{x \mid x < 3\}$ now looks like

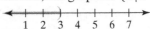

and can be represented in interval notation as $(-\infty, 3)$. The symbol $-\infty$, read as "negative infinity," does not indicate a number but does indicate that the shaded arrow to the left never ends. In other words, the interval $(-\infty, 3)$ includes *all* numbers less than 3.

Picturing the solutions of an inequality on a number line is called **graphing** the solutions or graphing the inequality, and the picture is called the **graph** of the inequality.

To graph $\{x \mid x \le 3\}$ or simply $x \le 3$, shade the numbers to the left of 3 and place a bracket at 3 on the number line. The bracket indicates that 3 **is** a solution: 3 **is** less than or equal to 3. In interval notation, we write $(-\infty, 3]$.

> ▶ **Helpful Hint**
>
> When writing an inequality in interval notation, it may be easier to graph the inequality first, then write it in interval notation. To help, think of the number line as approaching $-\infty$ to the left and $+\infty$ or ∞ to the right. Then simply write the interval notation by following your shading from left to right.
>
> $x > 5$ ∞ $-\infty$ $x \le -7$
>
> (5, ∞)   (−∞, −7]

EXAMPLE 1   Graph $x \ge -1$. Then write the solutions in interval notation.

Solution   We place a bracket at -1 since the inequality symbol is $\ge$ and -1 is greater than or equal to -1. Then we shade to the right of -1.

In interval notation, this is $[-1, \infty)$. □

PRACTICE

1   Graph $x < 5$. Then write the solutions in interval notation.

OBJECTIVE

2   **Solving Linear Inequalities** ▶

When solutions of a linear inequality are not immediately obvious, they are found through a process similar to the one used to solve a linear equation. Our goal is to get the variable alone, and we use properties of inequality similar to properties of equality.

> **Addition Property of Inequality**
>
> If a, b, and c are real numbers, then
>
> $$a < b \quad \text{and} \quad a + c < b + c$$
>
> are equivalent inequalities.

This property also holds true for subtracting values, since subtraction is defined in terms of addition. In other words, adding or subtracting the same quantity from both sides of an inequality does not change the solution of the inequality.

EXAMPLE 2 Solve $x + 4 \leq -6$ for x. Graph the solution set and write it in interval notation.

Solution To solve for x, subtract 4 from both sides of the inequality.

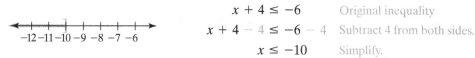

$$x + 4 \leq -6 \qquad \text{Original inequality}$$
$$x + 4 - 4 \leq -6 - 4 \qquad \text{Subtract 4 from both sides.}$$
$$x \leq -10 \qquad \text{Simplify.}$$

The solution set is $(-\infty, -10]$.

PRACTICE

2 Solve $x + 11 \geq 6$. Graph the solution set and write it in interval notation.

▶ **Helpful Hint**

Notice that any number less than or equal to -10 is a solution to $x \leq -10$. For example, solutions include

$$-10, \ -200, \ -11\frac{1}{2}, \ -7\pi, \ -\sqrt{130}, \ -50.3$$

An important difference between linear equations and linear inequalities is shown when we multiply or divide both sides of an inequality by a nonzero real number. For example, start with the true statement $6 < 8$ and multiply both sides by 2. As we see below, the resulting inequality is also true.

$$6 < 8 \qquad \text{True}$$
$$2(6) < 2(8) \qquad \text{Multiply both sides by 2.}$$
$$12 < 16 \qquad \text{True}$$

But if we start with the same true statement $6 < 8$ and multiply both sides by -2, the resulting inequality is not a true statement.

$$6 < 8 \qquad \text{True}$$
$$-2(6) < -2(8) \qquad \text{Multiply both sides by} -2.$$
$$-12 < -16 \qquad \text{False}$$

Notice, however, that if we reverse the direction of the inequality symbol, the resulting inequality is true.

$$-12 < -16 \qquad \text{False}$$
$$-12 > -16 \qquad \text{True}$$

This demonstrates the multiplication property of inequality.

Multiplication Property of Inequality

1. If a, b, and c are real numbers, and c is **positive,** then

$$a < b \qquad \text{and} \qquad ac < bc$$

are equivalent inequalities.

2. If a, b, and c are real numbers, and c is **negative,** then

$$a < b \qquad \text{and} \qquad ac > bc$$

are equivalent inequalities.

Because division is defined in terms of multiplication, this property also holds true when dividing both sides of an inequality by a nonzero number. If we multiply or divide both sides of an inequality by a negative number, **the direction of the inequality symbol must be reversed for the inequalities to remain equivalent.**

> ▶ Helpful Hint
> Whenever both sides of an inequality are multiplied or divided by a negative number, the direction of the inequality symbol **must be** reversed to form an equivalent inequality.

EXAMPLE 3 Solve $-2x \le -4$. Graph the solution set and write it in interval notation.

Solution Remember to reverse the direction of the inequality symbol when dividing by a negative number.

> ▶ Helpful Hint
> Don't forget to reverse the direction of the inequality symbol.

$$-2x \le -4$$
$$\frac{-2x}{-2} \ge \frac{-4}{-2} \quad \text{Divide both sides by } -2 \text{ and reverse the direction of the inequality symbol.}$$
$$x \ge 2 \quad \text{Simplify.}$$

The solution set $[2, \infty)$ is graphed as shown.

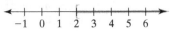

PRACTICE
3 Solve $-5x \ge -15$. Graph the solution set and write it in interval notation.

▶ **EXAMPLE 4** Solve $2x < -4$. Graph the solution set and write it in interval notation.

Solution

> ▶ Helpful Hint
> Do not reverse the inequality sign.

$$2x < -4$$
$$\frac{2x}{2} < \frac{-4}{2} \quad \text{Divide both sides by 2.}$$
$$\quad\quad\quad\quad \text{Do not reverse the direction of the inequality sign.}$$
$$x < -2 \quad \text{Simplify.}$$

The solution set $(-\infty, -2)$ is graphed as shown.

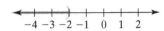

PRACTICE
4 Solve $3x > -9$. Graph the solution set and write it in interval notation.

✓CONCEPT CHECK
Fill in the blank with $<$, $>$, $\le$, or $\ge$.

a. Since $-8 < -4$, then $3(-8)$____ $3(-4)$.

b. Since $5 \ge -2$, then $\dfrac{5}{-7}$ ____ $\dfrac{-2}{-7}$.

c. If $a < b$, then $2a$ ____$2b$.

d. If $a \ge b$, then $\dfrac{a}{-3}$ ____ $\dfrac{b}{-3}$.

Answers to Concept Check:
a. $<$ **b.** $\le$ **c.** $<$ **d.** $\le$

The following steps may be helpful when solving inequalities. Notice that these steps are similar to the ones given in Section 2.3 for solving equations.

Solving Linear Inequalities in One Variable

Step 1. Clear the inequality of fractions by multiplying both sides of the inequality by the lowest common denominator (LCD) of all fractions in the inequality.

Step 2. Remove grouping symbols such as parentheses by using the distributive property.

Step 3. Simplify each side of the inequality by combining like terms.

Step 4. Write the inequality with variable terms on one side and numbers on the other side by using the addition property of inequality.

Step 5. Get the variable alone by using the multiplication property of inequality.

▶ Helpful Hint

Don't forget that if both sides of an inequality are multiplied or divided by a negative number, the direction of the inequality symbol must be reversed.

EXAMPLE 5 Solve $-4x + 7 \geq -9$. Graph the solution set and write it in interval notation.

Solution

$$-4x + 7 \geq -9$$

$$-4x + 7 - 7 \geq -9 - 7 \quad \text{Subtract 7 from both sides.}$$

$$-4x \geq -16 \quad \text{Simplify.}$$

$$\frac{-4x}{-4} \leq \frac{-16}{-4} \quad \text{Divide both sides by } -4 \text{ and reverse the direction of the inequality symbol.}$$

$$x \leq 4 \quad \text{Simplify.}$$

The solution set $(-\infty, 4]$ is graphed as shown.

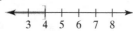

$$3 \quad 4 \quad 5 \quad 6 \quad 7 \quad 8$$

PRACTICE
5 Solve $45 - 7x \leq -4$. Graph the solution set and write it in interval notation.

EXAMPLE 6 Solve $2x + 7 \leq x - 11$. Graph the solution set and write it in interval notation.

Solution

$$2x + 7 \leq x - 11$$

$$2x + 7 - x \leq x - 11 - x \quad \text{Subtract } x \text{ from both sides.}$$

$$x + 7 \leq -11 \quad \text{Combine like terms.}$$

$$x + 7 - 7 \leq -11 - 7 \quad \text{Subtract 7 from both sides.}$$

$$x \leq -18 \quad \text{Combine like terms.}$$

The graph of the solution set $(-\infty, -18]$ is shown.

$$-20 \ -19 \ -18 \ -17 \ -16 \ -15 \ -14$$

PRACTICE
6 Solve $3x + 20 \leq 2x + 13$. Graph the solution set and write it in interval notation.

EXAMPLE 7 Solve $-5x + 7 < 2(x - 3)$. Graph the solution set and write it in interval notation.

Solution

$$-5x + 7 < 2(x - 3)$$
$$-5x + 7 < 2x - 6 \qquad \text{Apply the distributive property.}$$
$$-5x + 7 - 2x < 2x - 6 - 2x \qquad \text{Subtract } 2x \text{ from both sides.}$$
$$-7x + 7 < -6 \qquad \text{Combine like terms.}$$
$$-7x + 7 - 7 < -6 - 7 \qquad \text{Subtract } 7 \text{ from both sides.}$$
$$-7x < -13 \qquad \text{Combine like terms.}$$
$$\frac{-7x}{-7} > \frac{-13}{-7} \qquad \begin{array}{l}\text{Divide both sides by } -7 \text{ and reverse}\\\text{the direction of the inequality symbol.}\end{array}$$
$$x > \frac{13}{7} \qquad \text{Simplify.}$$

The graph of the solution set $\left(\dfrac{13}{7}, \infty\right)$ is shown.

$$\frac{13}{7}$$

```
   +---+---+---+---+--(+---+---+--->
  -2  -1   0   1   2   3   4
```

PRACTICE

7 Solve $6 - 5x > 3(x - 4)$. Graph the solution set and write it in interval notation.

EXAMPLE 8 Solve $2(x - 3) - 5 \le 3(x + 2) - 18$. Graph the solution set and write it in interval notation.

Solution

$$2(x - 3) - 5 \le 3(x + 2) - 18$$
$$2x - 6 - 5 \le 3x + 6 - 18 \qquad \text{Apply the distributive property.}$$
$$2x - 11 \le 3x - 12 \qquad \text{Combine like terms.}$$
$$-x - 11 \le -12 \qquad \text{Subtract } 3x \text{ from both sides.}$$
$$-x \le -1 \qquad \text{Add 11 to both sides.}$$
$$\frac{-x}{-1} \ge \frac{-1}{-1} \qquad \begin{array}{l}\text{Divide both sides by } -1 \text{ and reverse}\\\text{the direction of the inequality symbol.}\end{array}$$
$$x \ge 1 \qquad \text{Simplify.}$$

The graph of the solution set $[1, \infty)$ is shown.

```
   +---+---+---+---[---+---+--->
  -3  -2  -1   0   1   2   3
```

PRACTICE

8 Solve $3(x - 4) - 5 \le 5(x - 1) - 12$. Graph the solution set and write it in interval notation.

OBJECTIVE

3 Solving Compound Inequalities

Inequalities containing one inequality symbol are called **simple inequalities,** while inequalities containing two inequality symbols are called **compound inequalities.** A compound inequality is really two simple inequalities in one. The compound inequality

$$3 < x < 5 \quad \text{means} \quad 3 < x \textbf{ and } x < 5$$

This can be read "x is greater than 3 and less than 5."

A solution of a compound inequality is a value that is a solution of both of the simple inequalities that make up the compound inequality. For example,

$$4\frac{1}{2} \text{ is a solution of } 3 < x < 5 \text{ since } 3 < 4\frac{1}{2} \textbf{ and } 4\frac{1}{2} < 5.$$

To graph $3 < x < 5$, place parentheses at both 3 and 5 and shade between.

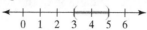

EXAMPLE 9   Graph $2 < x \le 4$. Write the solutions in interval notation.

Solution   Graph all numbers greater than 2 and less than or equal to 4. Place a parenthesis at 2, a bracket at 4, and shade between.

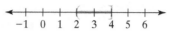

In interval notation, this is $(2, 4]$.

PRACTICE
9   Graph $-3 \le x < 1$. Write the solutions in interval notation.

When we solve a simple inequality, we isolate the variable on one side of the inequality. When we solve a compound inequality, we isolate the variable in the middle part of the inequality. Also, when solving a compound inequality, we must perform the same operation to all **three** parts of the inequality: left, middle, and right.

EXAMPLE 10   Solve $-1 \le 2x - 3 < 5$. Graph the solution set and write it in interval notation.

Solution

$$-1 \le 2x - 3 < 5$$
$$-1 + 3 \le 2x - 3 + 3 < 5 + 3 \quad \text{Add 3 to all three parts.}$$
$$2 \le 2x < 8 \quad \text{Combine like terms.}$$
$$\frac{2}{2} \le \frac{2x}{2} < \frac{8}{2} \quad \text{Divide all three parts by 2.}$$
$$1 \le x < 4 \quad \text{Simplify.}$$

The graph of the solution set $[1, 4)$ is shown.

PRACTICE
10   Solve $-4 < 3x + 2 \le 8$. Graph the solution set and write it in interval notation.

EXAMPLE 11   Solve $3 \le \dfrac{3x}{2} + 4 \le 5$. Graph the solution set and write it in interval notation.

Solution

$$3 \le \frac{3x}{2} + 4 \le 5$$

$$2(3) \le 2\left(\frac{3x}{2} + 4\right) \le 2(5) \quad \text{Multiply all three parts by 2 to clear the fraction.}$$
$$6 \le 3x + 8 \le 10 \quad \text{Distribute.}$$
$$-2 \le 3x \le 2 \quad \text{Subtract 8 from all three parts.}$$
$$\frac{-2}{3} \le \frac{3x}{3} \le \frac{2}{3} \quad \text{Divide all three parts by 3.}$$
$$-\frac{2}{3} \le x \le \frac{2}{3} \quad \text{Simplify.}$$

The graph of the solution set $\left[-\dfrac{2}{3}, \dfrac{2}{3}\right]$ is shown.

$$-\frac{2}{3} \quad \frac{2}{3}$$

$$\xleftarrow{\hspace{1cm}} \underset{-2\;-10123}{\vert\;\;\vert\;\vert\,\vert\!\vert\;\vert\;\;\vert\;\;\vert} \xrightarrow{\hspace{1cm}}$$

PRACTICE

11   Solve $1 < \dfrac{3}{4}x + 5 < 6$. Graph the solution set and write it in interval notation.

OBJECTIVE

4   **Solving Inequality Applications**

Problems containing words such as "at least," "at most," "between," "no more than," and "no less than" usually indicate that an inequality should be solved instead of an equation. In solving applications involving linear inequalities, use the same procedure you use to solve applications involving linear equations.

Some Inequality Translations			
≥	≤	<	>
at least	at most	is less than	is greater than
no less than	no more than		

EXAMPLE 12   12 subtracted from 3 times a number is less than 21. Find all numbers that make this statement true.

Solution

1. UNDERSTAND. Read and reread the problem. This is a direct translation problem, and let's let
   x = the unknown number

2. TRANSLATE.

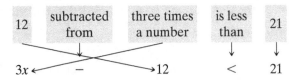

3. SOLVE. $3x - 12 < 21$

              $3x < 33$ Add 12 to both sides.

              $\dfrac{3x}{3} < \dfrac{33}{3}$ Divide both sides by 3 and do not reverse the direction of the inequality symbol.

              $x < 11$ Simplify.

4. INTERPRET.

Check: Check the translation; then let's choose a number less than 11 to see if it checks. For example, let's check 10. 12 subtracted from 3 times 10 is 12 subtracted from 30, or 18. Since 18 is less than 21, the number 10 checks.

State: All numbers less than 11 make the original statement true.

PRACTICE

12   Twice a number, subtracted from 35, is greater than 15. Find all numbers that make this true.

EXAMPLE 13 **Staying within Budget**

Marie Chase and Jonathan Edwards are having their wedding reception at the Gallery Reception Hall. They may spend at most $2000 for the reception. If the reception hall charges a $100 cleanup fee plus $36 per person, find the greatest number of people that they can invite and still stay within their budget.

Solution

1. UNDERSTAND. Read and reread the problem. Next, guess a solution. If 40 people attend the reception, the cost is $100 + $36(40) = $100 + $1440 = $1540. Let x = the number of people who attend the reception.

2. TRANSLATE.

In words:	cleanup fee	+	cost per person	must be less than or equal to	2000
	↓		↓	↓	↓
Translate:	100	+	36x	≤	2000

3. SOLVE.

$$100 + 36x \leq 2000$$
$$36x \leq 1900 \quad \text{Subtract 100 from both sides.}$$
$$x \leq 52\frac{7}{9} \quad \text{Divide both sides by 36.}$$

4. INTERPRET.

Check: Since x represents the number of people, we round down to the nearest whole, or 52. Notice that if 52 people attend, the cost is

$100 + $36(52) = $1972. If 53 people attend, the cost is

$100 + $36(53) = $2008, which is more than the given 2000.

State: Marie Chase and Jonathan Edwards can invite at most 52 people to the reception. □

PRACTICE
13 Kasonga is eager to begin his education at his local community college. He has budgeted $1500 for college this semester. His local college charges a $300 matriculation fee and costs an average of $375 for tuition, fees, and books for each three-credit course. Find the greatest number of classes Kasonga can afford to take this semester.

Vocabulary, Readiness & Video Check

Use the choices below to fill in each blank.

expression   inequality   equation

1. $6x - 7(x + 9)$ _____
2. $6x = 7(x + 9)$ _____
3. $6x < 7(x + 9)$ _____
4. $5y - 2 \geq -38$ _____

Decide which number listed is not a solution to each given inequality.

5. $x \geq -3; \quad -3, 0, -5, \pi$ _____
6. $x < 6; \quad -6, |-6|, 0, -3.2$ _____

Martin-Gay Interactive Videos

See Video 2.8 🍎

Watch the section lecture video and answer the following questions.

OBJECTIVE 1

7. Using Example 1 from the video as a reference, explain the connection between the graph of an inequality and interval notation.

OBJECTIVE 2

8. The steps for solving a linear inequality in one variable are discussed in the lecture before Example 6. Why are you told to be very careful when you use Step 5?

OBJECTIVE 3

9. For Example 8, explain how the solving would change if the compound inequality simplified to $0 < -3x < 14$ instead of $0 < 3x < 14$.

OBJECTIVE 4

10. What is the phrase in Example 9 that tells you to translate to an *inequality*? What does this phrase translate to?

2.8 Exercise Set MyMathLab®

Graph each set of numbers given in interval notation. Then write an inequality statement in x describing the numbers graphed.

1. $[2, \infty)$
2. $(-3, \infty)$
3. $(-\infty, -5)$
4. $(-\infty, 4]$

Graph each inequality on a number line. Then write the solutions in interval notation. See Example 1.

5. $x \le -1$
6. $y < 0$
7. $x < \dfrac{1}{2}$
8. $z < -\dfrac{2}{3}$
9. $y \ge 5$
10. $x > 3$

Solve each inequality. Graph the solution set and write it in interval notation. See Examples 2 through 4.

11. $2x < -6$
12. $3x > -9$
13. $x - 2 \ge -7$
14. $x + 4 \le 1$
15. $-8x \le 16$
16. $-5x < 20$

Solve each inequality. Graph the solution set and write it in interval notation. See Examples 5 and 6.

17. $3x - 5 > 2x - 8$
18. $3 - 7x \ge 10 - 8x$
19. $4x - 1 \le 5x - 2x$
20. $7x + 3 < 9x - 3x$

Solve each inequality. Graph the solution set and write it in interval notation. See Examples 7 and 8.

21. $x - 7 < 3(x + 1)$
22. $3x + 9 \le 5(x - 1)$
23. $-6x + 2 \ge 2(5 - x)$
24. $-7x + 4 > 3(4 - x)$
25. $4(3x - 1) \le 5(2x - 4)$

26. $3(5x - 4) \le 4(3x - 2)$
27. $3(x + 2) - 6 > -2(x - 3) + 14$
28. $7(x - 2) + x \le -4(5 - x) - 12$

MIXED PRACTICE

Solve the following inequalities. Graph each solution set and write it in interval notation.

29. $-2x \le -40$
30. $-7x > 21$
31. $-9 + x > 7$
32. $y - 4 \le 1$
33. $3x - 7 < 6x + 2$
34. $2x - 1 \ge 4x - 5$
35. $5x - 7x \ge x + 2$
36. $4 - x < 8x + 2x$
37. $\dfrac{3}{4}x > 2$
38. $\dfrac{5}{6}x \ge -8$
39. $3(x - 5) < 2(2x - 1)$
40. $5(x + 4) < 4(2x + 3)$
41. $4(2x + 1) < 4$
42. $6(2 - x) \ge 12$
43. $-5x + 4 \ge -4(x - 1)$
44. $-6x + 2 < -3(x + 4)$
45. $-2(x - 4) - 3x < -(4x + 1) + 2x$
46. $-5(1 - x) + x \le -(6 - 2x) + 6$
47. $\dfrac{1}{4}(x + 4) < \dfrac{1}{5}(2x + 3)$
48. $\dfrac{1}{3}(3x - 1) < \dfrac{1}{2}(x + 4)$

Graph each inequality. Then write the solutions in interval nota-tion. See Example 9.

49. $-1 < x < 3$

50. $2 \le y \le 3$

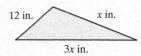 **51.** $0 \le y < 2$

52. $-1 \le x \le 4$

Solve each inequality. Graph the solution set and write it in interval notation. See Examples 10 and 11.

53. $-3 < 3x < 6$

54. $-5 < 2x < -2$

55. $2 \le 3x - 10 \le 5$

56. $4 \le 5x - 6 \le 19$

57. $-4 < 2(x - 3) \le 4$

58. $0 < 4(x + 5) \le 8$

59. $-2 < 3x - 5 < 7$

60. $1 < 4 + 2x \le 7$

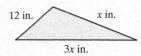 **61.** $-6 < 3(x - 2) \le 8$

62. $-5 \le 2(x + 4) < 8$

Solve the following. For Exercises 65 and 66, the solutions have been started for you. See Examples 12 and 13.

63. Six more than twice a number is greater than negative four-teen. Find all numbers that make this statement true.

64. One more than five times a number is less than or equal to ten. Find all such numbers.

65. The perimeter of a rectangle is to be no greater than 100 centimeters and the width must be 15 centimeters. Find the maximum length of the rectangle.

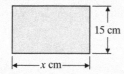

Start the solution:

1. **UNDERSTAND** the problem. Reread it as many times as needed.

2. **TRANSLATE** into an equation. (Fill in the blanks below.)

the perimeter of the rectangle	is no greater than	100
↓	↓	↓
$x + 15 + x + 15$	_____	100

Finish with:

3. **SOLVE** and 4. **INTERPRET**

66. One side of a triangle is three times as long as another side, and the third side is 12 inches long. If the perimeter can be no longer than 32 inches, find the maximum lengths of the other two sides.

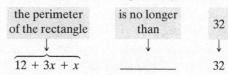

Start the solution:

1. **UNDERSTAND** the problem. Reread it as many times as needed.

2. **TRANSLATE** into an equation. (Fill in the blanks below.)

the perimeter of the rectangle	is no longer than	32
↓	↓	↓
$12 + 3x + x$	_____	32

Finish with:

3. **SOLVE** and 4. **INTERPRET**

67. Ben Holladay bowled 146 and 201 in his first two games. What must he bowl in his third game to have an average of at least 180? (*Hint:* The average of a list of numbers is their sum divided by the number of numbers in the list.)

68. On an NBA team, the two forwards measure 6'8" and 6'6" tall and the two guards measure 6'0" and 5'9" tall. How tall should the center be if they wish to have a starting team average height of at least 6'5"?

69. Dennis and Nancy Wood are celebrating their 30th wedding anniversary by having a reception at Tiffany Oaks reception hall. They have budgeted $3000 for their reception. If the reception hall charges a $50.00 cleanup fee plus $34 per person, find the greatest number of people that they may invite and still stay within their budget.

70. A surprise retirement party is being planned for Pratap Puri. A total of $860 has been collected for the event, which is to be held at a local reception hall. This reception hall charges a cleanup fee of $40 and $15 per person for drinks and light snacks. Find the greatest number of people that may be invited and still stay within the $860 budget.

71. A 150-pound person uses 5.8 calories per minute when walking at a speed of 4 mph. How long must a person walk at this speed to use at least 200 calories? Round up to the nearest minute. (*Source:* Home & Garden Bulletin No. 72)

72. A 170-pound person uses 5.3 calories per minute when bicy-cling at a speed of 5.5 mph. How long must a person ride a bike at this speed to use at least 200 calories? Round up to the nearest minute. (*Source:* Same as Exercise 71)

73. Twice a number, increased by one, is between negative five and seven. Find all such numbers.

74. Half a number, decreased by four, is between two and three. Find all such numbers.

REVIEW AND PREVIEW

Evaluate the following. See Section 1.4.

75. $(2)^3$

76. $(3)^3$

77. $(1)^{12}$

78. 0^5

79. $\left(\dfrac{4}{7}\right)^2$

80. $\left(\dfrac{2}{3}\right)^3$

CONCEPT EXTENSIONS

Fill in the box with $<$, $>$, $\leq$, or $\geq$. See the Concept Check in this section.

81. Since $3 < 5$, then $3(-4) \,\Box\, 5(-4)$.

82. If $m \leq n$, then $2m \,\Box\, 2n$.

83. If $m \leq n$, then $-2m \,\Box\, -2n$.

84. If $-x < y$, then $x \,\Box\, -y$.

85. When solving an inequality, when must you reverse the direction of the inequality symbol?

86. If both sides of the inequality $-3x < 30$ are divided by -3, do you reverse the direction of the inequality symbol? Why or why not?

Solve.

87. Eric Daly has scores of 75, 83, and 85 on his history tests. Use an inequality to find the scores he can make on his final exam to receive a B in the class. The final exam counts as **two** tests, and a B is received if the final course average is greater than or equal to 80.

88. Maria Lipco has scores of 85, 95, and 92 on her algebra tests. Use an inequality to find the scores she can make on her final exam to receive an A in the course. The final exam counts as **three** tests, and an A is received if the final course average is greater than or equal to 90. Round to one decimal place.

89. Explain how solving a linear inequality is similar to solving a linear equation.

90. Explain how solving a linear inequality is different from solving a linear equation.

91. Explain how solving a linear inequality is different from solving a compound inequality.

92. Explain how solving a linear inequality is similar to solving a compound inequality.

93. The formula $C = 3.14d$ can be used to approximate the circumference of a circle given its diameter. Waldo Manufacturing manufactures and sells a certain washer with an outside circumference of 3 centimeters. The company has decided that a washer whose actual circumference is in the interval $2.9 \leq C \leq 3.1$ centimeters is acceptable. Use a compound inequality and find the corresponding interval for diameters of these washers. (Round to 3 decimal places.)

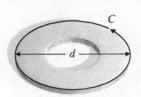

94. Bunnie Supplies manufactures plastic Easter eggs that open. The company has determined that if the circumference of the opening of each part of the egg is in the interval $118 \leq C \leq 122$ millimeters, the eggs will open and close comfortably. Use a compound inequality and find the corresponding interval for diameters of these openings. (Round to 2 decimal places.)

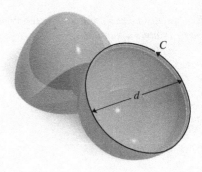

For Exercises 95 through 98, see the example below.

Solve $x(x - 6) > x^2 - 5x + 6$. Graph the solution set and write it in interval notation.

Solution

$$x(x - 6) > x^2 - 5x + 6$$
$$x^2 - 6x > x^2 - 5x + 6$$
$$x^2 - 6x - x^2 > x^2 - 5x + 6 - x^2$$
$$-6x > -5x + 6$$
$$-x > 6$$
$$\frac{-x}{-1} < \frac{6}{-1}$$
$$x < -6$$

The solution set $(-\infty, -6)$ is graphed as shown.

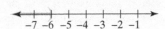

Solve each inequality. Graph the solution set and write it in interval notation.

95. $x(x + 4) > x^2 - 2x + 6$

96. $x(x - 3) \geq x^2 - 5x - 8$

97. $x^2 + 6x - 10 < x(x - 10)$

98. $x^2 - 4x + 8 < x(x + 8)$

Chapter 2 Vocabulary Check

Fill in each blank with one of the words or phrases listed below.

like terms   numerical coefficient   linear inequality in one variable   no solution

equivalent equations   formula   compound inequalities   reversed

linear equation in one variable   unlike terms   all real numbers   the same

1. Terms with the same variables raised to exactly the same powers are called _____.

2. If terms are not like terms, they are _____.

3. A(n) _____ can be written in the form $ax + b = c$.

4. A(n) _____ can be written in the form $ax + b < c$ (or $>$, $\leq$, $\geq$).

5. Inequalities containing two inequality symbols are called _____.

6. An equation that describes a known relationship among quantities is called a(n) _____.

7. The _____ of a term is its numerical factor.

8. Equations that have the same solution are called _____.

9. The solution(s) to the equation $x + 5 = x + 5$ is/are _____.

10. The solution(s) to the equation $x + 5 = x + 4$ is/are _____.

11. If both sides of an inequality are multiplied or divided by the same positive number, the direction of the inequality symbol is _____.

12. If both sides of an inequality are multiplied by the same negative number, the direction of the inequality symbol is _____.

Chapter 2 Highlights

DEFINITIONS AND CONCEPTS	EXAMPLES

Section 2.1   Simplifying Algebraic Expressions

The **numerical coefficient** of a **term** is its numerical factor.

Term	Numerical Coefficient
$-7y$	-7
x	1
$\frac{1}{5}a^2b$	$\frac{1}{5}$

Terms with the same variables raised to exactly the same powers are **like terms.**

Like Terms	Unlike Terms
$12x, -x$	$3y, 3y^2$
$-2xy, 5yx$	$7a^2b, -2ab^2$

To combine like terms, add the numerical coefficients and multiply the result by the common variable factor.

$$9y + 3y = 12y$$
$$-4z^2 + 5z^2 - 6z^2 = -5z^2$$

To remove parentheses, apply the distributive property.

$$-4(x + 7) + 10(3x - 1)$$
$$= -4x - 28 + 30x - 10$$
$$= 26x - 38$$

DEFINITIONS AND CONCEPTS	EXAMPLES

Section 2.2   The Addition and Multiplication Properties of Equality

A **linear equation in one variable** can be written in the form $ax + b = c$ where a, b, and c are real numbers and $a \neq 0$.

Equivalent equations are equations that have the same solution.

Addition Property of Equality

Adding the same number to or subtracting the same number from both sides of an equation does not change its solution.

Multiplication Property of Equality

Multiplying both sides or dividing both sides of an equation by the same nonzero number does not change its solution.

Linear Equations

$$-3x + 7 = 2$$

$$3(x - 1) = -8(x + 5) + 4$$

$x - 7 = 10$ and $x = 17$
are equivalent equations.

$$y + 9 = 3$$
$$y + 9 - 9 = 3 - 9$$
$$y = -6$$

$$\frac{2}{3}a = 18$$
$$\frac{3}{2}\left(\frac{2}{3}a\right) = \frac{3}{2}(18)$$
$$a = 27$$

Section 2.3   Solving Linear Equations

To Solve Linear Equations

1. Clear the equation of fractions.

2. Remove any grouping symbols such as parentheses.
3. Simplify each side by combining like terms.
4. Write variable terms on one side and numbers on the other side using the addition property of equality.

5. Get the variable alone using the multiplication property of equality.

6. Check by substituting in the original equation.

Solve: $\dfrac{5(-2x + 9)}{6} + 3 = \dfrac{1}{2}$

1. $6 \cdot \dfrac{5(-2x + 9)}{6} + 6 \cdot 3 = 6 \cdot \dfrac{1}{2}$

   $$5(-2x + 9) + 18 = 3$$

2. $\quad -10x + 45 + 18 = 3 \qquad$ Distributive property
3. $\qquad\quad -10x + 63 = 3 \qquad$ Combine like terms.
4. $\quad -10x + 63 - 63 = 3 - 63 \quad$ Subtract 63.

   $$-10x = -60$$

5. $\qquad\quad \dfrac{-10x}{-10} = \dfrac{-60}{-10} \qquad$ Divide by -10.

   $$x = 6$$

6. $\dfrac{5(-2x + 9)}{6} + 3 = \dfrac{1}{2}$

   $\dfrac{5(-2 \cdot 6 + 9)}{6} + 3 \overset{?}{=} \dfrac{1}{2}$

   $\dfrac{5(-3)}{6} + 3 \overset{?}{=} \dfrac{1}{2}$

   $-\dfrac{5}{2} + \dfrac{6}{2} \overset{?}{=} \dfrac{1}{2}$

   $\dfrac{1}{2} = \dfrac{1}{2} \qquad$ True

DEFINITIONS AND CONCEPTS	EXAMPLES

Section 2.4   An Introduction to Problem Solving

Problem-Solving Steps	The height of the Hudson volcano in Chile is twice the height of the Kiska volcano in the Aleutian Islands. If the sum of their heights is 12,870 feet, find the height of each.
1. UNDERSTAND the problem.	**1.** Read and reread the problem. Guess a solution and check your guess. Let x be the height of the Kiska volcano. Then $2x$ is the height of the Hudson volcano. $x \rceil$ $2x \rceil$ Kiska Hudson
2. TRANSLATE the problem.	**2.** In words: height of Kiska / added to / height of Hudson / is / 12,870 Translate: x $+$ $2x$ $=$ 12,870
3. SOLVE.	**3.** $\qquad x + 2x = 12{,}870$ $\qquad\qquad 3x = 12{,}870$ $\qquad\qquad\ x = 4290$
4. INTERPRET the results.	**4.** *Check:* If x is 4290, then $2x$ is 2(4290) or 8580. Their sum is 4290 + 8580 or 12,870, the required amount. *State:* The Kiska volcano is 4290 feet high and the Hudson volcano is 8580 feet high.

Section 2.5   Formulas and Problem Solving

	Formulas $A = lw$ (area of a rectangle) $I = PRT$ (simple interest)
An equation that describes a known relationship among quantities is called a **formula.**	
If all values for the variables in a formula are known except for one, this unknown value may be found by substituting in the known values and solving.	If $d = 182$ miles and $r = 52$ miles per hour in the formula $d = r \cdot t$, find t. $\qquad d = r \cdot t$ $\quad 182 = 52 \cdot t$ Let $d = 182$ and $r = 52$. $\quad 3.5 = t$ The time is 3.5 hours.
To solve a formula for a specified variable, use the same steps as for solving a linear equation. Treat the specified variable as the only variable of the equation.	Solve: $P = 2l + 2w$ for l. $\qquad\qquad P = 2l + 2w$ $\quad P - 2w = 2l + 2w - 2w$ Subtract $2w$. $\quad P - 2w = 2l$ $\quad \dfrac{P - 2w}{2} = \dfrac{2l}{2}$ Divide by 2. $\quad \dfrac{P - 2w}{2} = l$ Simplify.

DEFINITIONS AND CONCEPTS	EXAMPLES

Section 2.6 Percent and Mixture Problem Solving

Use the same problem-solving steps to solve a problem containing percents.

1. UNDERSTAND.

2. TRANSLATE.

3. SOLVE.

4. INTERPRET.

32% of what number is 36.8?

1. Read and reread. Propose a solution and check. Let $x =$ the unknown number.

2.
$$
\begin{array}{ccccc}
32\% & \text{of} & \text{what number} & \text{is} & 36.8 \\
\downarrow & \downarrow & \downarrow & \downarrow & \downarrow \\
32\% & \cdot & x & = & 36.8
\end{array}
$$

3. *Solve:* $\quad 32\% \cdot x = 36.8$
$$0.32x = 36.8$$
$$\frac{0.32x}{0.32} = \frac{36.8}{0.32} \quad \text{Divide by 0.32.}$$
$$x = 115 \quad \text{Simplify.}$$

4. *Check, then state:* 32% of 115 is 36.8.

---

1. UNDERSTAND.

2. TRANSLATE.

How many liters of a 20% acid solution must be mixed with a 50% acid solution to obtain 12 liters of a 30% solution?

1. Read and reread. Guess a solution and check.

Let $x =$ number of liters of 20% solution.

Then $12 - x =$ number of liters of 50% solution.

2.

	No. of Liters $\cdot$	Acid Strength $=$	Amount of Acid
20% Solution	x	20%	$0.20x$
50% Solution	$12 - x$	50%	$0.50(12 - x)$
30% Solution Needed	12	30%	$0.30(12)$

In words:

$$
\begin{array}{ccccc}
\text{acid in} & & \text{acid in} & & \text{acid in} \\
20\% & + & 50\% & = & 30\% \\
\text{solution} & & \text{solution} & & \text{solution} \\
\downarrow & & \downarrow & & \downarrow
\end{array}
$$

Translate: $\quad 0.20x \quad + \quad 0.50(12 - x) \quad = \quad 0.30(12)$

3. SOLVE.

4. INTERPRET.

3. Solve: $\ 0.20x + 0.50(12 - x) = 0.30(12)$

$$0.20x + 6 - 0.50x = 3.6 \quad \text{Apply the distributive}$$
$$-0.30x + 6 = 3.6 \quad \text{property.}$$
$$-0.30x = -2.4 \quad \text{Subtract 6.}$$
$$x = 8 \quad \text{Divide by } -0.30.$$

4. *Check, then state:*

If 8 liters of a 20% acid solution are mixed with $12 - 8$ or 4 liters of a 50% acid solution, the result is 12 liters of a 30% solution.

DEFINITIONS AND CONCEPTS	EXAMPLES

Section 2.7   Further Problem Solving

Problem-Solving Steps

A collection of dimes and quarters has a total value of $19.55. If there are three times as many quarters as dimes, find the number of quarters.

1. UNDERSTAND.

1. Read and reread. Propose a solution and check.

$$\text{Let } x = \text{number of dimes and}$$
$$3x = \text{number of quarters.}$$

2. TRANSLATE.

2. In words:

value of dimes	+	value of quarters	=	19.55
↓		↓		↓
Translate: $0.10x$	+	$0.25(3x)$	=	19.55

3. SOLVE.

3. Solve: $0.10x + 0.75x = 19.55$ Multiply.

$$0.85x = 19.55 \quad \text{Add like terms.}$$
$$x = 23 \quad \text{Divide by 0.85.}$$

4. INTERPRET.

4. *Check, then state:*

The number of dimes is 23 and the number of quarters is 3(23) or 69. The total value of this money is

$$0.10(23) + 0.25(69) = 19.55, \text{ so our result checks.}$$

The number of quarters is 69.

Section 2.8   Solving Linear Inequalities

A **linear inequality in one variable** is an inequality that can be written in one of the forms:

$$ax + b < c \qquad ax + b \le c$$
$$ax + b > c \qquad ax + b \ge c$$

where $a, b,$ and c are real numbers and a is not 0.

Linear Inequalities

$$2x + 3 < 6 \qquad 5(x - 6) \ge 10$$
$$\frac{x - 2}{5} > \frac{5x + 7}{2} \qquad \frac{-(x + 8)}{9} \le \frac{-2x}{11}$$

Addition Property of Inequality

Adding the same number to or subtracting the same number from both sides of an inequality does not change the solutions.

$$y + 4 \le -1$$
$$y + 4 - 4 \le -1 - 4 \quad \text{Subtract 4.}$$
$$y \le -5$$

$(-\infty, -5)$ ←————|——+——+——+——+——+——+——→
   $-6\ -5\ -4\ -3\ -2\ -1\ \ 0\ \ 1\ \ 2$

Multiplication Property of Inequality

Multiplying or dividing both sides of an inequality by the same positive number does not change its solutions.

$$\frac{1}{3}x > -2$$
$$3\left(\frac{1}{3}x\right) > 3 \cdot -2 \quad \text{Multiply by 3.}$$
$$x > -6 \quad (-6, \infty)$$

←+———+———+———+———+→
$-6\ -4\ -2\ \ 0\ \ 2$

Multiplying or dividing both sides of an inequality by the same **negative number and reversing the direction of the inequality symbol** does not change its solutions.

$$-2x \le 4$$
$$\frac{-2x}{-2} \ge \frac{4}{-2} \quad \text{Divide by } -2, \text{ reverse inequality symbol.}$$
$$x \ge -2 \quad [-2, \infty)$$

←+——+——+——+——+——+→
$-3\ -2\ -1\ \ 0\ \ 1\ \ 2$

(continued)

DEFINITIONS AND CONCEPTS	EXAMPLES

Section 2.8 Solving Linear Inequalities (continued)

To Solve Linear Inequalities

1. Clear the equation of fractions.
2. Remove grouping symbols.
3. Simplify each side by combining like terms.
4. Write variable terms on one side and numbers on the other side, using the addition property of inequality.

5. Get the variable alone, using the multiplication property of inequality.

Solve: $3(x + 2) \le -2 + 8$

1. No fractions to clear. $3(x + 2) \le -2 + 8$

2. $\qquad\qquad 3x + 6 \le -2 + 8$ Distributive property

3. $\qquad\qquad\quad 3x + 6 \le 6$ Combine like terms.

4. $\qquad\quad 3x + 6 - 6 \le 6 - 6$ Subtract 6.

$$3x \le 0$$

5. $\qquad\qquad\qquad \dfrac{3x}{3} \le \dfrac{0}{3}$ Divide by 3.

$x \le 0 \quad (-\infty, 0)$

Inequalities containing two inequality symbols are called **compound inequalities.**

Compound Inequalities

$$-2 < x < 6$$

$$5 \le 3(x - 6) < \frac{20}{3}$$

To solve a compound inequality, isolate the variable in the middle part of the inequality. Perform the same operation to all three parts of the inequality: left, middle, right.

Solve: $\qquad -2 < 3x + 1 < 7$

$-2 - 1 < 3x + 1 - 1 < 7 - 1$ Subtract 1.

$$-3 < 3x < 6$$

$$\frac{-3}{3} < \frac{3x}{3} < \frac{6}{3}$$ Divide by 3.

$-1 < x < 2 \quad (-1, 2)$

Chapter 2 Review

(2.1) Simplify the following expressions.

1. $5x - x + 2x$

2. $0.2z - 4.6x - 7.4z$

3. $\dfrac{1}{2}x + 3 + \dfrac{7}{2}x - 5$

4. $\dfrac{4}{5}y + 1 + \dfrac{6}{5}y + 2$

5. $2(n - 4) + n - 10$

6. $3(w + 2) - (12 - w)$

7. Subtract $7x - 2$ from $x + 5$.

8. Subtract $1.4y - 3$ from $y - 0.7$.

Write each of the following as algebraic expressions.

9. Three times a number decreased by 7

10. Twice the sum of a number and 2.8 added to 3 times the number

(2.2) Solve each equation.

11. $8x + 4 = 9x$

12. $5y - 3 = 6y$

13. $\dfrac{2}{7}x + \dfrac{5}{7}x = 6$

14. $3x - 5 = 4x + 1$

15. $2x - 6 = x - 6$

16. $4(x + 3) = 3(1 + x)$

17. $6(3 + n) = 5(n - 1)$

18. $5(2 + x) - 3(3x + 2) = -5(x - 6) + 2$

Use the addition property to fill in the blank so that the middle equation simplifies to the last equation.

19. $\qquad x - 5 = 3$

$x - 5 + \underline{\quad} = 3 + \underline{\quad}$

$\qquad\quad x = 8$

20. $\qquad x + 9 = -2$

$x + 9 - \underline{\quad} = -2 - \underline{\quad}$

$\qquad\quad x = -11$

Choose the correct algebraic expression.

21. The sum of two numbers is 10. If one number is x, express the other number in terms of x.

  a. $x - 10$ **b.** $10 - x$

  c. $10 + x$ **d.** $10x$

22. Mandy is 5 inches taller than Melissa. If x inches represents the height of Mandy, express Melissa's height in terms of x.

  a. $x - 5$ **b.** $5 - x$

  c. $5 + x$ **d.** $5x$

23. If one angle measures $x°$, express the measure of its complement in terms of x.

  a. $(180 - x)°$ **b.** $(90 - x)°$

  c. $(x - 180)°$ **d.** $(x - 90)°$

24. If one angle measures $(x + 5)°$, express the measure of its supplement in terms of x.

a. $(185 + x)°$

b. $(95 + x)°$

c. $(175 - x)°$

d. $(x - 170)°$

Solve each equation.

25. $\dfrac{3}{4}x = -9$

26. $\dfrac{x}{6} = \dfrac{2}{3}$

27. $-5x = 0$

28. $-y = 7$

29. $0.2x = 0.15$

30. $\dfrac{-x}{3} = 1$

31. $-3x + 1 = 19$

32. $5x + 25 = 20$

33. $7(x - 1) + 9 = 5x$

34. $7x - 6 = 5x - 3$

35. $-5x + \dfrac{3}{7} = \dfrac{10}{7}$

36. $5x + x = 9 + 4x - 1 + 6$

37. Write the sum of three consecutive integers as an expression in x. Let x be the first integer.

38. Write the sum of the first and fourth of four consecutive even integers. Let x be the first even integer.

(2.3) Solve each equation.

39. $\dfrac{5}{3}x + 4 = \dfrac{2}{3}x$

40. $\dfrac{7}{8}x + 1 = \dfrac{5}{8}x$

41. $-(5x + 1) = -7x + 3$

42. $-4(2x + 1) = -5x + 5$

43. $-6(2x - 5) = -3(9 + 4x)$

44. $3(8y - 1) = 6(5 + 4y)$

45. $\dfrac{3(2 - z)}{5} = z$

46. $\dfrac{4(n + 2)}{5} = -n$

47. $0.5(2n - 3) - 0.1 = 0.4(6 + 2n)$

48. $-9 - 5a = 3(6a - 1)$

49. $\dfrac{5(c + 1)}{6} = 2c - 3$

50. $\dfrac{2(8 - a)}{3} = 4 - 4a$

51. $200(70x - 3560) = -179(150x - 19{,}300)$

52. $1.72y - 0.04y = 0.42$

(2.4) Solve each of the following.

53. The height of the Washington Monument is 50.5 inches more than 10 times the length of a side of its square base. If the sum of these two dimensions is 7327 inches, find the height of the Washington Monument. (*Source:* National Park Service)

54. A 12-foot board is to be divided into two pieces so that one piece is twice as long as the other. If x represents the length of the shorter piece, find the length of each piece.

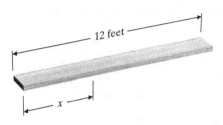

55. In a recent year, Kellogg Company acquired Keebler Foods Company. After the merger, the total number of Kellogg and Keebler manufacturing plants was 53. The number of Kellogg plants was one less than twice the number of Keebler plants. How many of each type of plant were there? (*Source: Kellogg Company 2000 Annual Report*)

56. Find three consecutive integers whose sum is -114.

57. The quotient of a number and 3 is the same as the difference of the number and two. Find the number.

58. Double the sum of a number and 6 is the opposite of the number. Find the number.

(2.5) Substitute the given values into the given formulas and solve for the unknown variable.

59. $P = 2l + 2w$; $P = 46, l = 14$

60. $V = lwh$; $V = 192, l = 8, w = 6$

Solve each equation as indicated.

61. $y = mx + b$ for m

62. $r = vst - 5$ for s

63. $2y - 5x = 7$ for x

64. $3x - 6y = -2$ for y

65. $C = \pi D$ for π

66. $C = 2\pi r$ for π

67. A swimming pool holds 900 cubic meters of water. If its length is 20 meters and its height is 3 meters, find its width.

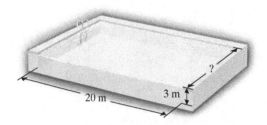

68. The perimeter of a rectangular billboard is 60 feet and has a length 6 feet longer than its width. Find the dimensions of the billboard.

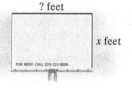

69. A charity 10K race is given annually to benefit a local hospice organization. How long will it take to run/walk a 10K race (10 kilometers or 10,000 meters) if your average pace is 125 **meters** per minute? Give your time in hours and minutes.

70. On April 28, 2001, the highest temperature recorded in the United States was 104°F, which occurred in Death Valley, California. Convert this temperature to degrees Celsius. (*Source:* National Weather Service)

(2.6) Find each of the following.

71. The number 9 is what percent of 45?

72. The number 59.5 is what percent of 85?

73. The number 137.5 is 125% of what number?

74. The number 768 is 60% of what number?

75. The price of a small diamond ring was recently increased by 11%. If the ring originally cost $1900, find the mark-up and the new price of the ring.

76. A recent survey found that 79% of Americans use the Internet. If a city has a population of 76,000 how many people in that city would you expect to use the Internet? (*Source:* PEW)

77. Thirty gallons of a 20% acid solution is needed for an experiment. Only 40% and 10% acid solutions are available. How much of each should be mixed to form the needed solution?

78. The ACT Assessment is a college entrance exam taken by about 60% of college-bound students. The national average score was 20.7 in 1993 and rose to 21.0 in 2008. Find the percent increase. (Round to the nearest hundredth of a percent.)

The graph below shows the percent(s) of cell phone users who have engaged in various behaviors while driving and talking on their cell phones. Use this graph to answer Exercises 79 through 82.

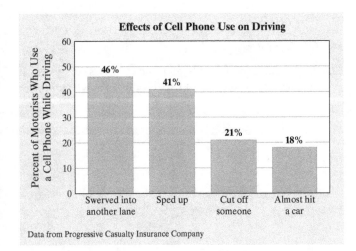

Effects of Cell Phone Use on Driving

Data from Progressive Casualty Insurance Company

79. What percent of motorists who use a cell phone while driving have almost hit another car?

80. What is the most common effect of cell phone use on driving?

Suppose that a cell phone service has an estimated 4600 customers who use their cell phones while driving. Use this information for Exercises 81 and 82.

81. How many of these customers would you expect to have cut someone off while driving and talking on their cell phones?

82. How many of these customers would you expect to have sped up while driving and talking on their cell phones?

83. If a price decreases from $250 to $170, what is the percent decrease?

84. Find the original price of a DVD if the sale price is $19.20 after a 20% discount.

85. In 2005, Lance Armstrong incredibly won his seventh Tour de France, the first man in history to win more than five Tour de France Championships. Suppose he rides a bicycle up a category 2 climb at 10 km/hr and rides down the same distance at a speed of 50 km/hr. Find the distance traveled if the total time on the mountain was 3 hours.

(2.7) Solve.

86. A $50,000 retirement pension is to be invested into two accounts: a money market fund that pays 8.5% and a certificate of deposit that pays 10.5%. How much should be invested at each rate to provide a yearly interest income of $4550?

87. A pay phone is holding its maximum number of 500 coins consisting of nickels, dimes, and quarters. The number of quarters is twice the number of dimes. If the value of all the coins is $88.00, how many nickels are in the pay phone?

88. How long will it take an Amtrak passenger train to catch up to a freight train if their speeds are 60 and 45 mph and the freight train had an hour and a half head start?

(2.8) Solve and graph the solutions of each of the following inequalities.

89. $x > 0$

90. $x \leq -2$

91. $0.5 \leq y < 1.5$

92. $-1 < x < 1$

93. $-3x > 12$

94. $-2x \geq -20$

95. $x + 4 \geq 6x - 16$

96. $5x - 7 > 8x + 5$

97. $-3 < 4x - 1 < 2$

98. $2 \leq 3x - 4 < 6$

99. $4(2x - 5) \leq 5x - 1$

100. $-2(x - 5) > 2(3x - 2)$

101. Tina earns $175 per week plus a 5% commission on all her sales. Find the minimum amount of sales to ensure that she earns at least $300 per week.

102. Ellen Catarella shot rounds of 76, 82, and 79 golfing. What must she shoot on her next round so that her average will be below 80?

MIXED REVIEW

Solve each equation.

103. $6x + 2x - 1 = 5x + 11$

104. $2(3y - 4) = 6 + 7y$

105. $4(3 - a) - (6a + 9) = -12a$

106. $\dfrac{x}{3} - 2 = 5$

107. $2(y + 5) = 2y + 10$

108. $7x - 3x + 2 = 2(2x - 1)$

Solve.

109. The sum of six and twice a number is equal to seven less than the number. Find the number.

110. A 23-inch piece of string is to be cut into two pieces so that the length of the longer piece is three more than four times the shorter piece. If x represents the length of the shorter piece, find the lengths of both pieces.

Solve for the specified variable.

111. $V = \dfrac{1}{3} Ah$ for h

112. What number is 26% of 85?

113. The number 72 is 45% of what number?

114. A company recently increased its number of employees from 235 to 282. Find the percent increase.

Solve each inequality. Graph the solution set.

115. $4x - 7 > 3x + 2$

116. $-5x < 20$

117. $-3(1 + 2x) + x \geq -(3 - x)$

Chapter 2 Test   MyMathLab®    Test Prep VIDEOS   You Tube™

Simplify each of the following expressions.

1. $2y - 6 - y - 4$

2. $2.7x + 6.1 + 3.2x - 4.9$

3. $4(x - 2) - 3(2x - 6)$

4. $7 + 2(5y - 3)$

Solve each of the following equations.

5. $-\dfrac{4}{5}x = 4$

6. $4(n - 5) = -(4 - 2n)$

7. $5y - 7 + y = -(y + 3y)$

8. $4z + 1 - z = 1 + z$

9. $\dfrac{2(x + 6)}{3} = x - 5$

10. $\dfrac{1}{2} - x + \dfrac{3}{2} = x - 4$

11. $-0.3(x - 4) + x = 0.5(3 - x)$

12. $-4(a + 1) - 3a = -7(2a - 3)$

13. $-2(x - 3) = x + 5 - 3x$

14. Find the value of x if $y = -14$, $m = -2$, and $b = -2$ in the formula $y = mx + b$.

Solve each of the following equations for the indicated variable.

15. $V = \pi r^2 h$ for h

16. $3x - 4y = 10$ for y

Solve each of the following inequalities. Graph each solution set and write it in interval notation.

17. $3x - 5 \geq 7x + 3$

18. $x + 6 > 4x - 6$

19. $-2 < 3x + 1 < 8$

20. $\dfrac{2(5x + 1)}{3} > 2$

Solve each of the following applications.

21. A number increased by two-thirds of the number is 35. Find the number.

22. A rectangular deck is to be built so that the width and length are two consecutive even integers and the perimeter is 252 feet. Find the dimensions of the deck.

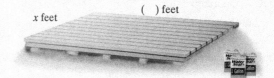

x feet   ( ) feet

23. Some states have a single area code for the entire state. Two such states have area codes where one is double the other. If the sum of these integers is 1203, find the two area codes. *(Source:* North American Numbering Plan Administration)

24. Sedric Angell invested an amount of money in Amoxil stock that earned an annual 10% return, and then he invested twice that amount in IBM stock that earned an annual 12% return. If his total return from both investments was $2890, find how much he invested in each stock.

The following graph shows the breakdown of tornadoes occurring in the United States by strength. The corresponding Fujita Tornado Scale categories are shown in parentheses. Use this graph to answer Exercise 26.

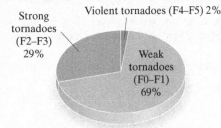

Strong tornadoes (F2–F3) 29%

Violent tornadoes (F4–F5) 2%

Weak tornadoes (F0–F1) 69%

Data from National Climatic Data Center

25. Two trains leave Los Angeles simultaneously traveling on the same track in opposite directions at speeds of 50 and 64 mph. How long will it take before they are 285 miles apart?

26. According to the National Climatic Data Center, in an average year, about 800 tornadoes are reported in the United States. How many of these would you expect to be classified as "weak" tornadoes?

27. The number 72 is what percent of 180?

28. The number of employees of a company decreased from 225 to 189. Find this percent decrease.

Chapter 2 **Cumulative Review**

1. Given the set $\left\{-2, 0, \frac{1}{4}, -1.5, 112, -3, 11, \sqrt{2}\right\}$, list the numbers in this set that belong to the set of:

  a. Natural numbers

  b. Whole numbers

  c. Integers

  d. Rational numbers

  e. Irrational numbers

  f. Real numbers

2. Given the set $\left\{7, 2, -\frac{1}{5}, 0, \sqrt{3}, -185, 8\right\}$, list the numbers in this set that belong to the set of:

  a. Natural numbers

  b. Whole numbers

  c. Integers

  d. Rational numbers

  e. Irrational numbers

  f. Real numbers

3. Find the absolute value of each number.

  a. $|4|$ **b.** $|-5|$

  c. $|0|$ **d.** $\left|-\frac{1}{2}\right|$

  e. $|5.6|$

4. Find the absolute value of each number.

  a. $|5|$ **b.** $|-8|$ **c.** $\left|-\frac{2}{3}\right|$

5. Write each of the following numbers as a product of primes.

  a. 40   **b.** 63

6. Write each number as a product of primes.

  a. 44   **b.** 90

7. Write $\frac{2}{5}$ as an equivalent fraction with a denominator of 20.

8. Write $\frac{2}{3}$ as an equivalent fraction with a denominator of 24.

9. Simplify $3[4 + 2(10 - 1)]$.

10. Simplify $5[16 - 4(2 + 1)]$.

11. Decide whether 2 is a solution of $3x + 10 = 8x$.

12. Decide whether 3 is a solution of $5x - 2 = 4x$.

Add.

13. $-1 + (-2)$ **14.** $(-2) + (-8)$

15. $-4 + 6$ **16.** $-3 + 10$

17. Simplify each expression.

  a. $-(-10)$ **b.** $-\left(-\frac{1}{2}\right)$

  c. $-(-2x)$ **d.** $-|-6|$

18. Simplify each expression.

  a. $-(-5)$ **b.** $-\left(-\frac{2}{3}\right)$

  c. $-(-a)$ **d.** $-|-3|$

19. Subtract.

  a. $5.3 - (-4.6)$ **b.** $-\frac{3}{10} - \frac{5}{10}$

  c. $-\frac{2}{3} - \left(-\frac{4}{5}\right)$

20. Subtract

  a. $-2.7 - 8.4$ **b.** $-\dfrac{4}{5} - \left(-\dfrac{3}{5}\right)$

  c. $\dfrac{1}{4} - \left(-\dfrac{1}{2}\right)$

21. Find each unknown complementary or supplementary angle.

  a.   **b.**

22. Find each unknown complementary or supplementary angle.

  a.   **b.**

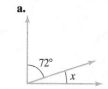

23. Multiply.

  a. $(-1.2)(0.05)$ **b.** $\dfrac{2}{3} \cdot \left(-\dfrac{7}{10}\right)$

  c. $\left(-\dfrac{4}{5}\right)(-20)$

24. Multiply.

  a. $(4.5)(-0.08)$ **b.** $-\dfrac{3}{4} \cdot \left(-\dfrac{8}{17}\right)$

25. Divide.

  a. $\dfrac{-24}{-4}$ **b.** $\dfrac{-36}{3}$

  c. $\dfrac{2}{3} \div \left(-\dfrac{5}{4}\right)$ **d.** $-\dfrac{3}{2} \div 9$

26. Divide.

  a. $\dfrac{-32}{8}$ **b.** $\dfrac{-108}{-12}$

  c. $\dfrac{-5}{7} \div \left(\dfrac{-9}{2}\right)$

27. Use a commutative property to complete each statement.

  a. $x + 5 = $ _____

  b. $3 \cdot x = $ _____

28. Use a commutative property to complete each statement.

  a. $y + 1 = $ _____

  b. $y \cdot 4 = $ _____

29. Use the distributive property to write each sum as a product.

  a. $8 \cdot 2 + 8 \cdot x$

  b. $7s + 7t$

30. Use the distributive property to write each sum as a product.

  a. $4 \cdot y + 4 \cdot \dfrac{1}{3}$

  b. $0.10x + 0.10y$

31. Subtract $4x - 2$ from $2x - 3$.

32. Subtract $10x + 3$ from $-5x + 1$.

Solve.

33. $y + 0.6 = -1.0$

34. $\dfrac{5}{6} + x = \dfrac{2}{3}$

35. $7 = -5(2a - 1) - (-11a + 6)$

36. $-3x + 1 - (-4x - 6) = 10$

37. $\dfrac{y}{7} = 20$

38. $\dfrac{x}{4} = 18$

39. $4(2x - 3) + 7 = 3x + 5$

40. $6x + 5 = 4(x + 4) - 1$

41. Twice the sum of a number and 4 is the same as four times the number, decreased by 12. Find the number.

42. A number increased by 4 is the same as 3 times the number decreased by 8. Find the number.

43. Solve $V = lwh$ for l.

44. Solve $C = 2\pi r$ for r.

45. Solve $x + 4 \le -6$ for x. Graph the solution set and write it in interval notation.

46. Solve $x - 3 > 2$ for x. Graph the solution set and write it in interval notation.

Appendix A

Operations on Decimals/Table of Percent, Decimal, and Fraction Equivalents

A.1 Operations on Decimals

To **add** or **subtract** decimals, write the numbers vertically with decimal points lined up. Add or subtract as with whole numbers and place the decimal point in the answer directly below the decimal points in the problem.

EXAMPLE 1   Add $5.87 + 23.279 + 0.003$.

Solution

$$
\begin{array}{r}
5.87 \\
23.279 \\
+\,0.003 \\
\hline
29.152
\end{array}
$$

EXAMPLE 2   Subtract $32.15 - 11.237$.

Solution

$$
\begin{array}{r}
3\;\;\overset{1}{\cancel{2}}\;.\;\overset{11}{\cancel{1}}\;\overset{4}{\cancel{5}}\;\overset{10}{\cancel{0}} \\
-\;1\;\;1\;.\;2\;\;3\;\;7 \\
\hline
2\;\;0\;.\;9\;\;1\;\;3
\end{array}
$$

To **multiply** decimals, multiply the numbers as if they were whole numbers. The decimal point in the product is placed so that the number of decimal places in the product is the same as the sum of the number of decimal places in the factors.

EXAMPLE 3   Multiply 0.072×3.5.

Solution

$$
\begin{array}{r}
0.072 \quad \text{3 decimal places} \\
\times \quad 3.5 \quad \text{1 decimal place} \\
\hline
360 \\
216 \quad\;\; \\
\hline
0.2520 \quad \text{4 decimal places}
\end{array}
$$

To **divide** decimals, move the decimal point in the divisor to the right of the last digit. Move the decimal point in the dividend the same number of places that the decimal point in the divisor was moved. The decimal point in the quotient lies directly above the decimal point in the dividend.

EXAMPLE 4   Divide $9.46 \div 0.04$.

Solution

$$
\begin{array}{r}
236.5 \\
04.\overline{)946.0} \\
-8 \\
\hline
14 \\
-12 \\
\hline
26 \\
-24 \\
\hline
20 \\
-20
\end{array}
$$

MyMathLab®

Perform the indicated operations.

1. 9.076 + 8.004

2.   6.3
       × 0.05

3.   27.004
       −14.2

4.   0.0036
         7.12
        32.502
       + 0.05

5.   107.92
       + 3.04

6. 7.2 ÷ 4

7. 10 − 7.6

8. 40 ÷ 0.25

9. 126.32 − 97.89

10.   3.62
          7.11
         12.36
          4.15
        + 2.29

11.   3.25
         × 70

12.   26.014
         − 7.8

13. 8.1 ÷ 3

14.   1.2366
          0.005
         15.17
        + 0.97

15. 55.405 − 6.1711

16. 8.09 + 0.22

17. 60 ÷ 0.75

18. 20 − 12.29

19. 7.612 ÷ 100

20.   8.72
          1.12
         14.86
          3.98
        + 1.99

21. 12.312 ÷ 2.7

22. 0.443 ÷ 100

23.   569.2
          71.25
        + 8.01

24. 3.706 − 2.91

25. 768 − 0.17

26. 63 ÷ 0.28

27. 12 + 0.062

28. 0.42 + 18

29. 76 − 14.52

30. 1.1092 ÷ 0.47

31. 3.311 ÷ 0.43

32. 7.61 + 0.0004

33.   762.12
          89.7
        + 11.55

34. 444 ÷ 0.6

35. 23.4 − 0.821

36. 3.7 + 5.6

37. 476.12 − 112.97

38. 19.872 ÷ 0.54

39. 0.007 + 7

40.   51.77
        + 3.6

A.2 Table of Percent, Decimal, and Fraction Equivalents

Percent, Decimal, and Fraction Equivalents		
Percent	**Decimal**	**Fraction**
1%	0.01	$\frac{1}{100}$
5%	0.05	$\frac{1}{20}$
10%	0.1	$\frac{1}{10}$
12.5% or $12\frac{1}{2}$%	0.125	$\frac{1}{8}$
$16.\overline{6}$% or $16\frac{2}{3}$%	$0.1\overline{6}$	$\frac{1}{6}$
20%	0.2	$\frac{1}{5}$
25%	0.25	$\frac{1}{4}$
30%	0.3	$\frac{3}{10}$
$33.\overline{3}$% or $33\frac{1}{3}$%	$0.\overline{3}$	$\frac{1}{3}$
37.5% or $37\frac{1}{2}$%	0.375	$\frac{3}{8}$
40%	0.4	$\frac{2}{5}$
50%	0.5	$\frac{1}{2}$
60%	0.6	$\frac{3}{5}$
62.5% or $62\frac{1}{2}$%	0.625	$\frac{5}{8}$
$66.\overline{6}$% or $66\frac{2}{3}$%	$0.\overline{6}$	$\frac{2}{3}$
70%	0.7	$\frac{7}{10}$
75%	0.75	$\frac{3}{4}$
80%	0.8	$\frac{4}{5}$
$83.\overline{3}$% or $83\frac{1}{3}$%	$08.\overline{3}$	$\frac{5}{6}$
87.5% or $87\frac{1}{2}$%	0.875	$\frac{7}{8}$
90%	0.9	$\frac{9}{10}$
100%	1.0	1
110%	1.1	$1\frac{1}{10}$
125%	1.25	$1\frac{1}{4}$
$133.\overline{3}$% or $133\frac{1}{3}$%	$1.\overline{3}$	$1\frac{1}{3}$
150%	1.5	$1\frac{1}{2}$
$166.\overline{6}$% or $166\frac{2}{3}$%	$1.\overline{6}$	$1\frac{2}{3}$
175%	1.75	$1\frac{3}{4}$
200%	2.0	2

Appendix B

Review of Algebra Topics

Recall that equations model many real-life problems. For example, we can use a linear equation to calculate the increase in the number (in millions) of Wi-Fi-enabled cell phones.

Wi-Fi-enabled cell phones let you carry your Internet access with you. There are already several of these smart phones available, and this technology will continue to expand. Predicted numbers of Wi-Fi-enabled cell phones in the United States for various years are shown below.

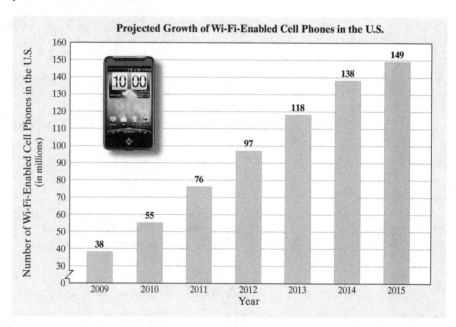

To find the projected increase in the number of Wi-Fi-enabled cell phones in the United States from 2014 to 2015, for example, we can use the equation below.

In words:	Increase in cell phones	is	cell phones in 2015	minus	cell phones in 2014
Translate:	x	$=$	149	$-$	138

Since our variable x (increase in Wi-Fi-enabled cell phones) is by itself on one side of the equation, we can find the value of x by simplifying the right side.

$$x = 11$$

The projected increase in the number of Wi-Fi-enabled cell phones from 2014 to 2015 is 11 million.

The **equation** $x = 149 - 138$ is a linear equation in one variable. In this section, we review solving linear equations and quadratic equations that can be solved by factoring. We will learn other methods for solving quadratic equations in Chapter 11.

Equations (Linear and Quadratic Solved by Factoring)

OBJECTIVE

1 Solve linear and quadratic equations.

OBJECTIVE

1 Solving Linear and Quadratic Equations

EXAMPLE 1   Solve: $2(x - 3) = 5x - 9$.

Solution   First, use the distributive property.

$$2(x - 3) = 5x - 9$$
$$2x - 6 = 5x - 9 \quad \text{Use the distributive property.}$$

Next, get variable terms on the same side of the equation by subtracting $5x$ from both sides.

$$2x - 6 - 5x = 5x - 9 - 5x \quad \text{Subtract } 5x \text{ from both sides.}$$
$$-3x - 6 = -9 \quad \text{Simplify.}$$
$$-3x - 6 + 6 = -9 + 6 \quad \text{Add 6 to both sides.}$$
$$-3x = -3 \quad \text{Simplify.}$$
$$\frac{-3x}{-3} = \frac{-3}{-3} \quad \text{Divide both sides by } -3.$$
$$x = 1$$

Let $x = 1$ in the original equation to see that 1 is the solution.   □

PRACTICE

1   Solve: $3(x - 5) = 6x - 3$.

Don't forget, if an equation contains fractions, you may want to first clear the equation of fractions by multiplying both sides of the equation by the *least common denominator* (LCD) of all fractions in the equation.

EXAMPLE 2   Solve for y: $\dfrac{y}{3} - \dfrac{y}{4} = \dfrac{1}{6}$.

Solution   First, clear the equation of fractions by multiplying both sides of the equation by 12, the LCD of denominators 3, 4, and 6.

$$\frac{y}{3} - \frac{y}{4} = \frac{1}{6}$$

$$12\left(\frac{y}{3} - \frac{y}{4}\right) = 12\left(\frac{1}{6}\right) \quad \text{Multiply both sides by the LCD 12.}$$

$$12\left(\frac{y}{3}\right) - 12\left(\frac{y}{4}\right) = 2 \quad \text{Apply the distributive property.}$$

$$4y - 3y = 2 \quad \text{Simplify.}$$

$$y = 2 \quad \text{Simplify.}$$

Check: To check, let $y = 2$ in the original equation.

$$\frac{y}{3} - \frac{y}{4} = \frac{1}{6} \quad \text{Original equation.}$$

$$\frac{2}{3} - \frac{2}{4} \stackrel{?}{=} \frac{1}{6} \quad \text{Let } y = 2.$$

$$\frac{8}{12} - \frac{6}{12} \stackrel{?}{=} \frac{1}{6} \qquad \text{Write fractions with the LCD.}$$

$$\frac{2}{12} \stackrel{?}{=} \frac{1}{6} \qquad \text{Subtract.}$$

$$\frac{1}{6} = \frac{1}{6} \qquad \text{Simplify.}$$

This is a true statement, so the solution is 2.

PRACTICE
2   Solve for y: $\frac{y}{2} - \frac{y}{5} = \frac{1}{4}$.

EXAMPLE 3   Solve: $3(x^2 + 4) + 5 = -6(x^2 + 2x) + 13$.

Solution   Rewrite the equation so that one side is 0.

$$3(x^2 + 4) + 5 = -6(x^2 + 2x) + 13$$
$$3x^2 + 12 + 5 = -6x^2 - 12x + 13 \qquad \text{Apply the distributive property.}$$
$$9x^2 + 12x + 4 = 0 \qquad \text{Rewrite the equation so that one side is 0.}$$
$$(3x + 2)(3x + 2) = 0 \qquad \text{Factor.}$$
$$3x + 2 = 0 \quad \text{or} \quad 3x + 2 = 0 \qquad \text{Set each factor equal to 0.}$$
$$3x = -2 \quad \text{or} \quad 3x = -2$$
$$x = -\frac{2}{3} \quad \text{or} \quad x = -\frac{2}{3} \qquad \text{Solve each equation.}$$

The solution is $-\frac{2}{3}$. Check by substituting $-\frac{2}{3}$ into the original equation.

PRACTICE
3   Solve: $8(x^2 + 3) + 4 = -8x(x + 3) + 19$.

EXAMPLE 4   Solve for x: $\frac{x + 5}{2} + \frac{1}{2} = 2x - \frac{x - 3}{8}$.

Solution   Multiply both sides of the equation by 8, the LCD of 2 and 8.

$$8\left(\frac{x + 5}{2} + \frac{1}{2}\right) = 8\left(2x - \frac{x - 3}{8}\right) \qquad \text{Multiply both sides by 8.}$$

$$8\left(\frac{x + 5}{2}\right) + 8 \cdot \frac{1}{2} = 8 \cdot 2x - 8\left(\frac{x - 3}{8}\right) \qquad \text{Apply the distributive property.}$$

$$4(x + 5) + 4 = 16x - (x - 3) \qquad \text{Simplify.}$$
$$4x + 20 + 4 = 16x - x + 3 \qquad \text{Use the distributive property to remove parentheses.}$$
$$4x + 24 = 15x + 3 \qquad \text{Combine like terms.}$$
$$-11x + 24 = 3 \qquad \text{Subtract } 15x \text{ from both sides.}$$
$$-11x = -21 \qquad \text{Subtract 24 from both sides.}$$
$$\frac{-11x}{-11} = \frac{-21}{-11} \qquad \text{Divide both sides by } -11.$$
$$x = \frac{21}{11} \qquad \text{Simplify.}$$

> **Helpful Hint**
> When we multiply both sides of an equation by a number, the distributive property tells us that each term of the equation is multiplied by the number.

Check: To check, verify that replacing x with $\frac{21}{11}$ makes the original equation true. The solution is $\frac{21}{11}$.

PRACTICE
4   Solve for x: $x - \frac{x - 2}{12} = \frac{x + 3}{4} + \frac{1}{4}$.

EXAMPLE 5   Solve: $2x^2 = \frac{17}{3}x + 1$.

Solution

$$2x^2 = \frac{17}{3}x + 1$$

$$3(2x^2) = 3\left(\frac{17}{3}x + 1\right) \qquad \text{Clear the equation of fractions.}$$

$$6x^2 = 17x + 3 \qquad \text{Apply the distributive property.}$$

$$6x^2 - 17x - 3 = 0 \qquad \text{Rewrite the equation in standard form.}$$

$$(6x + 1)(x - 3) = 0 \qquad \text{Factor.}$$

$$6x + 1 = 0 \quad \text{or} \quad x - 3 = 0 \qquad \text{Set each factor equal to zero.}$$

$$6x = -1$$

$$x = -\frac{1}{6} \quad \text{or} \qquad x = 3 \qquad \text{Solve each equation.}$$

The solutions are $-\frac{1}{6}$ and 3.

PRACTICE
5   Solve: $4x^2 = \frac{15}{2}x + 1$.

B.1 Exercise Set   MyMathLab®

MIXED PRACTICE

Solve each equation. See Examples 1 through 5.

1. $x^2 + 11x + 24 = 0$
2. $y^2 - 10y + 24 = 0$
3. $3x - 4 - 5x = x + 4 + x$
4. $13x - 15x + 8 = 4x + 2 - 24$
5. $12x^2 + 5x - 2 = 0$
6. $3y^2 - y - 14 = 0$
7. $z^2 + 9 = 10z$
8. $n^2 + n = 72$
9. $5(y + 4) = 4(y + 5)$
10. $6(y - 4) = 3(y - 8)$
11. $0.6x - 10 = 1.4x - 14$
12. $0.3x + 2.4 = 0.1x + 4$
13. $x(5x + 2) = 3$
14. $n(2n - 3) = 2$
15. $6x - 2(x - 3) = 4(x + 1) + 4$
16. $10x - 2(x + 4) = 8(x - 2) + 6$
17. $\frac{3}{8} + \frac{b}{3} = \frac{5}{12}$
18. $\frac{a}{2} + \frac{7}{4} = 5$
19. $x^2 - 6x = x(8 + x)$
20. $n(3 + n) = n^2 + 4n$
21. $\frac{z^2}{6} - \frac{z}{2} - 3 = 0$

22. $\frac{c^2}{20} - \frac{c}{4} + \frac{1}{5} = 0$
23. $-z + 3(2 + 4z) = 6(z + 1) + 5z$
24. $4(m - 6) - m = 8(m - 3) - 5m$
25. $\frac{x^2}{2} + \frac{x}{20} = \frac{1}{10}$
26. $\frac{y^2}{30} = \frac{y}{15} + \frac{1}{2}$
27. $\frac{4t^2}{5} = \frac{t}{5} + \frac{3}{10}$
28. $\frac{5x^2}{6} - \frac{7x}{2} + \frac{2}{3} = 0$
29. $\frac{3t + 1}{8} = \frac{5 + 2t}{7} + 2$
30. $4 - \frac{2z + 7}{9} = \frac{7 - z}{12}$
31. $\frac{m - 4}{3} - \frac{3m - 1}{5} = 1$
32. $\frac{n + 1}{8} - \frac{2 - n}{3} = \frac{5}{6}$
33. $3x^2 = -x$
34. $y^2 = -5y$
35. $x(x - 3) = x^2 + 5x + 7$
36. $z^2 - 4z + 10 = z(z - 5)$
37. $3(t - 8) + 2t = 7 + t$
38. $7c - 2(3c + 1) = 5(4 - 2c)$
39. $-3(x - 4) + x = 5(3 - x)$

40. $-4(a + 1) - 3a = -7(2a - 3)$

41. $(x - 1)(x + 4) = 24$

42. $(2x - 1)(x + 2) = -3$

43. $\dfrac{x^2}{4} - \dfrac{5}{2}x + 6 = 0$

44. $\dfrac{x^2}{18} + \dfrac{x}{2} + 1 = 0$

45. $y^2 + \dfrac{1}{4} = -y$

46. $\dfrac{x^2}{10} + \dfrac{5}{2} = x$

47. Which solution strategies are incorrect? Why?

   a. Solve $(y - 2)(y + 2) = 4$ by setting each factor equal to 4.

   b. Solve $(x + 1)(x + 3) = 0$ by setting each factor equal to 0.

   c. Solve $z^2 + 5z + 6 = 0$ by factoring $z^2 + 5z + 6$ and setting each factor equal to 0.

   d. Solve $x^2 + 6x + 8 = 10$ by factoring $x^2 + 6x + 8$ and setting each factor equal to 0.

48. Describe two ways a linear equation differs from a quadratic equation.

Find the value of K such that the equations are equivalent.

49. $3.2x + 4 = 5.4x - 7$
$3.2x = 5.4x + K$

50. $-7.6y - 10 = -1.1y + 12$
$-7.6y = -1.1y + K$

51. $\dfrac{x}{6} + 4 = \dfrac{x}{3}$
$x + K = 2x$

52. $\dfrac{5x}{4} + \dfrac{1}{2} = \dfrac{x}{2}$
$5x + K = 2x$

Solve and check.

53. $2.569x = -12.48534$

54. $-9.112y = -47.537304$

55. $2.86z - 8.1258 = -3.75$

56. $1.25x - 20.175 = -8.15$

B.2 | Problem Solving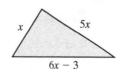

OBJECTIVES

1 Write Algebraic Expressions That Can Be Simplified.

2 Apply the Steps for Problem Solving.

OBJECTIVE

1   Writing and Simplifying Algebraic Expressions

In order to prepare for problem solving, we practice writing algebraic expressions that can be simplified.

   Our first example involves consecutive integers and perimeter. Recall that *consecutive integers* are integers that follow one another in order. Study the examples of consecutive, even, and odd integers and their representations.

Consecutive Integers:

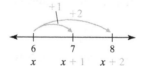

Consecutive Even Integers:

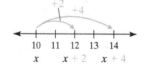

Consecutive Odd Integers:

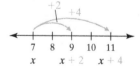

EXAMPLE 1   Write the following as algebraic expressions. Then simplify.

   a. The sum of three consecutive integers, if x is the first consecutive integer.

   △ **b.** The perimeter of the triangle with sides of length x, $5x$, and $6x - 3$.

(Continued on next page)

Solution

a. Recall that if x is the first integer, then the next consecutive integer is 1 more, or $x + 1$, and the next consecutive integer is 1 more than $x + 1$, or $x + 2$.

In words:	first integer	plus	next consecutive integer	plus	next consecutive integer
	↓	↓	↓	↓	↓
Translate:	x	$+$	$(x + 1)$	$+$	$(x + 2)$

Then $x + (x + 1) + (x + 2) = x + x + 1 + x + 2$

$\qquad\qquad\qquad\qquad\qquad = 3x + 3$ Simplify by combining like terms.

b. The perimeter of a triangle is the sum of the lengths of the sides.

In words:	side	$+$	side	$+$	side
	↓		↓		↓
Translate:	x	$+$	$5x$	$+$	$(6x - 3)$

Then $x + 5x + (6x - 3) = x + 5x + 6x - 3$

$\qquad\qquad\qquad\qquad\qquad = 12x - 3$ Simplify.   □

PRACTICE

1   Write the following algebraic expressions. Then simplify.

a. The sum of three consecutive odd integers if x is the first consecutive odd integer

b. The perimeter of a trapezoid with bases x and $2x$ and sides of $x + 2$ and $2x - 3$

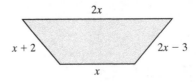

EXAMPLE 2   **Writing Algebraic Expressions Representing Metropolitan Regions**

The most populous metropolitan region in the United States is New York City, although it is only the sixth most populous metropolis in the world. Tokyo is the most populous metropolitan region. Mexico City is the fifth most populous metropolis in the world. Mexico City's population is 0.03 million more than New York's, and Tokyo's is twice that of New York, decreased by 2.19 million. Write the sum of the populations of these three metropolitan regions as an algebraic expression. Let x be the population of New York (in millions). (*Source:* United Nations, Department of Economic and Social Affairs)

Solution:

$$\text{If } x = \text{the population of New York (in millions), then}$$
$$x + 0.03 = \text{the population of Mexico City (in millions) and}$$
$$2x - 2.19 = \text{the population of Tokyo (in millions)}$$

In words:	population of New York		population of Mexico City		population of Tokyo
	↓		↓		↓
Translate:	x	$+$	$(x + 0.03)$	$+$	$(2x - 2.19)$

Then $x + (x + 0.03) + (2x - 2.19) = x + x + 2x + 0.03 - 2.19$

$\qquad\qquad\qquad\qquad\qquad\qquad\qquad = 4x - 2.16$ Combine like terms.

In Exercise 57, we will find the actual populations of these cities.   □

PRACTICE
2   The three busiest airports in Europe are in London, England; Paris, France; and Frankfurt, Germany. The airport in London has 12.9 million more arrivals and departures than the Frankfurt airport. The Paris airport has 5.2 million more arrivals and departures than the Frankfurt airport. Write the sum of the arrivals and departures from these three cities as a simplified algebraic expression. Let *x* be the number of arrivals and departures at the Frankfurt airport. (*Source:* Association of European Airlines)

OBJECTIVE
2   Applying Steps for Problem Solving

Our main purpose for studying algebra is to solve problems. The following problem-solving strategy will be used throughout this text and may also be used to solve real-life problems that occur outside the mathematics classroom.

General Strategy for Problem Solving

1. UNDERSTAND the problem. During this step, become comfortable with the problem. Some ways of doing this are to:

   Read and reread the problem.

   Propose a solution and check. Pay careful attention to how you check your proposed solution. This will help when writing an equation to model the problem.

   Construct a drawing.

   Choose a variable to represent the unknown. (Very important part)

2. TRANSLATE the problem into an equation.

3. SOLVE the equation.

4. INTERPRET the results: *Check* the proposed solution in the stated problem and *state* your conclusion.

Let's review this strategy by solving a problem involving unknown numbers.

EXAMPLE 3   **Finding Unknown Numbers**

Find three numbers such that the second number is 3 more than twice the first number, and the third number is four times the first number. The sum of the three numbers is 164.

Solution

▶ Helpful Hint

The purpose of guessing a solution is not to guess correctly but to gain confidence and to help understand the problem and how to model it.

1. UNDERSTAND the problem. First let's read and reread the problem and then propose a solution. For example, if the first number is 25, then the second number is 3 more than twice 25, or 53. The third number is four times 25, or 100. The sum of 25, 53, and 100 is 178, not the required sum, but we have gained some valuable information about the problem. First, we know that the first number is less than 25 since our guess led to a sum greater than the required sum. Also, we have gained some information as to how to model the problem.

   Next let's assign a variable and use this variable to represent any other unknown quantities. If we let

$$x = \text{the first number, then}$$

$$2x + 3 = \text{the second number}$$

3 more than
twice the first number

$$4x = \text{the third number}$$

(Continued on next page)

2. TRANSLATE the problem into an equation. To do so, we use the fact that the sum of the numbers is 164. First let's write this relationship in words and then translate to an equation.

In words:

first number	added to	second number	added to	third number	is	164
↓	↓	↓	↓	↓	↓	↓

Translate: x $+$ $(2x + 3)$ $+$ $4x$ $=$ 164

3. SOLVE the equation.

$$x + (2x + 3) + 4x = 164$$
$$x + 2x + 4x + 3 = 164 \quad \text{Remove parentheses.}$$
$$7x + 3 = 164 \quad \text{Combine like terms.}$$
$$7x = 161 \quad \text{Subtract 3 from both sides.}$$
$$x = 23 \quad \text{Divide both sides by 7.}$$

4. INTERPRET. Here, we *check* our work and *state* the solution. Recall that if the first number $x = 23$, then the second number $2x + 3 = 2 \cdot 23 + 3 = 49$ and the third number $4x = 4 \cdot 23 = 92$.

Check: Is the second number 3 more than twice the first number? Yes, since 3 more than twice 23 is $46 + 3$, or 49. Also, their sum, $23 + 49 + 92 = 164$, is the required sum.

State: The three numbers are 23, 49, and 92.   ☐

PRACTICE
3   Find three numbers such that the second number is 8 less than triple the first number, the third number is five times the first number, and the sum of the three numbers is 118.

Many of today's rates and statistics are given as percents. Interest rates, tax rates, nutrition labeling, and percent of households in a given category are just a few examples. Before we practice solving problems containing percents, let's briefly review the meaning of percent and how to find a percent of a number.

The word *percent* means "per hundred," and the symbol % denotes percent.

This means that 23% is 23 per hundred, or $\dfrac{23}{100}$. Also,

$$41\% = \frac{41}{100} = 0.41$$

To find a percent of a number, we multiply.

$$16\% \text{ of } 25 = 16\% \cdot 25 = 0.16 \cdot 25 = 4$$

Thus, 16% of 25 is 4.

Study the table below. It will help you become more familiar with finding percents.

Percent	*Meaning/Shortcut*	*Example*
50%	$\dfrac{1}{2}$ or half of a number	50% of 60 is 30.
25%	$\dfrac{1}{4}$ or a quarter of a number	25% of 60 is 15.
10%	0.1 or $\dfrac{1}{10}$ of a number (move the decimal point 1 place to the left)	10% of 60 is 6.0 or 6.
1%	0.01 or $\dfrac{1}{100}$ of a number (move the decimal point 2 places to the left)	1% of 60 is 0.60 or 0.6.
100%	1 or all of a number	100% of 60 is 60.
200%	2 or double a number	200% of 60 is 120.

✓CONCEPT CHECK

Suppose you are finding 112% of a number x. Which of the following is a correct description of the result? Explain.

a. The result is less than x.   **b.** The result is equal to x.   **c.** The result is greater than x.

Next, we solve a problem containing a percent.

EXAMPLE 4   Finding the Original Price of a Computer

Suppose that a computer store just announced an 8% decrease in the price of a particular computer model. If this computer sells for $2162 after the decrease, find the original price of this computer.

Solution

1. UNDERSTAND. Read and reread the problem. Recall that a percent decrease means a percent of the original price. Let's guess that the original price of the computer is $2500. The amount of decrease is then 8% of $2500, or $(0.08)(\$2500) = \$200$. This means that the new price of the computer is the original price minus the decrease, or $\$2500 - \$200 = \$2300$. Our guess is incorrect, but we now have an idea of how to model this problem. In our model, we will let $x =$ the original price of the computer.

2. TRANSLATE.

In words:	the original price of computer	minus	8% of the original price	is	the new price
	↓	↓	↓	↓	↓
Translate:	x	$-$	$0.08x$	$=$	2162

3. SOLVE the equation.

$$x - 0.08x = 2162$$
$$0.92x = 2162 \qquad \text{Combine like terms.}$$
$$x = \frac{2162}{0.92} = 2350 \qquad \text{Divide both sides by 0.92.}$$

4. INTERPRET.

Check: If the original price of the computer was $2350, the new price is
$$\$2350 - (0.08)(\$2350) = \$2350 - \$188$$
$$= \$2162 \qquad \text{The given new price}$$

State: The original price of the computer was $2350. ☐

PRACTICE

4   At the end of the season, the cost of a snowboard was reduced by 40%. If the snowboard sells for $270 after the decrease, find the original price of the board.

Vocabulary & Readiness Check

Fill in each blank with $<$, $>$, *or* $=$. *(Assume that the unknown number is a positive number.)*

1. 130% of a number ___ the number.   **2.** 70% of a number ___ the number.

3. 100% of a number ___ the number.   **4.** 200% of a number ___ the number.

Complete the table. The first row has been completed for you.

	First Integer	All Described Integers
Three consecutive integers	18	18, 19, 20
5. Four consecutive integers	31	
6. Three consecutive odd integers	31	
7. Three consecutive even integers	18	
8. Four consecutive even integers	92	
9. Three consecutive integers	y	
10. Three consecutive even integers	z (z is even)	
11. Four consecutive integers	p	
12. Three consecutive odd integers	s (s is odd)	

B.2 Exercise Set

MyMathLab®

Write the following as algebraic expressions. Then simplify. See Examples 1 and 2.

△ **1.** The perimeter of a square with side length y.

△ **2.** The perimeter of a rectangle with length x and width $x - 5$.

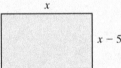

● **3.** The sum of three consecutive integers if the first is z.

4. The sum of three consecutive odd integers if the first integer is z.

● **5.** The total amount of money (in cents) in x nickels, $(x + 3)$ dimes, and $2x$ quarters. (*Hint:* The value of a nickel is 5 cents, the value of a dime is 10 cents, and the value of a quarter is 25 cents.)

6. The total amount of money (in cents) in y quarters, $7y$ dimes, and $(2y - 1)$ nickels. (Use the hint for Exercise 5.)

△ **7.** A piece of land along Bayou Liberty is to be fenced and subdivided as shown so that each rectangle has the same dimensions. Express the total amount of fencing needed as an algebraic expression in x.

8. A flooded piece of land near the Mississippi River in New Orleans is to be surveyed and divided into 4 rectangles of equal dimension. Express the total amount of fencing needed as an algebraic expression in x.

△ **9.** Write the perimeter of the floor plan shown as an algebraic expression in x.

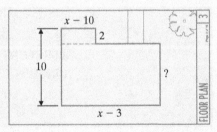

10. Write the perimeter of the floor plan shown as an algebraic expression in x.

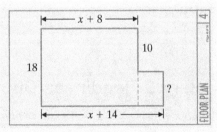

Solve. For Exercises 11 and 12, the solutions have been started for you. See Example 3.

11. Four times the difference of a number and 2 is the same as 2, increased by four times the number, plus twice the number. Find the number.

Start the solution:

1. UNDERSTAND the problem. Reread it as many times as needed.

2. TRANSLATE into an equation. (Fill in the blanks below.)

Four times	the difference of a number and 2	is the same as	2	increased by	four times the number	plus	twice the number
↓	↓	↓	↓	↓	↓	↓	↓
4 ·	(x − 2)	=	2	___	___	___	___

Finish with:

3. SOLVE and 4. INTERPRET

12. Twice the sum of a number and 3 is the same as five times the number, minus 1, minus four times the number. Find the number.

Start the solution:

1. UNDERSTAND the problem. Reread it as many times as needed.

2. TRANSLATE into an equation. (Fill in the blanks below.)

Twice	the sum of a number and 3	is the same as	five times the number	minus	1	minus	four times the number
↓	↓	↓	↓	↓	↓	↓	↓
2	(x + 3)	=	___	___	1	___	___

Finish with:

3. SOLVE and 4. INTERPRET

13. A second number is five times a first number. A third number is 100 more than the first number. If the sum of the three numbers is 415, find the numbers.

14. A second number is 6 less than a first number. A third number is twice the first number. If the sum of the three numbers is 306, find the numbers.

Solve. See Example 4.

15. The United States consists of 2271 million acres of land. Approximately 29% of this land is federally owned. Find the number of acres that are not federally owned. (*Source:* U.S. General Services Administration)

16. The state of Nevada contains the most federally owned acres of land in the United States. If 90% of the state's 70 million acres of land is federally owned, find the number of acres that are not federally owned. (*Source:* U.S. General Services Administration)

17. In 2010, 8476 earthquakes occurred in the United States. Of these, 91.4% were minor tremors with magnitudes of 3.9 or less on the Richter scale. How many minor earthquakes occurred in the United States in 2010? Round to the nearest whole. (*Source:* U.S. Geological Survey National Earthquake Information Center)

18. Of the 1543 tornadoes that occurred in the United States during 2010, 27.7% occurred during the month of June. How many tornadoes occurred in the United States during June 2010? Round to the nearest whole. (*Source:* Storm Prediction Center)

19. In a recent survey, 15% of online shoppers in the United States say that they prefer to do business only with large, well-known retailers. In a group of 1500 online shoppers, how many are willing to do business with any size retailers? (*Source:* Inc.com)

20. In 2010, the restaurant industry employed 9% of the U.S. workforce. If there are estimated to be 141 million Americans in the workforce, how many people are employed by the restaurant industry? Round to the nearest tenth. (*Source:* National Restaurant Association, U.S. Bureau of Labor Statistics)

The following graph is called a circle graph or a pie chart. The circle represents a whole, or in this case, 100%. This particular graph shows the number of minutes per day that people use email at work. Use this graph to answer Exercises 21 through 24.

Time Spent on Email at Work

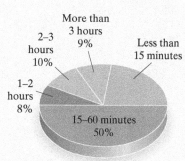

Source: Pew Internet & American Life Project

21. What percent of email users at work spend less than 15 minutes on email per day?

22. Among email users at work, what is the most common time spent on email per day?

23. If it were estimated that a large company has 4633 employees, how many of these would you expect to be using email more than 3 hours per day?

24. If it were estimated that a medium-size company has 250 employees, how many of these would you expect to be using email between 2 and 3 hours per day?

MIXED PRACTICE

Use the diagrams to find the unknown measures of angles or lengths of sides. Recall that the sum of the angle measures of a triangle is 180°.

25.

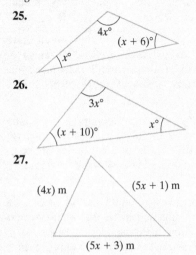

26.

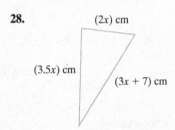

27.

$(4x)$ m $(5x + 1)$ m

$(5x + 3)$ m

Perimeter is 102 meters.

28. $(2x)$ cm

$(3.5x)$ cm $(3x + 7)$ cm

Perimeter is 75 centimeters.

29. $(2.5x - 9)$ in.

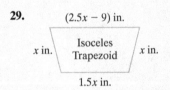

$1.5x$ in.

Perimeter is 99 inches.

30. $(9.2x - 3)$ ft

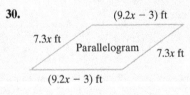

$(9.2x - 3)$ ft

Perimeter is 324 feet.

Solve.

31. The sum of three consecutive integers is 228. Find the integers.

32. The sum of three consecutive odd integers is 327. Find the integers.

33. The ZIP codes of three Nevada locations—Fallon, Fernley, and Gardnerville Ranchos—are three consecutive even integers. If twice the first integer added to the third is 268,222, find each ZIP code.

34. During a recent year, the average SAT scores in math for the states of Alabama, Louisiana, and Michigan were 3 consecutive integers. If the sum of the first integer, second

integer, and three times the third integer is 2637, find each score.

Many companies predict the growth or decline of various technologies. The following data is based on information from Techcrunchies, a technological information site. Notice that the first table is the predicted increase in the number of Wi-Fi-enabled cell phones (in millions), and the second is the predicted percent increase in the number of Wi-Fi-enabled cell phones in the United States.

35. Use the middle column in the table to find the predicted number of Wi-Fi-enabled cell phones for each year.

Year	Increase in Wi-Fi-Enabled Cell Phones	Predicted Number
2010	$2x - 21$	
2012	$\frac{5}{2}x + 2$	
2014	$3x + 24$	
Total	290 million	

36. Use the middle column in the table to find the predicted percent increase in the number of Wi-Fi-enabled cell phones for each year.

Year	Percent Increase in Wi-Fi-Enabled Cell Phones since 2009	Predicted Percent Increase
2010	x	
2011	$2x + 10$	
2012	$4x - 25$	
	300%	

Solve.

37. The occupations of biomedical engineers, skin care specialists, and physician assistants are among the 10 with the largest growth from 2008 to 2018. The number of physician assistant jobs will grow 7 thousand less than three times the number of biomedical engineer jobs. The number of skin care specialist jobs will grow 9 thousand more than half the number of biomedical engineer jobs. If the total growth of these three jobs is predicted to be 56 thousand, find the predicted growth of each job. (*Source:* U.S. Department of Labor, Bureau of Labor Statistics)

38. The occupations of farmer or rancher, file clerk, and telemarketer are among the 10 jobs with the largest decline from 2008 to 2018. The number of file clerk jobs is predicted to decline 11 thousand more than the number of telemarketer jobs. The number of farmer or rancher jobs is predicted to decline 3 thousand more than twice the number of telemarketer jobs. If the total decline of these three jobs is predicted to be 166 thousand, find the predicted decline of each job. (*Source:* U.S. Department of Labor, Bureau of Labor Statistics)

39. The B767-300ER aircraft has 88 more seats than the B737-200 aircraft. The F-100 has 32 fewer seats than the B737-200 aircraft. If their total number of seats is 413, find the number of seats for each aircraft. (*Source:* Air Transport Association of America)

40. Cowboy Stadium, home of the Dallas Cowboys of the NFL, seats approximately 9800 more fans than does Candlestick Park, home of the San Francisco 49ers. Soldier Field, home of the Chicago Bears, seats 8700 fewer fans than Candlestick Park. If the total seats in these three stadiums is 211,700, how many seats are in each of the three stadiums?

41. A new fax machine was recently purchased for an office in Hopedale for $464.40 including tax. If the tax rate in Hopedale is 8%, find the price of the fax machine before tax.

42. A premedical student at a local university was complaining that she had just paid $158.60 for her human anatomy book, including tax. Find the price of the book before taxes if the tax rate at this university is 9%.

43. The median compensation for a U.S. university president was $436,000 for the 2008–2009 academic year. Calculate the salary of a university president who received a 2.3% raise.

44. In 2009, the population of Brazil was 191.5 million. This represented a decrease in population of 3.7% from 2000. What was the population of Brazil in 2000? Round to the nearest tenth of a million. (*Source:* Population Reference Bureau)

45. In 2010, the population of Swaziland was 1,200,000 people. From 2010 to 2050, Swaziland's population is expected to increase by 50%. Find the expected population of Swaziland in 2050. (*Source:* Population Reference Bureau)

46. Dana, an auto parts supplier headquartered in Toledo, Ohio, recently announced it would be cutting 11,000 jobs worldwide. This is equivalent to 15% of Dana's workforce. Find the size of Dana's workforce prior to this round of job layoffs. Round to the nearest whole. (*Source:* Dana Corporation)

Recall that two angles are complements of each other if their sum is 90°. Two angles are supplements of each other if their sum is 180°. Find the measure of each angle.

47. One angle is three times its supplement increased by 20°. Find the measures of the two supplementary angles.

48. One angle is twice its complement increased by 30°. Find the measure of the two complementary angles.

Recall that the sum of the angle measures of a triangle is 180°.

49. Find the measures of the angles of a triangle if the measure of one angle is twice the measure of a second angle and the third angle measures 3 times the second angle decreased by 12.

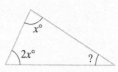

50. Find the angles of an isoceles triangle whose two base angles are equal and whose third angle is 10° less than three times a base angle.

51. Two frames are needed with the same perimeter: one frame in the shape of a square and one in the shape of an equilateral triangle. Each side of the triangle is 6 centimeters longer than each side of the square. Find the dimensions of each frame. (An equilateral triangle has sides that are the same length.)

52. Two frames are needed with the same perimeter: one frame in the shape of a square and one in the shape of a regular pentagon. Each side of the square is 7 inches longer than each side of the pentagon. Find the dimensions of each frame. (A regular polygon has sides that are the same length.)

53. The sum of the first and third of three consecutive even integers is 156. Find the three even integers.

54. The sum of the second and fourth of four consecutive integers is 110. Find the four integers.

55. Daytona International Speedway in Florida has 37,000 more grandstand seats than twice the number of grandstand seats at Darlington Motor Raceway in South Carolina. Together, these two race tracks seat 220,000 NASCAR fans. How many seats does each race track have? (*Source:* NASCAR)

56. For the 2010–2011 National Hockey League season, the payroll for the San Jose Sharks was $5,986,667 more than that for the Montreal Canadiens. The total payroll for these two teams was $113,103,333. What were the payrolls for these two teams for the 2010–2011 NHL season?

57. The sum of the populations of the metropolitan regions of New York, Tokyo, and Mexico City is 75.56 million. Use this information and Example 2 in this section to find the population of each metropolitan region. (*Source:* United Nations Department of Economic and Social Affairs)

58. The airports in London, Paris, and Frankfurt have a total of 177.1 million annual arrivals and departures. Use this information and Practice 2 in this section to find the number from each airport.

59. Suppose the perimeter of the triangle in Example 1b in this section is 483 feet. Find the length of each side.

60. Suppose the perimeter of the trapezoid in Practice 1b in this section is 110 meters. Find the lengths of its sides and bases.

61. Incandescent, fluorescent, and halogen bulbs are lasting longer today than ever before. On average, the number of bulb hours for a fluorescent bulb is 25 times the number of bulb hours for a halogen bulb. The number of bulb hours for an incandescent bulb is 2500 less than the halogen bulb. If the total number of bulb hours for the three types of bulbs is 105,500, find the number of bulb hours for each type. (*Source: Popular Science* magazine)

62. Falkland Islands, Iceland, and Norway are the top three countries that have the greatest Internet penetration rate (percent of population) in the world. Falkland Islands has a 6.8 percent greater penetration rate than Iceland. Norway has a 2.3 percent less penetration rate than Iceland. If the sum of the penetration rates is 284.1, find the Internet penetration rate in each of these countries. (*Source:* Internet World Stats)

63. During the 2010 Major League Baseball season, the number of wins for the Milwaukee Brewers, Houston Astros, and Chicago Cubs was three consecutive integers. Of these three teams, the Milwaukee Brewers had the most wins. The Chicago Cubs had the least wins. The total number of wins by these three teams was 228. How many wins did each team have in the 2010 season?

64. In the 2010 Winter Olympics, Austria won more medals than the Russian Federation, which won more medals than South Korea. If the numbers of medals won by these three countries is three consecutive integers whose sum is 45, find the number of medals won by each. (*Source:* Vancouver 2010)

65. The three tallest hospitals in the world are Guy's Tower in London, Queen Mary Hospital in Hong Kong, and Galter Pavilion in Chicago. These buildings have a total height of 1320 feet. Guy's Tower is 67 feet taller than Galter Pavilion, and the Queen Mary Hospital is 47 feet taller than Galter Pavilion. Find the heights of the three hospitals.

66. The official manual for traffic signs is the *Manual on Uniform Traffic Control Devices* published by the Government Printing Office. The rectangular sign below has a length 12 inches more than twice its height. If the perimeter of the sign is 312 inches, find its dimensions.

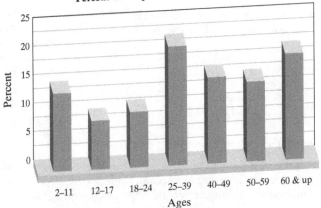

B.3 Graphing

OBJECTIVES
1 Plot Ordered Pairs.
2 Graph Linear Equations.

OBJECTIVE
1   Plotting Ordered Pairs

Graphs are widely used today in newspapers, magazines, and all forms of newsletters. A few examples of graphs are shown here.

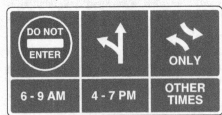

Percent of People Who Go to the Movies

Source: Motion Picture Association of America

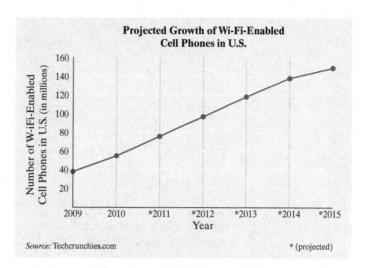

Source: Techcrunchies.com   * (projected)

To review how to read these graphs, we review their origin—the rectangular coordinate system. One way to locate points on a plane is by using a **rectangular coordinate system,** which is also called a **Cartesian coordinate system** after its inventor, René Descartes (1596–1650). The next diagram to the left shows the rectangular coordinate system. For further review of this system, see Section 3.1.

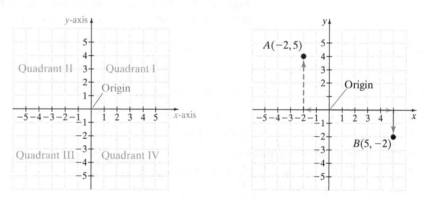

Recall that the location of point A in the figure above is described as 2 units to the left of the origin along the x-axis and 5 units upward parallel to the y-axis. Thus, we identify point A with the ordered pair $(-2, 5)$. Notice that the order of these numbers is *critical.* The x-value -2 is called the **x-coordinate** and is associated with the x-axis. The y-value 5 is called the **y-coordinate** and is associated with the y-axis. Compare the location of point A with the location of point B, which corresponds to the ordered pair $(5, -2)$.

Keep in mind that **each ordered pair corresponds to exactly one point in the real plane and that each point in the plane corresponds to exactly one ordered pair.** Thus, we may refer to the ordered pair (x, y) as the point (x, y).

EXAMPLE 1   Plot each ordered pair on a Cartesian coordinate system and name the quadrant or axis in which the point is located.

a. $(2, -1)$ **b.** $(0, 5)$ **c.** $(-3, 5)$

d. $(-2, 0)$ **e.** $\left(-\frac{1}{2}, -4\right)$ **f.** $(1.5, 1.5)$

Solution   The six points are graphed as shown on the next page.

a. $(2, -1)$ is in quadrant IV.   **b.** $(0, 5)$ is on the y-axis.

c. $(-3, 5)$ is in quadrant II.   **d.** $(-2, 0)$ is on the x-axis.

e. $\left(-\frac{1}{2}, -4\right)$ is in quadrant III.   **f.** $(1.5, 1.5)$ is in quadrant I.

(Continued on next page)

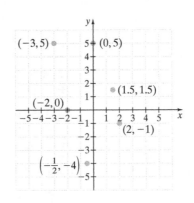

1 Plot each ordered pair on a Cartesian coordinate system and name the quadrant or axis in which the point is located.

a. $(3, -4)$ **b.** $(0, -2)$ **c.** $(-2, 4)$ **d.** $(4, 0)$ **e.** $\left(-1\frac{1}{2}, -2\right)$ **f.** $(2.5, 3.5)$

Notice that the y-coordinate of any point on the x-axis is 0. For example, the point with coordinates $(-2, 0)$ lies on the x-axis. Also, the x-coordinate of any point on the y-axis is 0. For example, the point with coordinates $(0, 5)$ lies on the y-axis. These points that lie on the axes do not lie in any quadrants.

✓CONCEPT CHECK

Which of the following correctly describes the location of the point $(3, -6)$ in a rectangular coordinate system?

a. 3 units to the left of the y-axis and 6 units above the x-axis

b. 3 units above the x-axis and 6 units to the left of the y-axis

c. 3 units to the right of the y-axis and 6 units below the x-axis

d. 3 units below the x-axis and 6 units to the right of the y-axis

---

2 Graphing Linear Equations

Recall that an equation such as $3x - y = 12$ is called a linear equation in two variables, and **the graph of every linear equation in two variables is a line.**

> ### Linear Equation in Two Variables
>
> A linear equation in two variables is an equation that can be written in the form
>
> $$Ax + By = C$$
>
> where A and B are not both 0. This form is called **standard form.**

Some examples of equations in standard form:

$$3x - y = 12$$
$$-2.1x + 5.6y = 0$$

> ▶ Helpful Hint
>
> Remember: A linear equation is written in standard form when all of the variable terms are on one side of the equation and the constant is on the other side.

Answer to Concept Check:
c

EXAMPLE 2   Graph the equation $y = -2x + 3$.

Solution   This is a linear equation. (In standard form it is $2x + y = 3$.) Find three ordered pair solutions, and plot the ordered pairs. The line through the plotted points is the graph. Since the equation is solved for y, let's choose three x-values. We'll choose $0, 2,$ and then -1 for x to find our three ordered pair solutions.

Let $x = 0$	Let $x = 2$	Let $x = -1$
$y = -2x + 3$	$y = -2x + 3$	$y = -2x + 3$
$y = -2 \cdot 0 + 3$	$y = -2 \cdot 2 + 3$	$y = -2(-1) + 3$
$y = 3$ Simplify.	$y = -1$ Simplify.	$y = 5$ Simplify.

The three ordered pairs $(0, 3)$, $(2, -1)$, and $(-1, 5)$ are listed in the table and the graph is shown.

x	y
0	3
2	-1
-1	5

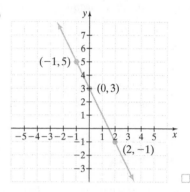

PRACTICE
2   Graph the equation $y = -3x - 2$.

Notice that the graph crosses the y-axis at the point $(0, 3)$. This point is called the **y-intercept.** (You may sometimes see just the number 3 called the y-intercept.) This graph also crosses the x-axis at the point $\left(\frac{3}{2}, 0\right)$. This point is called the **x-intercept.** (You may also see just the number $\frac{3}{2}$ called the x-intercept.)

Since every point on the y-axis has an x-value of 0, we can find the y-intercept of a graph by letting $x = 0$ and solving for y. Also, every point on the x-axis has a y-value of 0. To find the x-intercept, we let $y = 0$ and solve for x.

Finding x- and y-Intercepts

To find an x-intercept, let $y = 0$ and solve for x.
To find a y-intercept, let $x = 0$ and solve for y.

EXAMPLE 3   Graph the linear equation $y = \frac{1}{3}x$.

Solution   To graph, we find ordered pair solutions, plot the ordered pairs, and draw a line through the plotted points. We will choose x-values and substitute in the equation. To avoid fractions, we choose x-values that are multiples of 3. To find the y-intercept, we let $x = 0$.

▶ Helpful Hint
Notice that by using multiples of 3 for x, we avoid fractions.

▶ Helpful Hint
Since the equation $y = \frac{1}{3}x$ is solved for y, we choose x-values for finding points. This way, we simply need to evaluate an expression to find the y-value, as shown.

$$y = \frac{1}{3}x$$

If $x = 0$, then $y = \frac{1}{3}(0)$, or 0.

If $x = 6$, then $y = \frac{1}{3}(6)$, or 2.

If $x = -3$, then $y = \frac{1}{3}(-3)$, or -1.

x	y
0	0
6	2
-3	-1

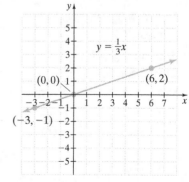

(Continued on next page)

This graph crosses the *x*-axis at $(0, 0)$ and the *y*-axis at $(0, 0)$. This means that the *x*-intercept is $(0, 0)$ and that the *y*-intercept is $(0, 0)$. ☐

PRACTICE
3 Graph the linear equation $y = -\frac{1}{2}x$.

 B.3 Exercise Set MyMathLab®

Determine the coordinates of each point on the graph.

1. Point *A*
2. Point *B*
3. Point *C*
4. Point *D*
5. Point *E*
6. Point *F*
7. Point *G*
8. Point *H*

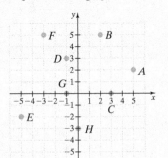

Without graphing, visualize the location of each point. Then give its location by quadrant or x- or y-axis. See Example 1.

9. $(2, 3)$
10. $(0, 5)$
11. $(-2, 7)$
12. $(-3, 0)$
13. $(-1, -4)$
14. $(4, -2)$
15. $(0, -100)$
16. $(10, 30)$
17. $(-10, -30)$
18. $(0, 0)$
19. $(-87, 0)$
20. $(-42, 17)$

Given that x is a positive number and that y is a positive number, determine the quadrant or axis in which each point lies.

21. $(x, -y)$
22. $(-x, y)$
23. $(x, 0)$
24. $(0, -y)$
25. $(-x, -y)$
26. $(0, 0)$

Graph each linear equation. See Examples 2 and 3.

27. $y = -x - 2$
28. $y = -2x + 1$
29. $3x - 4y = 8$
30. $x - 9y = 3$
31. $y = \frac{1}{3}x$
32. $y = \frac{3}{2}x$
33. $y + 4 = 0$
34. $x = -1.5$

Recall that if $f(2) = 7$, for example, this corresponds to the ordered pair $(2, 7)$ on the graph of f. Use this information and the graphs of f and g below to answer Exercises 35 through 42.

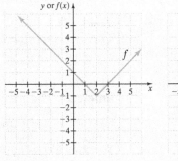 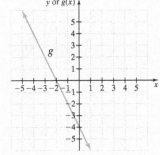

35. $f(4) =$
36. $f(0) =$
37. $g(0) =$
38. $g(-1) =$
39. Find all values for *x* such that $f(x) = 0$.
40. Find all values for *x* such that $g(x) = 0$.
41. If $(-1, -2)$ is a point on the graph of *g*, write this using function notation.
42. If $(-1, 2)$ is a point on the graph of *f*, write this using function notation.

B.4 Polynomials and Factoring

OBJECTIVES

1 Review Operations on Polynomials.

2 Review Factoring Polynomials.

OBJECTIVE
1 Operations on Polynomials

B.4 Exercise Set, Part 1 MyMathLab®

Perform each indicated operation.

1. $(-y^2 + 6y - 1) + (3y^2 - 4y - 10)$
2. $(5z^4 - 6z^2 + z + 1) - (7z^4 - 2z + 1)$
3. Subtract $(x - 5)$ from $(x^2 - 6x + 2)$.
4. $(2x^2 + 6x - 5) + (5x^2 - 10x)$
5. $(5x - 3)^2$
6. $(5x^2 - 14x - 3) \div (5x + 1)$

7. $(2x^4 - 3x^2 + 5x - 2) \div (x + 2)$

8. $(4x - 1)(x^2 - 3x - 2)$

OBJECTIVE
2   Factoring Strategies

The key to proficiency in factoring polynomials is to practice until you are comfortable with each technique. A strategy for factoring polynomials completely is given next.

Factoring a Polynomial

Step 1.   Are there any common factors? If so, factor out the greatest common factor.

Step 2.   How many terms are in the polynomial?

    a. If there are *two* terms, decide if one of the following formulas may be applied:

        i. Difference of two squares: $a^2 - b^2 = (a - b)(a + b)$

        ii. Difference of two cubes: $a^3 - b^3 = (a - b)(a^2 + ab + b^2)$

        iii. Sum of two cubes: $a^3 + b^3 = (a + b)(a^2 - ab + b^2)$

    b. If there are *three* terms, try one of the following:

        i. Perfect square trinomial: $a^2 + 2ab + b^2 = (a + b)^2$
                                       $a^2 - 2ab + b^2 = (a - b)^2$

        ii. If not a perfect square trinomial, factor by using the methods presented in Sections 6.2 through 6.4.

    c. If there are *four* or more terms, try factoring by grouping.

Step 3.   See whether any factors in the factored polynomial can be factored further.

A few examples are worked for you below.

EXAMPLE 1   Factor each polynomial completely.

a. $8a^2b - 4ab$ **b.** $36x^2 - 9$ **c.** $2x^2 - 5x - 7$
d. $5p^2 + 5 + qp^2 + q$ **e.** $9x^2 + 24x + 16$ **f.** $y^2 + 25$

Solution

a. Step 1.   The terms have a common factor of $4ab$, which we factor out.

$$8a^2b - 4ab = 4ab(2a - 1)$$

    Step 2.   There are two terms, but the binomial $2a - 1$ is not the difference of two squares or the sum or difference of two cubes.

    Step 3.   The factor $2a - 1$ cannot be factored further.

b. Step 1.   Factor out a common factor of 9.

$$36x^2 - 9 = 9(4x^2 - 1)$$

    Step 2.   The factor $4x^2 - 1$ has two terms, and it is the difference of two squares.

$$9(4x^2 - 1) = 9(2x + 1)(2x - 1)$$

    Step 3.   No factor with more than one term can be factored further.

c. Step 1.   The terms of $2x^2 - 5x - 7$ contain no common factor other than 1 or -1.

    Step 2.   There are three terms. The trinomial is not a perfect square, so we factor by methods from Section 6.3 or 6.4.

$$2x^2 - 5x - 7 = (2x - 7)(x + 1)$$

    Step 3.   No factor with more than one term can be factored further.

(Continued on next page)

d. Step 1. There is no common factor of all terms of $5p^2 + 5 + qp^2 + q$.

   Step 2. The polynomial has four terms, so try factoring by grouping.

$$5p^2 + 5 + qp^2 + q = (5p^2 + 5) + (qp^2 + q) \quad \text{Group the terms.}$$
$$= 5(p^2 + 1) + q(p^2 + 1)$$
$$= (p^2 + 1)(5 + q)$$

   Step 3. No factor can be factored further.

e. Step 1. The terms of $9x^2 + 24x + 16$ contain no common factor other than 1 or -1.

   Step 2. The trinomial $9x^2 + 24x + 16$ is a perfect square trinomial, and $9x^2 + 24x + 16 = (3x + 4)^2$.

   Step 3. No factor can be factored further.

f. Step 1. There is no common factor of $y^2 + 25$ other than 1.

   Step 2. This binomial is the sum of two squares and is prime.

   Step 3. The binomial $y^2 + 25$ cannot be factored further.   □

PRACTICE

1   Factor each polynomial completely.

a. $12x^2y - 3xy$

b. $49x^2 - 4$

c. $5x^2 + 2x - 3$

d. $3x^2 + 6 + x^3 + 2x$

e. $4x^2 + 20x + 25$

f. $b^2 + 100$

EXAMPLE 2   Factor each polynomial completely.

a. $27a^3 - b^3$ **b.** $3n^2m^4 - 48m^6$ **c.** $2x^2 - 12x + 18 - 2z^2$

d. $8x^4y^2 + 125xy^2$ **e.** $(x - 5)^2 - 49y^2$

Solution

a. This binomial is the difference of two cubes.

$$27a^3 - b^3 = (3a)^3 - b^3$$
$$= (3a - b)[(3a)^2 + (3a)(b) + b^2]$$
$$= (3a - b)(9a^2 + 3ab + b^2)$$

b. $3n^2m^4 - 48m^6 = 3m^4(n^2 - 16m^2)$ Factor out the GCF $3m^4$.
$$= 3m^4(n + 4m)(n - 4m) \quad \text{Factor the difference of squares.}$$

c. $2x^2 - 12x + 18 - 2z^2 = 2(x^2 - 6x + 9 - z^2)$ The GCF is 2.
$$= 2[(x^2 - 6x + 9) - z^2] \quad \begin{array}{l}\text{Group the first three}\\ \text{terms together.}\end{array}$$
$$= 2[(x - 3)^2 - z^2] \quad \begin{array}{l}\text{Factor the perfect}\\ \text{square trinomial.}\end{array}$$
$$= 2[(x - 3) + z][(x - 3) - z] \quad \begin{array}{l}\text{Factor the difference}\\ \text{of squares.}\end{array}$$
$$= 2(x - 3 + z)(x - 3 - z)$$

d. $8x^4y^2 + 125xy^2 = xy^2(8x^3 + 125)$ The GCF is xy^2.
$$= xy^2[(2x)^3 + 5^3]$$
$$= xy^2(2x + 5)[(2x)^2 - (2x)(5) + 5^2] \quad \text{Factor the sum of cubes.}$$
$$= xy^2(2x + 5)(4x^2 - 10x + 25)$$

e. This binomial is the difference of squares.

$$(x - 5)^2 - 49y^2 = (x - 5)^2 - (7y)^2$$
$$= [(x - 5) + 7y][(x - 5) - 7y]$$
$$= (x - 5 + 7y)(x - 5 - 7y) \quad □$$

PRACTICE
2   Factor each polynomial completely.

a. $64x^3 + y^3$

b. $7x^2y^2 - 63y^4$

c. $3x^2 + 12x + 12 - 3b^2$

d. $x^5y^4 + 27x^2y$

e. $(x + 7)^2 - 81y^2$

B.4   Exercise Set, Part 2   MyMathLab

Factor completely.

9. $x^2 - 8x + 16 - y^2$

10. $12x^2 - 22x - 20$

11. $x^4 - x$

12. $(2x + 1)^2 - 3(2x + 1) + 2$

13. $14x^2y - 2xy$

14. $24ab^2 - 6ab$

15. $4x^2 - 16$

16. $9x^2 - 81$

17. $3x^2 - 8x - 11$

18. $5x^2 - 2x - 3$

19. $4x^2 + 8x - 12$

20. $6x^2 - 6x - 12$

21. $4x^2 + 36x + 81$

22. $25x^2 + 40x + 16$

23. $8x^3 + 125y^3$

24. $27x^3 - 64y^3$

25. $64x^2y^3 - 8x^2$

26. $27x^5y^4 - 216x^2y$

27. $(x + 5)^3 + y^3$

28. $(y - 1)^3 + 27x^3$

29. $(5a - 3)^2 - 6(5a - 3) + 9$

30. $(4r + 1)^2 + 8(4r + 1) + 16$

31. $7x^2 - 63x$

32. $20x^2 + 23x + 6$

33. $ab - 6a + 7b - 42$

34. $20x^2 - 220x + 600$

35. $x^4 - 1$

36. $15x^2 - 20x$

37. $10x^2 - 7x - 33$

38. $45m^3n^3 - 27m^2n^2$

39. $5a^3b^3 - 50a^3b$

40. $x^4 + x$

41. $16x^2 + 25$

42. $20x^3 + 20y^3$

43. $10x^3 - 210x^2 + 1100x$

44. $9y^2 - 42y + 49$

45. $64a^3b^4 - 27a^3b$

46. $y^4 - 16$

47. $2x^3 - 54$

48. $2sr + 10s - r - 5$

49. $3y^5 - 5y^4 + 6y - 10$

50. $64a^2 + b^2$

51. $100z^3 + 100$

52. $250x^4 - 16x$

53. $4b^2 - 36b + 81$

54. $2a^5 - a^4 + 6a - 3$

55. $(y - 6)^2 + 3(y - 6) + 2$

56. $(c + 2)^2 - 6(c + 2) + 5$

△ **57.** Express the area of the shaded region as a polynomial. Factor the polynomial completely.

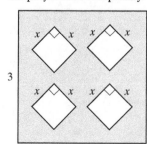

B.5 | Rational Expressions

OBJECTIVE

1 **Performing Operations on Rational Expressions and Solving Equations Containing Rational Expressions**

It is very important that you understand the difference between an expression and an equation containing rational expressions. An equation contains an equal sign; an expression does not.

Expression to be Simplified

$$\frac{x}{2} + \frac{x}{6}$$

Write both rational expressions with the LCD, 6, as the denominator.

$$\frac{x}{2} + \frac{x}{6} = \frac{x \cdot 3}{2 \cdot 3} + \frac{x}{6}$$

$$= \frac{3x}{6} + \frac{x}{6}$$

$$= \frac{4x}{6} = \frac{2x}{3}$$

Equation to be Solved

$$\frac{x}{2} + \frac{x}{6} = \frac{2}{3}$$

Multiply both sides by the LCD, 6.

$$6\left(\frac{x}{2} + \frac{x}{6}\right) = 6\left(\frac{2}{3}\right)$$

$$3x + x = 4$$

$$4x = 4$$

$$x = 1$$

Check to see that the solution is 1.

> ▶ **Helpful Hint**
> Remember: Equations can be cleared of fractions; expressions cannot.

EXAMPLE 1 Multiply. $\dfrac{x^3 - 1}{-3x + 3} \cdot \dfrac{15x^2}{x^2 + x + 1}$

Solution

$$\frac{x^3 - 1}{-3x + 3} \cdot \frac{15x^2}{x^2 + x + 1} = \frac{(x - 1)(x^2 + x + 1)}{-3(x - 1)} \cdot \frac{15x^2}{x^2 + x + 1} \qquad \text{Factor.}$$

$$= \frac{(x - 1)(x^2 + x + 1) \cdot 3 \cdot 5x^2}{-1 \cdot 3(x - 1)(x^2 + x + 1)} \qquad \text{Factor.}$$

$$= \frac{5x^2}{-1} = -5x^2 \qquad \text{Simplest form} \quad \square$$

PRACTICE

1 Multiply.

a. $\dfrac{2 + 5n}{3n} \cdot \dfrac{6n + 3}{5n^2 - 3n - 2}$

b. $\dfrac{x^3 - 8}{-6x + 12} \cdot \dfrac{6x^2}{x^2 + 2x + 4}$

EXAMPLE 2 Divide. $\dfrac{8m^2}{3m^2 - 12} \div \dfrac{40}{2 - m}$

Solution

$$\frac{8m^2}{3m^2 - 12} \div \frac{40}{2 - m} = \frac{8m^2}{3m^2 - 12} \cdot \frac{2 - m}{40} \qquad \text{Multiply by the reciprocal of the divisor.}$$

$$= \frac{8m^2(2 - m)}{3(m + 2)(m - 2) \cdot 40} \qquad \text{Factor and multiply.}$$

$$= \frac{8 \, m^2 \cdot -1 \, (m - 2)}{3(m + 2) \, (m - 2) \cdot 8 \cdot 5} \qquad \text{Write } (2 - m) \text{ as } -1(m - 2).$$

$$= -\frac{m^2}{15(m + 2)} \qquad \text{Simplify.} \quad \square$$

PRACTICE
2   Divide.

a. $\dfrac{6y^3}{3y^2 - 27} \div \dfrac{42}{3 - y}$

b. $\dfrac{10x^2 + 23x - 5}{5x^2 - 51x + 10} \div \dfrac{2x^2 + 9x + 10}{7x^2 - 68x - 20}$

EXAMPLE 3   Perform the indicated operation.

$$\frac{3}{x + 2} + \frac{2x}{x - 2}$$

Solution   The LCD is the product of the two denominators: $(x + 2)(x - 2)$.

$$\frac{3}{x + 2} + \frac{2x}{x - 2} = \frac{3 \cdot (x - 2)}{(x + 2) \cdot (x - 2)} + \frac{2x \cdot (x + 2)}{(x - 2) \cdot (x + 2)} \quad \text{Write equivalent rational expressions.}$$

$$= \frac{3x - 6}{(x + 2)(x - 2)} + \frac{2x^2 + 4x}{(x + 2)(x - 2)} \quad \text{Multiply in the numerators.}$$

$$= \frac{3x - 6 + 2x^2 + 4x}{(x + 2)(x - 2)} \quad \text{Add the numerators.}$$

$$= \frac{2x^2 + 7x - 6}{(x + 2)(x - 2)} \quad \text{Simplify the numerator.} \quad \square$$

PRACTICE
3   Perform the indicated operation.

a. $\dfrac{4}{p^3 q} + \dfrac{3}{5p^4 q}$

b. $\dfrac{4}{y + 3} + \dfrac{5y}{y - 3}$

c. $\dfrac{3z - 18}{z - 5} - \dfrac{3}{5 - z}$

EXAMPLE 4   Solve: $\dfrac{2x}{x - 3} + \dfrac{6 - 2x}{x^2 - 9} = \dfrac{x}{x + 3}$.

Solution   We factor the second denominator to find that the LCD is $(x + 3)(x - 3)$. We multiply both sides of the equation by $(x + 3)(x - 3)$. By the distributive property, this is the same as multiplying each term by $(x + 3)(x - 3)$.

$$\frac{2x}{x - 3} + \frac{6 - 2x}{x^2 - 9} = \frac{x}{x + 3}$$

$$(x + 3)(x - 3) \cdot \frac{2x}{x - 3} + (x + 3)(x - 3) \cdot \frac{6 - 2x}{(x + 3)(x - 3)}$$

$$= (x + 3)(x - 3)\left(\frac{x}{x + 3}\right)$$

$$2x(x + 3) + (6 - 2x) = x(x - 3) \quad \text{Simplify.}$$

$$2x^2 + 6x + 6 - 2x = x^2 - 3x \quad \text{Use the distributive property.}$$

Next we solve this quadratic equation by the factoring method. To do so, we first write the equation so that one side is 0.

$$x^2 + 7x + 6 = 0$$

$$(x + 6)(x + 1) = 0 \quad \text{Factor.}$$

$$x = -6 \quad \text{or} \quad x = -1 \quad \text{Set each factor equal to 0.}$$

Neither -6 nor -1 makes any denominator 0, so they are both solutions. The solutions are -6 and -1. $\quad \square$

PRACTICE
4   Solve: $\dfrac{2}{x - 2} - \dfrac{5 + 2x}{x^2 - 4} = \dfrac{x}{x + 2}$.

B.5 Exercise Set MyMathLab®

Perform each indicated operation and simplify, or solve the equation for the variable.

1. $\dfrac{x}{2} = \dfrac{1}{8} + \dfrac{x}{4}$

2. $\dfrac{x}{4} = \dfrac{3}{2} + \dfrac{x}{10}$

3. $\dfrac{1}{8} + \dfrac{x}{4}$

4. $\dfrac{3}{2} + \dfrac{x}{10}$

5. $\dfrac{4}{x + 2} - \dfrac{2}{x - 1}$

6. $\dfrac{5}{x - 2} - \dfrac{10}{x + 4}$

7. $\dfrac{4}{x + 2} = \dfrac{2}{x - 1}$

8. $\dfrac{5}{x - 2} = \dfrac{10}{x + 4}$

9. $\dfrac{2}{x^2 - 4} = \dfrac{1}{x + 2} - \dfrac{3}{x - 2}$

10. $\dfrac{3}{x^2 - 25} = \dfrac{1}{x + 5} + \dfrac{2}{x - 5}$

11. $\dfrac{5}{x^2 - 3x} + \dfrac{4}{2x - 6}$

12. $\dfrac{5}{x^2 - 3x} \div \dfrac{4}{2x - 6}$

13. $\dfrac{x - 1}{x + 1} + \dfrac{x + 7}{x - 1} = \dfrac{4}{x^2 - 1}$

14. $\left(1 - \dfrac{y}{x}\right) \div \left(1 - \dfrac{x}{y}\right)$

15. $\dfrac{a^2 - 9}{a - 6} \cdot \dfrac{a^2 - 5a - 6}{a^2 - a - 6}$

16. $\dfrac{2}{a - 6} + \dfrac{3a}{a^2 - 5a - 6} - \dfrac{a}{5a + 5}$

17. $\dfrac{2x + 3}{3x - 2} = \dfrac{4x + 1}{6x + 1}$

18. $\dfrac{5x - 3}{2x} = \dfrac{10x + 3}{4x + 1}$

19. $\dfrac{a}{9a^2 - 1} + \dfrac{2}{6a - 2}$

20. $\dfrac{3}{4a - 8} - \dfrac{a + 2}{a^2 - 2a}$

21. $-\dfrac{3}{x^2} - \dfrac{1}{x} + 2 = 0$

22. $\dfrac{x}{2x + 6} + \dfrac{5}{x^2 - 9}$

23. $\dfrac{x - 8}{x^2 - x - 2} + \dfrac{2}{x - 2}$

24. $\dfrac{x - 8}{x^2 - x - 2} + \dfrac{2}{x - 2} = \dfrac{3}{x + 1}$

25. $\dfrac{3}{a} - 5 = \dfrac{7}{a} - 1$

26. $\dfrac{7}{3z - 9} + \dfrac{5}{z}$

Use $\dfrac{x}{5} - \dfrac{x}{4} = \dfrac{1}{10}$ and $\dfrac{x}{5} - \dfrac{x}{4} + \dfrac{1}{10}$ for Exercises 27 and 28.

27. **a.** Which one above is an expression?
   b. Describe the first step to simplify this expression.
   c. Simplify the expression.

28. **a.** Which one above is an equation?
   b. Describe the first step to solve this equation.
   c. Solve the equation.

For each exercise, choose the correct statement. *Each figure represents a real number, and no denominators are 0.*

29. **a.** $\dfrac{\triangle + \square}{\triangle} = \square$ **b.** $\dfrac{\triangle + \square}{\triangle} = 1 + \dfrac{\square}{\triangle}$

   c. $\dfrac{\triangle + \square}{\triangle} = \dfrac{\square}{\triangle}$ **d.** $\dfrac{\triangle + \square}{\triangle} = 1 + \square$

   e. $\dfrac{\triangle + \square}{\triangle - \square} = -1$

*My thanks to Kelly Champagne for permission to use her Exercises for 29 through 33.

▶ **Helpful Hint**
Remember: Equations can be cleared of fractions; expressions cannot.

30. **a.** $\dfrac{\triangle}{\square} + \dfrac{\square}{\triangle} = \dfrac{\triangle + \square}{\square + \triangle} = 1$

b. $\dfrac{\triangle}{\square} + \dfrac{\square}{\triangle} = \dfrac{\triangle + \square}{\triangle \square}$

c. $\dfrac{\triangle}{\square} + \dfrac{\square}{\triangle} = \triangle\triangle + \square\square$

d. $\dfrac{\triangle}{\square} + \dfrac{\square}{\triangle} = \dfrac{\triangle\triangle + \square\square}{\square\triangle}$

e. $\dfrac{\triangle}{\square} + \dfrac{\square}{\triangle} = \dfrac{\triangle\square}{\square\triangle} = 1$

31. **a.** $\dfrac{\triangle}{\square} \cdot \dfrac{\bigcirc}{\square} = \dfrac{\triangle\bigcirc}{\square}$ **b.** $\dfrac{\triangle}{\square} \cdot \dfrac{\bigcirc}{\square} = \triangle\bigcirc$

c. $\dfrac{\triangle}{\square} \cdot \dfrac{\bigcirc}{\square} = \dfrac{\triangle + \bigcirc}{\square + \square}$ **d.** $\dfrac{\triangle}{\square} \cdot \dfrac{\bigcirc}{\square} = \dfrac{\triangle\bigcirc}{\square\square}$

32. **a.** $\dfrac{\triangle}{\square} \div \dfrac{\bigcirc}{\triangle} = \dfrac{\triangle\triangle}{\square\bigcirc}$ **b.** $\dfrac{\triangle}{\square} \div \dfrac{\bigcirc}{\triangle} = \dfrac{\bigcirc\square}{\triangle\triangle}$

c. $\dfrac{\triangle}{\square} \div \dfrac{\bigcirc}{\triangle} = \dfrac{\bigcirc}{\square}$ **d.** $\dfrac{\triangle}{\square} \div \dfrac{\bigcirc}{\triangle} = \dfrac{\triangle + \triangle}{\square + \bigcirc}$

33. **a.** $\dfrac{\dfrac{\triangle + \square}{\bigcirc}}{\dfrac{\triangle}{\bigcirc}} = \square$ **b.** $\dfrac{\dfrac{\triangle + \square}{\bigcirc}}{\dfrac{\triangle}{\bigcirc}} = \dfrac{\triangle\triangle + \triangle\square}{\bigcirc\bigcirc}$

c. $\dfrac{\dfrac{\triangle + \square}{\bigcirc}}{\dfrac{\triangle}{\bigcirc}} = 1 + \square$ **d.** $\dfrac{\dfrac{\triangle + \square}{\bigcirc}}{\dfrac{\triangle}{\bigcirc}} = \dfrac{\triangle + \square}{\triangle}$

Appendix C

An Introduction to Using a Graphing Utility

The Viewing Window and Interpreting Window Settings

In this appendix, we will use the term **graphing utility** to mean a graphing calculator or a computer software graphing package. All graphing utilities graph equations by plotting points on a screen. While plotting several points can be slow and sometimes tedious for us, a graphing utility can quickly and accurately plot hundreds of points. How does a graphing utility show plotted points? A computer or calculator screen is made up of a grid of small rectangular areas called **pixels.** If a pixel contains a point to be plotted, the pixel is turned "on"; otherwise, the pixel remains "off." The graph of an equation is then a collection of pixels turned "on." The graph of $y = 3x + 1$ from a graphing calculator is shown in Figure A-1. Notice the irregular shape of the line caused by the rectangular pixels.

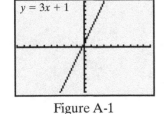

Figure A-1

The portion of the coordinate plane shown on the screen in Figure A-1 is called the **viewing window** or the **viewing rectangle.** Notice the x-axis and the y-axis on the graph. While tick marks are shown on the axes, they are not labeled. This means that from this screen alone, we do not know how many units each tick mark represents. To see what each tick mark represents and the minimum and maximum values on the axes, check the window setting of the graphing utility. It defines the viewing window. The window of the graph of $y = 3x + 1$ shown in Figure A-1 has the following settings (Figure A-2):

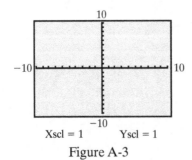

Figure A-2

$$\text{Xmin} = -10 \quad \text{The minimum } x\text{-value is } -10.$$
$$\text{Xmax} = 10 \quad \text{The maximum } x\text{-value is } 10.$$
$$\text{Xscl} = 1 \quad \text{The } x\text{-axis scale is 1 unit per tick mark.}$$
$$\text{Ymin} = -10 \quad \text{The minimum } y\text{-value is } -10.$$
$$\text{Ymax} = 10 \quad \text{The maximum } y\text{-value is } 10.$$
$$\text{Yscl} = 1 \quad \text{The } y\text{-axis scale is 1 unit per tick mark.}$$

By knowing the scale, we can find the minimum and the maximum values on the axes simply by counting tick marks. For example, if both the Xscl (x-axis scale) and the Yscl (y-axis scale) are 1 unit per tick mark on the graph in Figure A-3, we can count the tick marks and find that the minimum x-value is -10 and the maximum x-value is 10. Also, the minimum y-value is -10 and the maximum y-value is 10. If the Xscl changes to 2 units per tick mark (shown in Figure A-4), by counting tick marks, we see that the minimum x-value is now -20 and the maximum x-value is now 20.

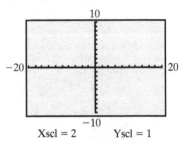

Figure A-3   Figure A-4

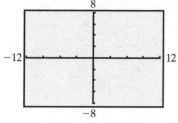

Figure A-5

It is also true that if we know the Xmin and the Xmax values, we can calculate the Xscl by the displayed axes. For example, the Xscl of the graph in Figure A-5 must be 3 units per tick mark for the maximum and minimum x-values to be as shown. Also, the Yscl of that graph must be 2 units per tick mark for the maximum and minimum y-values to be as shown.

We will call the viewing window in Figure A-3 a *standard* viewing window or rectangle. Although a standard viewing window is sufficient for much of this text, special care must be taken to ensure that all key features of a graph are shown. Figures A-6, A-7, and A-8 show the graph of $y = x^2 + 11x - 1$ on three different viewing windows. Note that certain viewing windows for this equation are misleading.

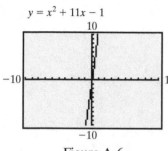

Figure A-6

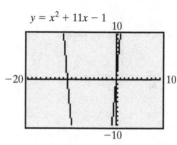

Figure A-7

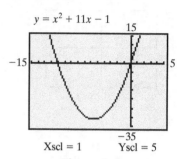

Figure A-8

How do we ensure that all distinguishing features of the graph of an equation are shown? It helps to know about the equation that is being graphed. For example, the equation $y = x^2 + 11x - 1$ is not a linear equation and its graph is not a line. This equation is a quadratic equation and, therefore, its graph is a parabola. By knowing this information, we know that the graph shown in Figure A-6, although correct, is misleading. Of the three viewing rectangles shown, the graph in Figure A-8 is best because it shows more of the distinguishing features of the parabola. Properties of equations needed for graphing will be studied in this text.

The Viewing Window and Interpreting Window Settings Exercise Set

In Exercises 1–4, determine whether all ordered pairs listed will lie within a standard viewing rectangle.

1. $(-9, 0), (5, 8), (1, -8)$

2. $(4, 7), (0, 0), (-8, 9)$

3. $(-11, 0), (2, 2), (7, -5)$

4. $(3, 5), (-3, -5), (15, 0)$

In Exercises 5–10, choose an Xmin, Xmax, Ymin, and Ymax so that all ordered pairs listed will lie within the viewing rectangle.

5. $(-90, 0), (55, 80), (0, -80)$

6. $(4, 70), (20, 20), (-18, 90)$

7. $(-11, 0), (2, 2), (7, -5)$

8. $(3, 5), (-3, -5), (15, 0)$

9. $(200, 200), (50, -50), (70, -50)$

10. $(40, 800), (-30, 500), (15, 0)$

Write the window setting for each viewing window shown. Use the following format:

Xmin =	Ymin =
Xmax =	Ymax =
Xscl =	Yscl =

11.

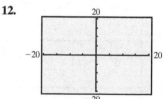

12.

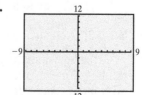

13.

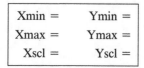

14.

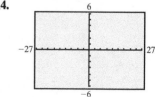

15.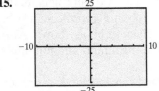

16.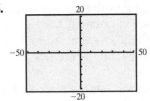

19.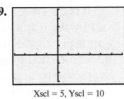

Xscl = 5, Yscl = 10

20.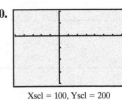

Xscl = 100, Yscl = 200

17.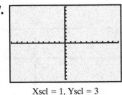

Xscl = 1, Yscl = 3

18.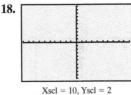

Xscl = 10, Yscl = 2

Graphing Equations and Square Viewing Window

In general, the following steps may be used to graph an equation on a standard viewing window.

> **Graphing an Equation in *X* and *Y* with a Graphing Utility on a Standard Viewing Window**
>
> **Step 1:** Solve the equation for *y*.
>
> **Step 2:** Using your graphing utility, enter the equation in the form
> Y = *expression involving x*.
>
> **Step 3:** Activate the graphing utility.

Special care must be taken when entering the *expression involving x* in Step 2. You must be sure that the graphing utility you are using interprets the expression as you want it to. For example, let's graph $3y = 4x$. To do so,

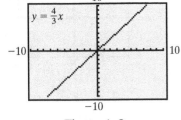

Figure A-9

Step 1: Solve the equation for *y*.

$$3y = 4x$$

$$\frac{3y}{3} = \frac{4x}{3}$$

$$y = \frac{4}{3}x$$

Step 2: Using your graphing utility, enter the expression $\frac{4}{3}x$ after the Y = prompt.
In order for your graphing utility to correctly interpret the expression, you may need to enter $(4/3)x$ or $(4 \div 3)x$.

Step 3: Activate the graphing utility. The graph should appear as in Figure A-9.

Distinguishing features of the graph of a line include showing all the intercepts of the line. For example, the window of the graph of the line in Figure A-10 does not show both intercepts of the line, but the window of the graph of the same line in Figure A-11 does show both intercepts. Notice the notation below each graph. This is a shorthand notation of the range setting of the graph. This notation means [Xmin, Xmax] by [Ymin, Ymax].

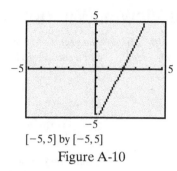

[−5, 5] by [−5, 5]

Figure A-10

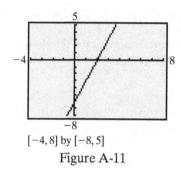

[−4, 8] by [−8, 5]

Figure A-11

On a standard viewing window, the tick marks on the *y*-axis are closer together than the tick marks on the *x*-axis. This happens because the viewing window is a rectangle, and so 10 equally spaced tick marks on the positive *y*-axis will be closer together than 10 equally spaced tick marks on the positive *x*-axis. This causes the appearance of graphs to be distorted.

For example, notice the different appearances of the same line graphed using different viewing windows. The line in Figure A-12 is distorted because the tick marks along the *x*-axis are farther apart than the tick marks along the *y*-axis. The graph of the same line in Figure A-13 is not distorted because the viewing rectangle has been selected so that there is equal spacing between tick marks on both axes.

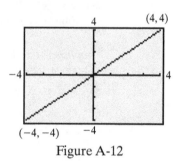

Figure A-12

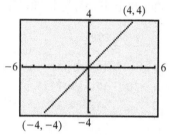

Figure A-13

We say that the line in Figure A-13 is graphed on a *square* setting. Some graphing utilities have a built-in program that, if activated, will automatically provide a square setting. A square setting is especially helpful when we are graphing perpendicular lines, circles, or when a true geometric perspective is desired. Some examples of square screens are shown in Figures A-14 and A-15.

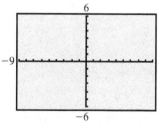

Figure A-14

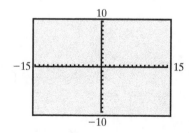

Figure A-15

Other features of a graphing utility such as Trace, Zoom, Intersect, and Table are discussed in appropriate Graphing Calculator Explorations in this text.

Graphing Equations and Square Viewing Window Exercise Set

Graph each linear equation in two variables using the two different range settings given. Determine which setting shows all intercepts of a line.

1. $y = 2x + 12$
   Setting A: $[-10, 10]$ by $[-10, 10]$
   Setting B: $[-10, 10]$ by $[-10, 15]$

2. $y = -3x + 25$
   Setting A: $[-5, 5]$ by $[-30, 10]$
   Setting B: $[-10, 10]$ by $[-10, 30]$

3. $y = -x - 41$
   Setting A: $[-50, 10]$ by $[-10, 10]$
   Setting B: $[-50, 10]$ by $[-50, 15]$

4. $y = 6x - 18$
   Setting A: $[-10, 10]$ by $[-20, 10]$
   Setting B: $[-10, 10]$ by $[-10, 10]$

5. $y = \dfrac{1}{2}x - 15$
   Setting B: $[-10, 10]$ by $[-20, 10]$
   Setting B: $[-10, 35]$ by $[-20, 15]$

6. $y = -\dfrac{2}{3}x - \dfrac{29}{3}$
   Setting A: $[-10, 10]$ by $[-10, 10]$
   Setting B: $[-15, 5]$ by $[-15, 5]$

The graph of each equation is a line. Use a graphing utility and a standard viewing window to graph each equation.

7. $3x = 5y$

8. $7y = -3x$

9. $9x - 5y = 30$

10. $4x + 6y = 20$

11. $y = -7$

12. $y = 2$

13. $x + 10y = -5$

14. $x - 5y = 9$

Graph the following equations using the square setting given. Some keystrokes that may be helpful are given.

15. $y = \sqrt{x}$ $[-12, 12]$ by $[-8, 8]$
    Suggested keystrokes: $\sqrt{\ }\,x$

16. $y = \sqrt{2x}$ $[-12, 12]$ by $[-8, 8]$
    Suggested keystrokes: $\sqrt{\ }(2x)$

17. $y = x^2 + 2x + 1$ $[-15, 15]$ by $[-10, 10]$
    Suggested keystrokes: $x^{\wedge}2 + 2x + 1$

18. $y = x^2 - 5$ $[-15, 15]$ by $[-10, 10]$
    Suggested keystrokes: $x^{\wedge}2 - 5$

19. $y = |x|$ $[-9, 9]$ by $[-6, 6]$
    Suggested keystrokes: $ABS\,(x)$

20. $y = |x - 2|$ $[-9, 9]$ by $[-6, 6]$
    Suggested keystrokes: $ABS\,(x - 2)$

Graph each line. Use a standard viewing window; then, if necessary, change the viewing window so that all intercepts of each line show.

21. $x + 2y = 30$

22. $1.5x - 3.7y = 40.3$

Appendix D

Solving Systems of Equations by Matrices

OBJECTIVES

1 Use Matrices to Solve a System of Two Equations.

2 Use Matrices to Solve a System of Three Equations.

By now, you may have noticed that the solution of a system of equations depends on the coefficients of the equations in the system and not on the variables. In this section, we introduce solving a system of equations by a **matrix.**

OBJECTIVE

1   Using Matrices to Solve a System of Two Equations

A matrix (plural: **matrices**) is a rectangular array of numbers. The following are examples of matrices.

$$\begin{bmatrix} 1 & 0 \\ 0 & 1 \end{bmatrix} \quad \begin{bmatrix} 2 & 1 & 3 & -1 \\ 0 & -1 & 4 & 5 \\ -6 & 2 & 1 & 0 \end{bmatrix} \quad \begin{bmatrix} a & b & c \\ d & e & f \end{bmatrix}$$

The numbers aligned horizontally in a matrix are in the same **row.** The numbers aligned vertically are in the same **column.**

$$\begin{array}{c} \text{row 1} \rightarrow \\ \text{row 2} \rightarrow \end{array} \begin{bmatrix} 2 & 1 & 0 \\ -1 & 6 & 2 \end{bmatrix}$$

column 1
column 2
column 3

This matrix has 2 rows and 3 columns. It is called a 2×3 (read "two by three") matrix.

To see the relationship between systems of equations and matrices, study the example below.

> **Helpful Hint**
> Before writing the corresponding matrix associated with a system of equations, make sure that the equations are written in standard form.

System of Equations (in standard form)	Corresponding Matrix

$$\begin{cases} 2x - 3y = 6 & \text{Equation 1} \\ x + y = 0 & \text{Equation 2} \end{cases} \qquad \begin{bmatrix} 2 & -3 & \vdots & 6 \\ 1 & 1 & \vdots & 0 \end{bmatrix} \begin{array}{l} \text{Row 1} \\ \text{Row 2} \end{array}$$

Notice that the rows of the matrix correspond to the equations in the system. The coefficients of each variable are placed to the left of a vertical dashed line. The constants are placed to the right. Each of the numbers in the matrix is called an **element.**

The method of solving systems by matrices is to write this matrix as an equivalent matrix from which we easily identify the solution. Two matrices are equivalent if they represent systems that have the same solution set. The following **row operations** can be performed on matrices, and the result is an equivalent matrix.

> **Helpful Hint**
> Notice that these *row* operations are the same operations that we can perform on *equations* in a system.

Elementary Row Operations

1. Any two rows in a matrix may be interchanged.

2. The elements of any row may be multiplied (or divided) by the same nonzero number.

3. The elements of any row may be multiplied (or divided) by a nonzero number and added to their corresponding elements in any other row.

To solve a system of two equations in x and y by matrices, write the corresponding matrix associated with the system. Then use elementary row operations to write equivalent matrices until you have a matrix of the form

$$\begin{bmatrix} 1 & a & | & b \\ 0 & 1 & | & c \end{bmatrix},$$

where a, b, and c are constants. Why? If a matrix associated with a system of equations is in this form, we can easily solve for x and y. For example,

Matrix		**System of Equations**

$$\begin{bmatrix} 1 & 2 & | & -3 \\ 0 & 1 & | & 5 \end{bmatrix} \quad \text{corresponds to} \quad \begin{cases} 1x + 2y = -3 \\ 0x + 1y = 5 \end{cases} \quad \text{or} \quad \begin{cases} x + 2y = -3 \\ y = 5 \end{cases}$$

In the second equation, we have $y = 5$. Substituting this in the first equation, we have $x + 2(5) = -3$ or $x = -13$. The solution of the system is the ordered pair $(-13, 5)$.

EXAMPLE 1 Use matrices to solve the system.

$$\begin{cases} x + 3y = 5 \\ 2x - y = -4 \end{cases}$$

Solution The corresponding matrix is $\begin{bmatrix} 1 & 3 & | & 5 \\ 2 & -1 & | & -4 \end{bmatrix}$. We use elementary row operations to write an equivalent matrix that looks like $\begin{bmatrix} 1 & a & | & b \\ 0 & 1 & | & c \end{bmatrix}$.

For the matrix given, the element in the first row, first column is already 1, as desired. Next we write an equivalent matrix with a 0 below the 1. To do this, we multiply row 1 by -2 and add to row 2. _We will change only row 2._

$$\begin{bmatrix} 1 & 3 & | & 5 \\ -2(1) + 2 & -2(3) + (-1) & | & -2(5) + (-4) \end{bmatrix} \quad \text{simplifies to} \quad \begin{bmatrix} 1 & 3 & | & 5 \\ 0 & -7 & | & -14 \end{bmatrix}$$

row 1 row 2 row 1 row 2 row 1 row 2
element element element element element element

Now we change the -7 to a 1 by use of an elementary row operation. We divide row 2 by -7, then

$$\begin{bmatrix} 1 & 3 & | & 5 \\ \frac{0}{-7} & \frac{-7}{-7} & | & \frac{-14}{-7} \end{bmatrix} \quad \text{simplifies to} \quad \begin{bmatrix} 1 & 3 & | & 5 \\ 0 & 1 & | & 2 \end{bmatrix}$$

This last matrix corresponds to the system

$$\begin{cases} x + 3y = 5 \\ y = 2 \end{cases}$$

To find x, we let $y = 2$ in the first equation, $x + 3y = 5$.

$$x + 3y = 5 \qquad \text{First equation}$$
$$x + 3(2) = 5 \qquad \text{Let } y = 2.$$
$$x = -1$$

The ordered pair solution is $(-1, 2)$. Check to see that this ordered pair satisfies both equations. □

PRACTICE

1 Use matrices to solve the system.

$$\begin{cases} x + 4y = -2 \\ 3x - y = 7 \end{cases}$$

EXAMPLE 2   Use matrices to solve the system.

$$\begin{cases} 2x - y = 3 \\ 4x - 2y = 5 \end{cases}$$

Solution   The corresponding matrix is $\begin{bmatrix} 2 & -1 & \vdots & 3 \\ 4 & -2 & \vdots & 5 \end{bmatrix}$. To get 1 in the row 1, column 1 position, we divide the elements of row 1 by 2.

$$\begin{bmatrix} \dfrac{2}{2} & -\dfrac{1}{2} & \vdots & \dfrac{3}{2} \\ 4 & -2 & \vdots & 5 \end{bmatrix} \quad \text{simplifies to} \quad \begin{bmatrix} 1 & -\dfrac{1}{2} & \vdots & \dfrac{3}{2} \\ 4 & -2 & \vdots & 5 \end{bmatrix}$$

To get 0 under the 1, we multiply the elements of row 1 by -4 and add the new elements to the elements of row 2.

$$\begin{bmatrix} 1 & -\dfrac{1}{2} & \vdots & \dfrac{3}{2} \\ -4(1) + 4 & -4\left(-\dfrac{1}{2}\right) - 2 & \vdots & -4\left(\dfrac{3}{2}\right) + 5 \end{bmatrix} \quad \text{simplifies to} \quad \begin{bmatrix} 1 & -\dfrac{1}{2} & \vdots & \dfrac{3}{2} \\ 0 & 0 & \vdots & -1 \end{bmatrix}$$

The corresponding system is $\begin{cases} x - \dfrac{1}{2}y = \dfrac{3}{2} \\ 0 = -1 \end{cases}$. The equation $0 = -1$ is false for all y or x values; hence, the system is inconsistent and has no solution. The solution set is $\{\ \}$ or $\varnothing$.

PRACTICE
2   Use matrices to solve the system.

$$\begin{cases} x - 3y = 3 \\ -2x + 6y = 4 \end{cases}$$

✓**CONCEPT CHECK**
Consider the system

$$\begin{cases} 2x - 3y = 8 \\ x + 5y = -3 \end{cases}$$

What is wrong with its corresponding matrix shown below?

$$\begin{bmatrix} 2 & -3 & \vdots & 8 \\ 0 & 5 & \vdots & -3 \end{bmatrix}$$

OBJECTIVE
2   **Using Matrices to Solve a System of Three Equations**

To solve a system of three equations in three variables using matrices, we will write the corresponding matrix in the form

$$\begin{bmatrix} 1 & a & b & \vdots & d \\ 0 & 1 & c & \vdots & e \\ 0 & 0 & 1 & \vdots & f \end{bmatrix}$$

Answer to Concept Check:

matrix should be $\begin{bmatrix} 2 & -3 & \vdots & 8 \\ 1 & 5 & \vdots & -3 \end{bmatrix}$

EXAMPLE 3 Use matrices to solve the system.

$$\begin{cases} x + 2y + z = 2 \\ -2x - y + 2z = 5 \\ x + 3y - 2z = -8 \end{cases}$$

Solution The corresponding matrix is $\begin{bmatrix} 1 & 2 & 1 & \vdots & 2 \\ -2 & -1 & 2 & \vdots & 5 \\ 1 & 3 & -2 & \vdots & -8 \end{bmatrix}$. Our goal is to write

an equivalent matrix with 1's along the diagonal (see the numbers in red) and 0's below the 1's. The element in row 1, column 1 is already 1. Next we get 0's for each element in the rest of column 1. To do this, first we multiply the elements of row 1 by 2 and add the new elements to row 2. Also, we multiply the elements of row 1 by -1 and add the new elements to the elements of row 3. We *do not change row 1*. Then

$$\begin{bmatrix} 1 & 2 & 1 & \vdots & 2 \\ 2(1)-2 & 2(2)-1 & 2(1)+2 & \vdots & 2(2)+5 \\ -1(1)+1 & -1(2)+3 & -1(1)-2 & \vdots & -1(2)-8 \end{bmatrix} \text{ simplifies to } \begin{bmatrix} 1 & 2 & 1 & \vdots & 2 \\ 0 & 3 & 4 & \vdots & 9 \\ 0 & 1 & -3 & \vdots & -10 \end{bmatrix}$$

We continue down the diagonal and use elementary row operations to get 1 where the element 3 is now. To do this, we interchange rows 2 and 3.

$$\begin{bmatrix} 1 & 2 & 1 & \vdots & 2 \\ 0 & 3 & 4 & \vdots & 9 \\ 0 & 1 & -3 & \vdots & -10 \end{bmatrix} \text{ is equivalent to } \begin{bmatrix} 1 & 2 & 1 & \vdots & 2 \\ 0 & 1 & -3 & \vdots & -10 \\ 0 & 3 & 4 & \vdots & 9 \end{bmatrix}$$

Next we want the new row 3, column 2 element to be 0. We multiply the elements of row 2 by -3 and add the result to the elements of row 3.

$$\begin{bmatrix} 1 & 2 & 1 & \vdots & 2 \\ 0 & 1 & -3 & \vdots & -10 \\ -3(0)+0 & -3(1)+3 & -3(-3)+4 & \vdots & -3(-10)+9 \end{bmatrix} \text{ simplifies to}$$

$$\begin{bmatrix} 1 & 2 & 1 & \vdots & 2 \\ 0 & 1 & -3 & \vdots & -10 \\ 0 & 0 & 13 & \vdots & 39 \end{bmatrix}$$

Finally, we divide the elements of row 3 by 13 so that the final diagonal element is 1.

$$\begin{bmatrix} 1 & 2 & 1 & \vdots & 2 \\ 0 & 1 & -3 & \vdots & -10 \\ \frac{0}{13} & \frac{0}{13} & \frac{13}{13} & \vdots & \frac{39}{13} \end{bmatrix} \text{ simplifies to } \begin{bmatrix} 1 & 2 & 1 & \vdots & 2 \\ 0 & 1 & -3 & \vdots & -10 \\ 0 & 0 & 1 & \vdots & 3 \end{bmatrix}$$

This matrix corresponds to the system

$$\begin{cases} x + 2y + z = 2 \\ y - 3z = -10 \\ z = 3 \end{cases}$$

We identify the z-coordinate of the solution as 3. Next, we replace z with 3 in the second equation and solve for y.

$$y - 3z = -10 \quad \text{Second equation}$$
$$y - 3(3) = -10 \quad \text{Let } z = 3.$$
$$y = -1$$

To find x, we let $z = 3$ and $y = -1$ in the first equation.

$$x + 2y + z = 2 \quad \text{First equation}$$
$$x + 2(-1) + 3 = 2 \quad \text{Let } z = 3 \text{ and } y = -1.$$
$$x = 1$$

The ordered triple solution is $(1, -1, 3)$. Check to see that it satisfies all three equations in the original system.

PRACTICE

3 Use matrices to solve the system.

$$\begin{cases} x + 3y - z = 0 \\ 2x + y + 3z = 5 \\ -x - 2y + 4z = 7 \end{cases}$$

D Exercise Set   MyMathLab®

Solve each system of linear equations using matrices. See Example 1.

1. $\begin{cases} x + y = 1 \\ x - 2y = 4 \end{cases}$

2. $\begin{cases} 2x - y = 8 \\ x + 3y = 11 \end{cases}$

3. $\begin{cases} x + 3y = 2 \\ x + 2y = 0 \end{cases}$

4. $\begin{cases} 4x - y = 5 \\ 3x + 3y = 0 \end{cases}$

Solve each system of linear equations using matrices. See Example 2.

5. $\begin{cases} x - 2y = 4 \\ 2x - 4y = 4 \end{cases}$

6. $\begin{cases} -x + 3y = 6 \\ 3x - 9y = 9 \end{cases}$

7. $\begin{cases} 3x - 3y = 9 \\ 2x - 2y = 6 \end{cases}$

8. $\begin{cases} 9x - 3y = 6 \\ -18x + 6y = -12 \end{cases}$

Solve each system of linear equations using matrices. See Example 3.

9. $\begin{cases} x + y = 3 \\ 2y = 10 \\ 3x + 2y - 4z = 12 \end{cases}$

10. $\begin{cases} 5x = 5 \\ 2x + y = 4 \\ 3x + y - 5z = -15 \end{cases}$

11. $\begin{cases} 2y - z = -7 \\ x + 4y + z = -4 \\ 5x - y + 2z = 13 \end{cases}$

12. $\begin{cases} 4y + 3z = -2 \\ 5x - 4y = 1 \\ -5x + 4y + z = -3 \end{cases}$

MIXED PRACTICE

Solve each system of linear equations using matrices. See Examples 1 through 3.

13. $\begin{cases} x - 4 = 0 \\ x + y = 1 \end{cases}$

14. $\begin{cases} 3y = 6 \\ x + y = 7 \end{cases}$

15. $\begin{cases} x + y + z = 2 \\ 2x - z = 5 \\ 3y + z = 2 \end{cases}$

16. $\begin{cases} x + 2y + z = 5 \\ x - y - z = 3 \\ y + z = 2 \end{cases}$

17. $\begin{cases} 5x - 2y = 27 \\ -3x + 5y = 18 \end{cases}$

18. $\begin{cases} 4x - y = 9 \\ 2x + 3y = -27 \end{cases}$

19. $\begin{cases} 4x - 7y = 7 \\ 12x - 21y = 24 \end{cases}$

20. $\begin{cases} 2x - 5y = 12 \\ -4x + 10y = 20 \end{cases}$

21. $\begin{cases} 4x - y + 2z = 5 \\ 2y + z = 4 \\ 4x + y + 3z = 10 \end{cases}$

22. $\begin{cases} 5y - 7z = 14 \\ 2x + y + 4z = 10 \\ 2x + 6y - 3z = 30 \end{cases}$

23. $\begin{cases} 4x + y + z = 3 \\ -x + y - 2z = -11 \\ x + 2y + 2z = -1 \end{cases}$

24. $\begin{cases} x + y + z = 9 \\ 3x - y + z = -1 \\ -2x + 2y - 3z = -2 \end{cases}$

CONCEPT EXTENSIONS

Solve. See the Concept Check in this section.

25. For the system $\begin{cases} x + z = 7 \\ y + 2z = -6 \\ 3x - y = 0 \end{cases}$, which is the correct corresponding matrix?

a. $\begin{bmatrix} 1 & 1 & | & 7 \\ 1 & 2 & | & -6 \\ 3 & -1 & | & 0 \end{bmatrix}$

b. $\begin{bmatrix} 1 & 0 & 1 & | & 7 \\ 1 & 2 & 0 & | & -6 \\ 3 & -1 & 0 & | & 0 \end{bmatrix}$

c. $\begin{bmatrix} 1 & 0 & 1 & | & 7 \\ 0 & 1 & 2 & | & -6 \\ 3 & -1 & 0 & | & 0 \end{bmatrix}$

Appendix E

Solving Systems of Equations by Determinants

OBJECTIVES

1 Define and Evaluate a 2 × 2 Determinant.

2 Use Cramer's Rule to Solve a System of Two Linear Equations in Two Variables.

3 Define and Evaluate a 3 × 3 Determinant.

4 Use Cramer's Rule to Solve a System of Three Linear Equations in Three Variables.

We have solved systems of two linear equations in two variables in four different ways: graphically, by substitution, by elimination, and by matrices. Now we analyze another method, called **Cramer's rule.**

OBJECTIVE

1   Evaluating 2 × 2 Determinants

Recall that a matrix is a rectangular array of numbers. If a matrix has the same number of rows and columns, it is called a **square matrix.** Examples of square matrices are

$$\begin{bmatrix} 1 & 6 \\ 5 & 2 \end{bmatrix} \qquad \begin{bmatrix} 2 & 4 & 1 \\ 0 & 5 & 2 \\ 3 & 6 & 9 \end{bmatrix}$$

A **determinant** is a real number associated with a square matrix. The determinant of a square matrix is denoted by placing vertical bars about the array of numbers. Thus,

The determinant of the square matrix $\begin{bmatrix} 1 & 6 \\ 5 & 2 \end{bmatrix}$ is $\begin{vmatrix} 1 & 6 \\ 5 & 2 \end{vmatrix}$.

The determinant of the square matrix $\begin{bmatrix} 2 & 4 & 1 \\ 0 & 5 & 2 \\ 3 & 6 & 9 \end{bmatrix}$ is $\begin{vmatrix} 2 & 4 & 1 \\ 0 & 5 & 2 \\ 3 & 6 & 9 \end{vmatrix}$.

We define the determinant of a 2 × 2 matrix first. (Recall that 2 × 2 is read "two by two." It means that the matrix has 2 rows and 2 columns.)

Determinant of a 2 × 2 Matrix

$$\begin{vmatrix} a & b \\ c & d \end{vmatrix} = ad - bc$$

EXAMPLE 1   Evaluate each determinant

a. $\begin{vmatrix} -1 & 2 \\ 3 & -4 \end{vmatrix}$ **b.** $\begin{vmatrix} 2 & 0 \\ 7 & -5 \end{vmatrix}$

Solution   First we identify the values of $a, b, c,$ and d. Then we perform the evaluation.

a. Here $a = -1, b = 2, c = 3,$ and $d = -4$.

$$\begin{vmatrix} -1 & 2 \\ 3 & -4 \end{vmatrix} = ad - bc = (-1)(-4) - (2)(3) = -2$$

b. In this example, $a = 2, b = 0, c = 7,$ and $d = -5$.

$$\begin{vmatrix} 2 & 0 \\ 7 & -5 \end{vmatrix} = ad - bc = 2(-5) - (0)(7) = -10$$

OBJECTIVE

2   Using Cramer's Rule to Solve a System of Two Linear Equations

To develop Cramer's rule, we solve the system $\begin{cases} ax + by = h \\ cx + dy = k \end{cases}$ using elimination. First, we eliminate y by multiplying both sides of the first equation by d and both sides of the second equation by $-b$ so that the coefficients of y are opposites. The result is that

$$\begin{cases} d(ax + by) = d \cdot h \\ -b(cx + dy) = -b \cdot k \end{cases} \quad \text{simplifies to} \quad \begin{cases} adx + bdy = hd \\ -bcx - bdy = -kb \end{cases}$$

We now add the two equations and solve for x.

$$
\begin{aligned}
adx + bdy &= hd \\
\underline{-bcx - bdy} &= \underline{-kb} \\
adx - bcx &= hd - kb \qquad \text{Add the equations.} \\
(ad - bc)x &= hd - kb \\
x &= \frac{hd - kb}{ad - bc} \qquad \text{Solve for } x.
\end{aligned}
$$

When we replace x with $\dfrac{hd - kb}{ad - bc}$ in the equation $ax + by = h$ and solve for y, we find that $y = \dfrac{ak - ch}{ad - bc}$.

Notice that the numerator of the value of x is the determinant of

$$\begin{vmatrix} h & b \\ k & d \end{vmatrix} = hd - kb$$

Also, the numerator of the value of y is the determinant of

$$\begin{vmatrix} a & h \\ c & k \end{vmatrix} = ak - hc$$

Finally, the denominators of the values of x and y are the same and are the determinant of

$$\begin{vmatrix} a & b \\ c & d \end{vmatrix} = ad - bc$$

This means that the values of x and y can be written in determinant notation:

$$x = \frac{\begin{vmatrix} h & b \\ k & d \end{vmatrix}}{\begin{vmatrix} a & b \\ c & d \end{vmatrix}} \quad \text{and} \quad y = \frac{\begin{vmatrix} a & h \\ c & k \end{vmatrix}}{\begin{vmatrix} a & b \\ c & d \end{vmatrix}}$$

For convenience, we label the determinants D, D_x, and D_y.

x-coefficients

y-coefficients

$$\begin{vmatrix} a & b \\ c & d \end{vmatrix} = D \qquad \begin{vmatrix} h & b \\ k & d \end{vmatrix} = D_x \qquad \begin{vmatrix} a & h \\ c & k \end{vmatrix} = D_y$$

↑ x-column replaced by constants

↑ y-column replaced by constants

These determinant formulas for the coordinates of the solution of a system are known as **Cramer's rule.**

Cramer's Rule for Two Linear Equations in Two Variables

The solution of the system $\begin{cases} ax + by = h \\ cx + dy = k \end{cases}$ is given by

$$x = \frac{\begin{vmatrix} h & b \\ k & d \end{vmatrix}}{\begin{vmatrix} a & b \\ c & d \end{vmatrix}} = \frac{D_x}{D} \qquad y = \frac{\begin{vmatrix} a & h \\ c & k \end{vmatrix}}{\begin{vmatrix} a & b \\ c & d \end{vmatrix}} = \frac{D_y}{D}$$

as long as $D = ad - bc$ is not 0.

When $D = 0$, the system is either inconsistent or the equations are dependent. When this happens, we need to use another method to see which is the case.

EXAMPLE 2　Use Cramer's rule to solve the system

$$\begin{cases} 3x + 4y = -7 \\ x - 2y = -9 \end{cases}$$

Solution　First we find D, D_x, and D_y.

$$\begin{cases} 3x + 4y = -7 \\ x - 2y = -9 \end{cases}$$

$$D = \begin{vmatrix} a & b \\ c & d \end{vmatrix} = \begin{vmatrix} 3 & 4 \\ 1 & -2 \end{vmatrix} = 3(-2) - 4(1) = -10$$

$$D_x = \begin{vmatrix} h & b \\ k & d \end{vmatrix} = \begin{vmatrix} -7 & 4 \\ -9 & -2 \end{vmatrix} = (-7)(-2) - 4(-9) = 50$$

$$D_y = \begin{vmatrix} a & h \\ c & k \end{vmatrix} = \begin{vmatrix} 3 & -7 \\ 1 & -9 \end{vmatrix} = 3(-9) - (-7)(1) = -20$$

Then $x = \dfrac{D_x}{D} = \dfrac{50}{-10} = -5$ and $y = \dfrac{D_y}{D} = \dfrac{-20}{-10} = 2$.

The ordered pair solution is $(-5, 2)$.
As always, check the solution in both original equations.

EXAMPLE 3　Use Cramer's rule to solve the system

$$\begin{cases} 5x + y = 5 \\ -7x - 2y = -7 \end{cases}$$

Solution　First we find D, D_x, and D_y.

$$D = \begin{vmatrix} 5 & 1 \\ -7 & -2 \end{vmatrix} = 5(-2) - (-7)(1) = -3$$

$$D_x = \begin{vmatrix} 5 & 1 \\ -7 & -2 \end{vmatrix} = 5(-2) - (-7)(1) = -3$$

$$D_y = \begin{vmatrix} 5 & 5 \\ -7 & -7 \end{vmatrix} = 5(-7) - 5(-7) = 0$$

Then

$$x = \frac{D_x}{D} = \frac{-3}{-3} = 1 \qquad y = \frac{D_y}{D} = \frac{0}{-3} = 0$$

The ordered pair solution is $(1, 0)$.

OBJECTIVE
3   Evaluating 3 × 3 Determinants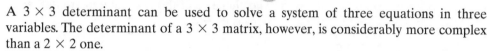

A 3×3 determinant can be used to solve a system of three equations in three variables. The determinant of a 3×3 matrix, however, is considerably more complex than a 2×2 one.

Determinant of a 3 × 3 Matrix

$$\begin{vmatrix} a_1 & b_1 & c_1 \\ a_2 & b_2 & c_2 \\ a_3 & b_3 & c_3 \end{vmatrix} = a_1 \cdot \begin{vmatrix} b_2 & c_2 \\ b_3 & c_3 \end{vmatrix} - a_2 \cdot \begin{vmatrix} b_1 & c_1 \\ b_3 & c_3 \end{vmatrix} + a_3 \cdot \begin{vmatrix} b_1 & c_1 \\ b_2 & c_2 \end{vmatrix}$$

Notice that the determinant of a 3×3 matrix is related to the determinants of three 2×2 matrices. Each determinant of these 2×2 matrices is called a **minor,** and every element of a 3×3 matrix has a minor associated with it. For example, the minor of c_2 is the determinant of the 2×2 matrix found by deleting the row and column containing c_2.

$$\begin{matrix} a_1 & b_1 & c_1 \\ a_2 & b_2 & c_2 \\ a_3 & b_3 & c_3 \end{matrix} \qquad \text{The minor of } c_2 \text{ is} \quad \begin{vmatrix} a_1 & b_1 \\ a_3 & b_3 \end{vmatrix}$$

Also, the minor of element a_1 is the determinant of the 2×2 matrix that has no row or column containing a_1.

$$\begin{matrix} a_1 & b_1 & c_1 \\ a_2 & b_2 & c_2 \\ a_3 & b_3 & c_3 \end{matrix} \qquad \text{The minor of } a_1 \text{ is} \quad \begin{vmatrix} b_2 & c_2 \\ b_3 & c_3 \end{vmatrix}$$

So the determinant of a 3×3 matrix can be written as

$$a_1 \cdot (\text{minor of } a_1) - a_2 \cdot (\text{minor of } a_2) + a_3 \cdot (\text{minor of } a_3)$$

Finding the determinant by using minors of elements in the first column is called **expanding** by the minors of the first column. *The value of a determinant can be found by expanding by the minors of any row or column.* The following **array of signs** is helpful in determining whether to add or subtract the product of an element and its minor.

$$\begin{matrix} + & - & + \\ - & + & - \\ + & - & + \end{matrix}$$

If an element is in a position marked $+$, we add. If marked $-$, we subtract.

EXAMPLE 4 Evaluate by expanding by the minors of the given row or column.

$$\begin{vmatrix} 0 & 5 & 1 \\ 1 & 3 & -1 \\ -2 & 2 & 4 \end{vmatrix}$$

a. First column   **b.** Second row

Solution

a. The elements of the first column are 0, 1, and −2. The first column of the array of signs is +, −, +.

$$\begin{vmatrix} 0 & 5 & 1 \\ 1 & 3 & -1 \\ -2 & 2 & 4 \end{vmatrix} = 0 \cdot \begin{vmatrix} 3 & -1 \\ 2 & 4 \end{vmatrix} - 1 \cdot \begin{vmatrix} 5 & 1 \\ 2 & 4 \end{vmatrix} + (-2) \cdot \begin{vmatrix} 5 & 1 \\ 3 & -1 \end{vmatrix}$$

$$= 0(12 - (-2)) - 1(20 - 2) + (-2)(-5 - 3)$$

$$= 0 - 18 + 16 = -2$$

b. The elements of the second row are 1, 3, and −1. This time, the signs begin with − and again alternate.

$$\begin{vmatrix} 0 & 5 & 1 \\ 1 & 3 & -1 \\ -2 & 2 & 4 \end{vmatrix} = -1 \cdot \begin{vmatrix} 5 & 1 \\ 2 & 4 \end{vmatrix} + 3 \cdot \begin{vmatrix} 0 & 1 \\ -2 & 4 \end{vmatrix} - (-1) \cdot \begin{vmatrix} 0 & 5 \\ -2 & 2 \end{vmatrix}$$

$$= -1(20 - 2) + 3(0 - (-2)) - (-1)(0 - (-10))$$

$$= -18 + 6 + 10 = -2$$

Notice that the determinant of the 3 × 3 matrix is the same regardless of the row or column you select to expand by.   □

✓CONCEPT CHECK

Why would expanding by minors of the second row be a good choice for the determinant $\begin{vmatrix} 3 & 4 & -2 \\ 5 & 0 & 0 \\ 6 & -3 & 7 \end{vmatrix}$?

OBJECTIVE

4   **Using Cramer's Rule to Solve a System of Three Linear Equations** ▶

A system of three equations in three variables may be solved with Cramer's rule also. Using the elimination process to solve a system with unknown constants as coefficients leads to the following.

Cramer's Rule for Three Equations in Three Variables

The solution of the system $\begin{cases} a_1x + b_1y + c_1z = k_1 \\ a_2x + b_2y + c_2z = k_2 \\ a_3x + b_3y + c_3z = k_3 \end{cases}$ is given by

$$x = \frac{D_x}{D} \qquad y = \frac{D_y}{D} \qquad \text{and} \qquad z = \frac{D_z}{D}$$

where

$$D = \begin{vmatrix} a_1 & b_1 & c_1 \\ a_2 & b_2 & c_2 \\ a_3 & b_3 & c_3 \end{vmatrix} \qquad D_x = \begin{vmatrix} k_1 & b_1 & c_1 \\ k_2 & b_2 & c_2 \\ k_3 & b_3 & c_3 \end{vmatrix}$$

$$D_y = \begin{vmatrix} a_1 & k_1 & c_1 \\ a_2 & k_2 & c_2 \\ a_3 & k_3 & c_3 \end{vmatrix} \qquad D_z = \begin{vmatrix} a_1 & b_1 & k_1 \\ a_2 & b_2 & k_2 \\ a_3 & b_3 & k_3 \end{vmatrix}$$

as long as D is not 0.

Answer to Concept Check:
Two elements of the second row are 0, which makes calculations easier.

EXAMPLE 5   Use Cramer's rule to solve the system

$$\begin{cases} x - 2y + z = 4 \\ 3x + y - 2z = 3 \\ 5x + 5y + 3z = -8 \end{cases}$$

Solution   First we find $D, D_x, D_y,$ and D_z. Beginning with D, we expand by the minors of the first column.

$$D = \begin{vmatrix} 1 & -2 & 1 \\ 3 & 1 & -2 \\ 5 & 5 & 3 \end{vmatrix} = 1 \cdot \begin{vmatrix} 1 & -2 \\ 5 & 3 \end{vmatrix} - 3 \cdot \begin{vmatrix} -2 & 1 \\ 5 & 3 \end{vmatrix} + 5 \cdot \begin{vmatrix} -2 & 1 \\ 1 & -2 \end{vmatrix}$$

$$= 1(3 - (-10)) - 3(-6 - 5) + 5(4 - 1)$$

$$= 13 + 33 + 15 = 61$$

$$D_x = \begin{vmatrix} 4 & -2 & 1 \\ 3 & 1 & -2 \\ -8 & 5 & 3 \end{vmatrix} = 4 \cdot \begin{vmatrix} 1 & -2 \\ 5 & 3 \end{vmatrix} - 3 \cdot \begin{vmatrix} -2 & 1 \\ 5 & 3 \end{vmatrix} + (-8) \cdot \begin{vmatrix} -2 & 1 \\ 1 & -2 \end{vmatrix}$$

$$= 4(3 - (-10)) - 3(-6 - 5) + (-8)(4 - 1)$$

$$= 52 + 33 - 24 = 61$$

$$D_y = \begin{vmatrix} 1 & 4 & 1 \\ 3 & 3 & -2 \\ 5 & -8 & 3 \end{vmatrix} = 1 \cdot \begin{vmatrix} 3 & -2 \\ -8 & 3 \end{vmatrix} - 3 \cdot \begin{vmatrix} 4 & 1 \\ -8 & 3 \end{vmatrix} + 5 \cdot \begin{vmatrix} 4 & 1 \\ 3 & -2 \end{vmatrix}$$

$$= 1(9 - 16) - 3(12 - (-8)) + 5(-8 - 3)$$

$$= -7 - 60 - 55 = -122$$

$$D_z = \begin{vmatrix} 1 & -2 & 4 \\ 3 & 1 & 3 \\ 5 & 5 & -8 \end{vmatrix} = 1 \cdot \begin{vmatrix} 1 & 3 \\ 5 & -8 \end{vmatrix} - 3 \cdot \begin{vmatrix} -2 & 4 \\ 5 & -8 \end{vmatrix} + 5 \cdot \begin{vmatrix} -2 & 4 \\ 1 & 3 \end{vmatrix}$$

$$= 1(-8 - 15) - 3(16 - 20) + 5(-6 - 4)$$

$$= -23 + 12 - 50 = -61$$

From these determinants, we calculate the solution:

$$x = \frac{D_x}{D} = \frac{61}{61} = 1 \quad y = \frac{D_y}{D} = \frac{-122}{61} = -2 \quad z = \frac{D_z}{D} = \frac{-61}{61} = -1$$

The ordered triple solution is $(1, -2, -1)$. Check this solution by verifying that it satisfies each equation of the system.   □

E   Exercise Set   MyMathLab®

Evaluate. See Example 1.

1. $\begin{vmatrix} 3 & 5 \\ -1 & 7 \end{vmatrix}$

2. $\begin{vmatrix} -5 & 1 \\ 0 & -4 \end{vmatrix}$

3. $\begin{vmatrix} 9 & -2 \\ 4 & -3 \end{vmatrix}$

4. $\begin{vmatrix} 4 & 0 \\ 9 & 8 \end{vmatrix}$

5. $\begin{vmatrix} -2 & 9 \\ 4 & -18 \end{vmatrix}$

6. $\begin{vmatrix} -40 & 8 \\ 70 & -14 \end{vmatrix}$

Use Cramer's rule, if possible, to solve each system of linear equations. See Examples 2 and 3.

7. $\begin{cases} 2y - 4 = 0 \\ x + 2y = 5 \end{cases}$

8. $\begin{cases} 4x - y = 5 \\ 3x - 3 = 0 \end{cases}$

9. $\begin{cases} 3x + y = 1 \\ 2y = 2 - 6x \end{cases}$

10. $\begin{cases} y = 2x - 5 \\ 8x - 4y = 20 \end{cases}$

11. $\begin{cases} 5x - 2y = 27 \\ -3x + 5y = 18 \end{cases}$

12. $\begin{cases} 4x - y = 9 \\ 2x + 3y = -27 \end{cases}$

Evaluate. See Example 4.

13. $\begin{vmatrix} 2 & 1 & 0 \\ 0 & 5 & -3 \\ 4 & 0 & 2 \end{vmatrix}$
14. $\begin{vmatrix} -6 & 4 & 2 \\ 1 & 0 & 5 \\ 0 & 3 & 1 \end{vmatrix}$

15. $\begin{vmatrix} 4 & -6 & 0 \\ -2 & 3 & 0 \\ 4 & -6 & 1 \end{vmatrix}$
16. $\begin{vmatrix} 5 & 2 & 1 \\ 3 & -6 & 0 \\ -2 & 8 & 0 \end{vmatrix}$

17. $\begin{vmatrix} 3 & 6 & -3 \\ -1 & -2 & 3 \\ 4 & -1 & 6 \end{vmatrix}$
18. $\begin{vmatrix} 2 & -2 & 1 \\ 4 & 1 & 3 \\ 3 & 1 & 2 \end{vmatrix}$

Use Cramer's rule, if possible, to solve each system of linear equations. See Example 5.

19. $\begin{cases} 3x \quad + z = -1 \\ -x - 3y + z = 7 \\ \quad 3y + z = 5 \end{cases}$
20. $\begin{cases} \quad 4y - 3z = -2 \\ 8x - 4y \quad = 4 \\ -8x + 4y + z = -2 \end{cases}$

21. $\begin{cases} x + y + z = 8 \\ 2x - y - z = 10 \\ x - 2y + 3z = 22 \end{cases}$
22. $\begin{cases} 5x + y + 3z = 1 \\ x - y - 3z = -7 \\ -x + y \quad = 1 \end{cases}$

MIXED PRACTICE

Evaluate.

23. $\begin{vmatrix} 10 & -1 \\ -4 & 2 \end{vmatrix}$
24. $\begin{vmatrix} -6 & 2 \\ 5 & -1 \end{vmatrix}$

25. $\begin{vmatrix} 1 & 0 & 4 \\ 1 & -1 & 2 \\ 3 & 2 & 1 \end{vmatrix}$
26. $\begin{vmatrix} 0 & 1 & 2 \\ 3 & -1 & 2 \\ 3 & 2 & -2 \end{vmatrix}$

27. $\begin{vmatrix} \frac{3}{4} & \frac{5}{2} \\ -\frac{1}{6} & \frac{7}{3} \end{vmatrix}$
28. $\begin{vmatrix} \frac{5}{7} & \frac{1}{3} \\ \frac{6}{7} & \frac{2}{3} \end{vmatrix}$

29. $\begin{vmatrix} 4 & -2 & 2 \\ 6 & -1 & 3 \\ 2 & 1 & 1 \end{vmatrix}$
30. $\begin{vmatrix} 1 & 5 & 0 \\ 7 & 9 & -4 \\ 3 & 2 & -2 \end{vmatrix}$

31. $\begin{vmatrix} -2 & 5 & 4 \\ 5 & -1 & 3 \\ 4 & 1 & 2 \end{vmatrix}$
32. $\begin{vmatrix} 5 & -2 & 4 \\ -1 & 5 & 3 \\ 1 & 4 & 2 \end{vmatrix}$

Use Cramer's rule, if possible, to solve each system of linear equations.

33. $\begin{cases} 2x - 5y = 4 \\ x + 2y = -7 \end{cases}$
34. $\begin{cases} 3x - y = 2 \\ -5x + 2y = 0 \end{cases}$

35. $\begin{cases} 4x + 2y = 5 \\ 2x + y = -1 \end{cases}$
36. $\begin{cases} 3x + 6y = 15 \\ 2x + 4y = 3 \end{cases}$

37. $\begin{cases} 2x + 2y + z = 1 \\ -x + y + 2z = 3 \\ x + 2y + 4z = 0 \end{cases}$
38. $\begin{cases} 2x - 3y + z = 5 \\ x + y + z = 0 \\ 4x + 2y + 4z = 4 \end{cases}$

39. $\begin{cases} \frac{2}{3}x - \frac{3}{4}y = -1 \\ -\frac{1}{6}x + \frac{3}{4}y = \frac{5}{2} \end{cases}$
40. $\begin{cases} \frac{1}{2}x - \frac{1}{3}y = -3 \\ \frac{1}{8}x + \frac{1}{6}y = 0 \end{cases}$

41. $\begin{cases} 0.7x - 0.2y = -1.6 \\ 0.2x - y = -1.4 \end{cases}$
42. $\begin{cases} -0.7x + 0.6y = 1.3 \\ 0.5x - 0.3y = -0.8 \end{cases}$

43. $\begin{cases} -2x + 4y - 2z = 6 \\ x - 2y + z = -3 \\ 3x - 6y + 3z = -9 \end{cases}$
44. $\begin{cases} -x - y + 3z = 2 \\ 4x + 4y - 12z = -8 \\ -3x - 3y + 9z = 6 \end{cases}$

45. $\begin{cases} x - 2y + z = -5 \\ 3y + 2z = 4 \\ 3x - y = -2 \end{cases}$
46. $\begin{cases} 4x + 5y = 10 \\ 3y + 2z = -6 \\ x + y + z = 3 \end{cases}$

CONCEPT EXTENSIONS

Find the value of x such that each is a true statement.

47. $\begin{vmatrix} 1 & x \\ 2 & 7 \end{vmatrix} = -3$
48. $\begin{vmatrix} 6 & 1 \\ -2 & x \end{vmatrix} = 26$

49. If all the elements in a single row of a square matrix are zero, to what does the determinant evaluate? Explain your answer.

50. If all the elements in a single column of a square matrix are 0, to what does the determinant evaluate? Explain your answer.

51. Suppose you are interested in finding the determinant of a 4×4 matrix. Study the pattern shown in the array of signs for a 3×3 matrix. Use the pattern to expand the array of signs for use with a 4×4 matrix.

52. Why would expanding by minors of the second row be a good choice for the determinant $\begin{vmatrix} 3 & 4 & -2 \\ 5 & 0 & 0 \\ 6 & -3 & 7 \end{vmatrix}$?

Find the value of each determinant. To evaluate a 4×4 determinant, select any row or column and expand by the minors. The array of signs for a 4×4 determinant is the same as for a 3×3 determinant except expanded.

53. $\begin{vmatrix} 5 & 0 & 0 & 0 \\ 0 & 4 & 2 & -1 \\ 1 & 3 & -2 & 0 \\ 0 & -3 & 1 & 2 \end{vmatrix}$
54. $\begin{vmatrix} 1 & 7 & 0 & -1 \\ 1 & 3 & -2 & 0 \\ 1 & 0 & -1 & 2 \\ 0 & -6 & 2 & 4 \end{vmatrix}$

55. $\begin{vmatrix} 4 & 0 & 2 & 5 \\ 0 & 3 & -1 & 1 \\ 0 & 0 & 2 & 0 \\ 0 & 0 & 0 & 1 \end{vmatrix}$
56. $\begin{vmatrix} 2 & 0 & -1 & 4 \\ 6 & 0 & 4 & 1 \\ 2 & 4 & 3 & -1 \\ 4 & 0 & 5 & -4 \end{vmatrix}$

Appendix F
Mean, Median, and Mode

It is sometimes desirable to be able to describe a set of data, or a set of numbers, by a single "middle" number. Three such **measures of central tendency** are the mean, the median, and the mode.

The most common measure of central tendency is the mean (sometimes called the arithmetic mean or the average). The **mean** of a set of data items, denoted by $\bar{x}$, is the sum of the items divided by the number of items.

EXAMPLE 1 Seven students in a psychology class conducted an experiment on mazes. Each student was given a pencil and asked to successfully complete the same maze. The timed results are below.

Student	Ann	Thanh	Carlos	Jesse	Melinda	Ramzi	Dayni
Time (Seconds)	13.2	11.8	10.7	16.2	15.9	13.8	18.5

a. Who completed the maze in the shortest time? Who completed the maze in the longest time?

b. Find the mean.

c. How many students took longer than the mean time? How many students took shorter than the mean time?

Solution

a. Carlos completed the maze in 10.7 seconds, the shortest time. Dayni completed the maze in 18.5 seconds, the longest time.

b. To find the mean, $\bar{x}$, find the sum of the data items and divide by 7, the number of items.

$$\bar{x} = \frac{13.2 + 11.8 + 10.7 + 16.2 + 15.9 + 13.8 + 18.5}{7} = \frac{100.1}{7} = 14.3$$

c. Three students, Jesse, Melinda, and Dayni, had times longer than the mean time. Four students, Ann, Thanh, Carlos, and Ramzi, had times shorter than the mean time. $\square$

Two other measures of central tendency are the median and the mode.

The **median** of an ordered set of numbers is the middle number. If the number of items is even, the median is the mean of the two middle numbers. The **mode** of a set of numbers is the number that occurs most often. It is possible for a data set to have no mode or more than one mode.

EXAMPLE 2 Find the median and the mode of the following list of numbers. These numbers were high temperatures for fourteen consecutive days in a city in Montana.

76, 80, 85, 86, 89, 87, 82, 77, 76, 79, 82, 89, 89, 92

(Continued on next page)

Solution

First, write the numbers in order.

$$76, 76, 77, 79, 80, 82, 82, 85, 86, 87, 89, 89, 89, 92$$

two
middle numbers   mode

Since there is an even number of items, the median is the mean of the two middle numbers.

$$\text{median} = \frac{82 + 85}{2} = 83.5$$

The mode is 89, since 89 occurs most often.

F Exercise Set

MyMathLab®

For each of the following data sets, find the mean, the median, and the mode. If necessary, round the mean to one decimal place.

1. 21, 28, 16, 42, 38

2. 42, 35, 36, 40, 50

3. 7.6, 8.2, 8.2, 9.6, 5.7, 9.1

4. 4.9, 7.1, 6.8, 6.8, 5.3, 4.9

5. 0.2, 0.3, 0.5, 0.6, 0.6, 0.9, 0.2, 0.7, 1.1

6. 0.6, 0.6, 0.8, 0.4, 0.5, 0.3, 0.7, 0.8, 0.1

7. 231, 543, 601, 293, 588, 109, 334, 268

8. 451, 356, 478, 776, 892, 500, 467, 780

The eight tallest buildings in the United States are listed below. Use this table for Exercises 9 through 12.

Building	Height (feet)
Willis Tower, Chicago, IL	1454
Empire State, New York, NY	1250
Amoco, Chicago, IL	1136
John Hancock Center, Chicago, IL	1127
First Interstate World Center, Los Angeles, CA	1107
Chrysler, New York, NY	1046
NationsBank Tower, Atlanta, GA	1023
Texas Commerce Tower, Houston, TX	1002

9. Find the mean height for the five tallest buildings.
10. Find the median height for the five tallest buildings.
11. Find the median height for the eight tallest buildings.
12. Find the mean height for the eight tallest buildings.

During an experiment, the following times (in seconds) were recorded: 7.8, 6.9, 7.5, 4.7, 6.9, 7.0.

13. Find the mean. Round to the nearest tenth.
14. Find the median.
15. Find the mode.

In a mathematics class, the following test scores were recorded for a student: 86, 95, 91, 74, 77, 85.

16. Find the mean. Round to the nearest hundredth.
17. Find the median.
18. Find the mode.

The following pulse rates were recorded for a group of fifteen students: 78, 80, 66, 68, 71, 64, 82, 71, 70, 65, 70, 75, 77, 86, 72.

19. Find the mean.
20. Find the median.
21. Find the mode.
22. How many rates were higher than the mean?
23. How many rates were lower than the mean?
24. Have each student in your algebra class take his/her pulse rate. Record the data and find the mean, the median, and the mode.

Find the missing numbers in each list of numbers. (These numbers are not necessarily in numerical order.)

25. __, __, 16, 18, __
    The mode is 21.   The mean is 20.
26. __, __, __, __, 40
    The mode is 35.   The median is 37.   The mean is 38.

Appendix G

Review of Angles, Lines, and Special Triangles

The word **geometry** is formed from the Greek words **geo,** meaning earth, and **metron,** meaning measure. Geometry literally means to measure the earth.

This section contains a review of some basic geometric ideas. It will be assumed that fundamental ideas of geometry such as point, line, ray, and angle are known. In this appendix, the notation $\angle 1$ is read "angle 1" and the notation $m\angle 1$ is read "the measure of angle 1."

We first review types of angles.

Angles

A **right angle** is an angle whose measure is 90°. A right angle can be indicated by a square drawn at the vertex of the angle, as shown below.

An angle whose measure is more than 0° but less than 90° is called an **acute angle.**

An angle whose measure is greater than 90° but less than 180° is called an **obtuse angle.**

An angle whose measure is 180° is called a **straight angle.**

Two angles are said to be **complementary** if the sum of their measures is 90°. Each angle is called the **complement** of the other.

Two angles are said to be **supplementary** if the sum of their measures is 180°. Each angle is called the **supplement** of the other.

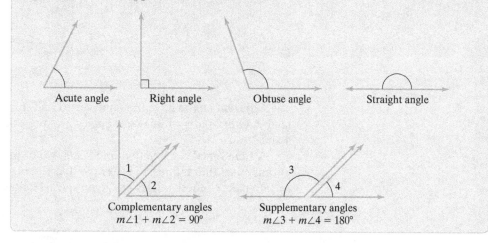

Acute angle   Right angle   Obtuse angle   Straight angle

Complementary angles
$m\angle 1 + m\angle 2 = 90°$

Supplementary angles
$m\angle 3 + m\angle 4 = 180°$

EXAMPLE 1   If an angle measures 28°, find its complement.

Solution   Two angles are complementary if the sum of their measures is 90°. The complement of a 28° angle is an angle whose measure is $90° - 28° = 62°$. To check, notice that $28° + 62° = 90°$.   □

Plane is an undefined term that we will describe. A plane can be thought of as a flat surface with infinite length and width, but no thickness. A plane is two dimensional.

The arrows in the following diagram indicate that a plane extends indefinitely and has no boundaries.

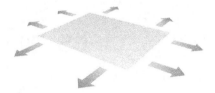

Figures that lie on a plane are called **plane figures.** Lines that lie in the same plane are called **coplanar.**

Lines

Two lines are **parallel** if they lie in the same plane but never meet.

Intersecting lines meet or cross in one point.

Two lines that form right angles when they intersect are said to be **perpendicular.**

Parallel lines   Intersecting lines   Intersecting lines that are perpendicular

---

Two intersecting lines form **vertical angles.** Angles 1 and 3 are vertical angles. Also, angles 2 and 4 are vertical angles. It can be shown that **vertical angles have equal measures.**

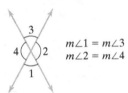

$$m\angle 1 = m\angle 3$$
$$m\angle 2 = m\angle 4$$

Adjacent angles have the same vertex and share a side. Angles 1 and 2 are adjacent angles. Other pairs of adjacent angles are angles 2 and 3, angles 3 and 4, and angles 4 and 1.

A **transversal** is a line that intersects two or more lines in the same plane. Line l is a transversal that intersects lines m and n. The eight angles formed are numbered and certain pairs of these angles are given special names.

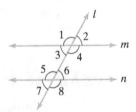

Corresponding angles: $\angle 1$ and $\angle 5$, $\angle 3$ and $\angle 7$, $\angle 2$ and $\angle 6$, and $\angle 4$ and $\angle 8$.

Exterior angles: $\angle 1$, $\angle 2$, $\angle 7$, and $\angle 8$.

Interior angles: $\angle 3$, $\angle 4$, $\angle 5$, and $\angle 6$.

Alternate interior angles: $\angle 3$ and $\angle 6$, $\angle 4$ and $\angle 5$.

These angles and parallel lines are related in the following manner.

Parallel Lines Cut by a Transversal

1. If two parallel lines are cut by a transversal, then
   a. corresponding angles are equal and
   b. alternate interior angles are equal.
2. If corresponding angles formed by two lines and a transversal are equal, then the lines are parallel.
3. If alternate interior angles formed by two lines and a transversal are equal, then the lines are parallel.

EXAMPLE 2   Given that lines m and n are parallel and that the measure of angle 1 is 100°, find the measures of angles 2, 3, and 4.

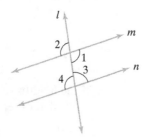

Solution $m\angle 2 = 100°$, since angles 1 and 2 are vertical angles.

$m\angle 4 = 100°$, since angles 1 and 4 are alternate interior angles.

$m\angle 3 = 180° - 100° = 80°$, since angles 4 and 3 are supplementary angles.   □

A **polygon** is the union of three or more coplanar line segments that intersect each other only at each end point, with each end point shared by exactly two segments.

A **triangle** is a polygon with three sides. The sum of the measures of the three angles of a triangle is 180°. In the following figure, $m\angle 1 + m\angle 2 + m\angle 3 = 180°$.

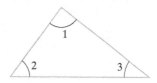

EXAMPLE 3   Find the measure of the third angle of the triangle shown.

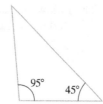

Solution   The sum of the measures of the angles of a triangle is 180°. Since one angle measures 45° and the other angle measures 95°, the third angle measures $180° - 45° - 95° = 40°$.   □

Two triangles are **congruent** if they have the same size and the same shape. In congruent triangles, the measures of corresponding angles are equal and the lengths of corresponding sides are equal. The following triangles are congruent.

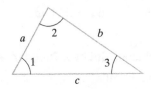
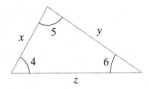

Corresponding angles are equal: $m\angle 1 = m\angle 4, m\angle 2 = m\angle 5$, and $m\angle 3 = m\angle 6$. Also, lengths of corresponding sides are equal: $a = x$, $b = y$, and $c = z$.

Any one of the following may be used to determine whether two triangles are congruent.

Congruent Triangles

1. If the measures of two angles of a triangle equal the measures of two angles of another triangle and the lengths of the sides between each pair of angles are equal, the triangles are congruent.

$m\angle 1 = m\angle 3$
$m\angle 2 = m\angle 4$
and
$a = x$

2. If the lengths of the three sides of a triangle equal the lengths of corresponding sides of another triangle, the triangles are congruent.

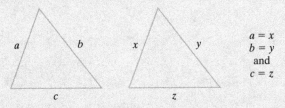

$a = x$
$b = y$
and
$c = z$

3. If the lengths of two sides of a triangle equal the lengths of corresponding sides of another triangle, and the measures of the angles between each pair of sides are equal, the triangles are congruent.

$a = x$
$b = y$
and
$m\angle 1 = m\angle 2$

Two triangles are **similar** if they have the same shape. In similar triangles, the measures of corresponding angles are equal and corresponding sides are in proportion. The following triangles are similar. (All similar triangles drawn in this appendix will be oriented the same.)

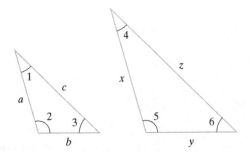

Corresponding angles are equal: $m\angle 1 = m\angle 4$, $m\angle 2 = m\angle 5$, and $m\angle 3 = m\angle 6$.

Also, corresponding sides are proportional: $\dfrac{a}{x} = \dfrac{b}{y} = \dfrac{c}{z}$.

Any one of the following may be used to determine whether two triangles are similar.

Similar Triangles

1. If the measures of two angles of a triangle equal the measures of two angles of another triangle, the triangles are similar.

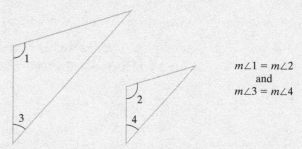

$$m\angle 1 = m\angle 2$$
and
$$m\angle 3 = m\angle 4$$

2. If three sides of one triangle are proportional to three sides of another triangle, the triangles are similar.

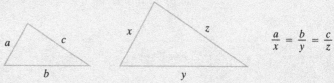

$$\frac{a}{x} = \frac{b}{y} = \frac{c}{z}$$

3. If two sides of a triangle are proportional to two sides of another triangle and the measures of the included angles are equal, the triangles are similar.

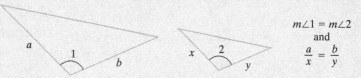

$$m\angle 1 = m\angle 2$$
and
$$\frac{a}{x} = \frac{b}{y}$$

EXAMPLE 4   Given that the following triangles are similar, find the missing length x.

Solution   Since the triangles are similar, corresponding sides are in proportion. Thus, $\frac{2}{3} = \frac{10}{x}$. To solve this equation for x, we multiply both sides by the LCD, $3x$.

$$3x\left(\frac{2}{3}\right) = 3x\left(\frac{10}{x}\right)$$
$$2x = 30$$
$$x = 15$$

The missing length is 15 units. □

A **right triangle** contains a right angle. The side opposite the right angle is called the **hypotenuse,** and the other two sides are called the **legs.** The **Pythagorean theorem** gives a formula that relates the lengths of the three sides of a right triangle.

The Pythagorean Theorem

If a and b are the lengths of the legs of a right triangle, and c is the length of the hypotenuse, then $a^2 + b^2 = c^2$.

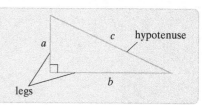

EXAMPLE 5   Find the length of the hypotenuse of a right triangle whose legs have lengths of 3 centimeters and 4 centimeters.

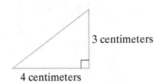

3 centimeters

4 centimeters

Solution   Because we have a right triangle, we use the Pythagorean theorem. The legs are 3 centimeters and 4 centimeters, so let $a = 3$ and $b = 4$ in the formula.

$$a^2 + b^2 = c^2$$
$$3^2 + 4^2 = c^2$$
$$9 + 16 = c^2$$
$$25 = c^2$$

Since c represents a length, we assume that c is positive. Thus, if c^2 is 25, c must be 5. The hypotenuse has a length of 5 centimeters.   □

G Exercise Set   MyMathLab®

Find the complement of each angle. See Example 1.

1. $19°$
2. $65°$
3. $70.8°$
4. $45\frac{2}{3}°$
5. $11\frac{1}{4}°$
6. $19.6°$

Find the supplement of each angle.

7. $150°$
8. $90°$
9. $30.2°$
10. $81.9°$
11. $79\frac{1}{2}°$
12. $165\frac{8}{9}°$

13. If lines m and n are parallel, find the measures of angles 1 through 7. See Example 2.

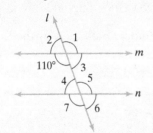

14. If lines m and n are parallel, find the measures of angles 1 through 5. See Example 2.

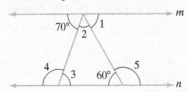

In each of the following, the measures of two angles of a triangle are given. Find the measure of the third angle. See Example 3.

15. $11°, 79°$
16. $8°, 102°$
17. $25°, 65°$
18. $44°, 19°$
19. $30°, 60°$
20. $67°, 23°$

In each of the following, the measure of one angle of a right triangle is given. Find the measures of the other two angles.

21. $45°$
22. $60°$
23. $17°$
24. $30°$
25. $39\frac{3}{4}°$
26. $72.6°$

Given that each of the following pairs of triangles is similar, find the missing lengths. See Example 4.

27.

28.

29.

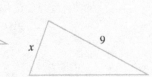

30.

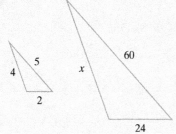

Use the Pythagorean theorem to find the missing lengths in the right triangles. See Example 5.

31.

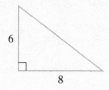

32.

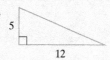

33.

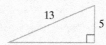

34.

Contents of Student Resources

Study Skills Builders

Attitude and Study Tips:
1. Have You Decided to Complete This Course Successfully?
2. Tips for Studying for an Exam
3. What to Do the Day of an Exam
4. Are You Satisfied with Your Performance on a Particular Quiz or Exam?
5. How Are You Doing?
6. Are You Preparing for Your Final Exam?

Organizing Your Work:
7. Learning New Terms
8. Are You Organized?
9. Organizing a Notebook
10. How Are Your Homework Assignments Going?

MyMathLab and MathXL:
11. Tips for Turning in Your Homework on Time
12. Tips for Doing Your Homework Online
13. Organizing Your Work
14. Getting Help with Your Homework Assignments
15. Tips for Preparing for an Exam
16. How Well Do You Know the Resources Available to You in MyMathLab?

Additional Help Inside and Outside Your Textbook:
17. How Well Do You Know Your Textbook?
18. Are You Familiar with Your Textbook Supplements?
19. Are You Getting All the Mathematics Help That You Need?

The Bigger Picture—Study Guide Outline

Practice Final Exam

Answers to Selected Exercises

Student Resources

Study Skills Builders

Attitude and Study Tips

Study Skills Builder 1
Have You Decided to Complete This Course Successfully?

Ask yourself if one of your current goals is to complete this course successfully.

If it is not a goal of yours, ask yourself why. One common reason is fear of failure. Amazingly enough, fear of failure alone can be strong enough to keep many of us from doing our best in any endeavor.

Another common reason is that you simply haven't taken the time to think about or write down your goals for this course. To help accomplish this, answer the following questions.

Exercises

1. Write down your goal(s) for this course.

2. Now list steps you will take to make sure your goal(s) in Exercise 1 are accomplished.

3. Rate your commitment to this course with a number between 1 and 5. Use the diagram below to help.

High Commitment		Average Commitment		Not Committed at All
5	4	3	2	1

4. If you have rated your personal commitment level (from the exercise above) as a 1, 2, or 3, list the reasons why this is so. Then determine whether it is possible to increase your commitment level to a 4 or 5.

Good luck, and don't forget that a positive attitude will make a big difference.

Study Skills Builder 2
Tips for Studying for an Exam

To prepare for an exam, try the following study techniques:

- Start the study process days before your exam.
- Make sure that you are up to date on your assignments.
- If there is a topic that you are unsure of, use one of the many resources that are available to you. For example,
  See your instructor.
  View a lecture video on the topic.
  Visit a learning resource center on campus.
  Read the textbook material and examples on the topic.
- Reread your notes and carefully review the Chapter Highlights at the end of any chapter.
- Work the review exercises at the end of the chapter.
- Find a quiet place to take the Chapter Test found at the end of the chapter. Do not use any resources when taking this sample test. This way, you will have a clear indication of how prepared you are for your exam. Check your answers and use the Chapter Test Prep Videos to make sure that you correct any missed exercises.

Good luck, and keep a positive attitude.

Exercises

Let's see how you did on your last exam.

1. How many days before your last exam did you start studying for that exam?

2. Were you up to date on your assignments at that time or did you need to catch up on assignments?

3. List the most helpful text supplement (if you used one).

4. List the most helpful campus supplement (if you used one).

5. List your process for preparing for a mathematics test.

6. Was this process helpful? In other words, were you satisfied with your performance on your exam?

7. If not, what changes can you make in your process that will make it more helpful to you?

Study Skills Builder 3
What to Do the Day of an Exam

Your first exam may be soon. On the day of an exam, don't forget to try the following:

- Allow yourself plenty of time to arrive.
- Read the directions on the test carefully.
- Read each problem carefully as you take your test. Make sure that you answer the question asked.
- Watch your time and pace yourself so that you may attempt each problem on your test.
- Check your work and answers.
- *Do not turn your test in early.* If you have extra time, spend it double-checking your work.

Good luck!

Exercises

Answer the following questions based on your most recent mathematics exam, whenever that was.

1. How soon before class did you arrive?
2. Did you read the directions on the test carefully?
3. Did you make sure you answered the question asked for each problem on the exam?
4. Were you able to attempt each problem on your exam?
5. If your answer to Exercise 4 is no, list reasons why.
6. Did you have extra time on your exam?
7. If your answer to Exercise 6 is yes, describe how you spent that extra time.

Study Skills Builder 4
Are You Satisfied with Your Performance on a Particular Quiz or Exam?

If not, don't forget to analyze your quiz or exam and look for common errors. Were most of your errors a result of:

- *Carelessness?* Did you turn in your quiz or exam before the allotted time expired? If so, resolve to use any extra time to check your work.
- *Running out of time?* Answer the questions you are sure of first. Then attempt the questions you are unsure of and delay checking your work until all questions have been answered.
- *Not understanding a concept?* If so, review that concept and correct your work so that you make sure you understand it before the next quiz or the final exam.
- *Test conditions?* When studying for a quiz or exam, make sure you place yourself in conditions similar to test conditions. For example, before your next quiz or exam, take a sample test without the aid of your notes or text.

(For a sample test, see your instructor or use the Chapter Test at the end of each chapter.)

Exercises

1. Have you corrected all your previous quizzes and exams?
2. List any errors you have found common to two or more of your graded papers.
3. Is one of your common errors not understanding a concept? If so, are you making sure you understand all the concepts for the next quiz or exam?
4. Is one of your common errors making careless mistakes? If so, are you now taking all the time allotted to check over your work so that you can minimize the number of careless mistakes?
5. Are you satisfied with your grades thus far on quizzes and tests?
6. If your answer to Exercise 5 is no, are there any more suggestions you can make to your instructor or yourself to help? If so, list them here and share these with your instructor.

Study Skills Builder 5
How Are You Doing?

If you haven't done so yet, take a few moments to think about how you are doing in this course. Are you working toward your goal of successfully completing this course? Is your performance on homework, quizzes, and tests satisfactory? If not, you might want to see your instructor to see whether he/she has any suggestions on how you can improve your performance. Reread Section 1.1 for ideas on places to get help with your mathematics course.

Exercises

Answer the following.

1. List any textbook supplements you are using to help you through this course.
2. List any campus resources you are using to help you through this course.
3. Write a short paragraph describing how you are doing in your mathematics course.
4. If improvement is needed, list ways that you can work toward improving your situation as described in Exercise 3.

Study Skills Builder 6
Are You Preparing for Your Final Exam?

To prepare for your final exam, try the following study techniques:

- Review the material that you will be responsible for on your exam. This includes material from your textbook, your notebook, and any handouts from your instructor.
- Review any formulas that you may need to memorize.
- Check to see if your instructor or mathematics department will be conducting a final exam review.
- Check with your instructor to see whether final exams from previous semesters/quarters are available to students for review.
- Use your previously taken exams as a practice final exam. To do so, rewrite the test questions in mixed order on blank sheets of paper. This will help you prepare for exam conditions.
- If you are unsure of a few concepts, see your instructor or visit a learning lab for assistance. Also, view the video segment of any troublesome sections.
- If you need further exercises to work, try the Cumulative Reviews at the end of the chapters.

Once again, good luck! I hope you are enjoying this textbook and your mathematics course.

Organizing Your Work

Study Skills Builder 7
Learning New Terms

Many of the terms used in this text may be new to you. It will be helpful to make a list of new mathematical terms and symbols as you encounter them and to review them frequently. Placing these new terms (including page references) on 3×5 index cards might help you later when you're preparing for a quiz.

Exercises

1. Name one way you might place a word and its definition on a 3×5 card.
2. How do new terms stand out in this text so that they can be found?

Study Skills Builder 8
Are You Organized?

Have you ever had trouble finding a completed assignment? When it's time to study for a test, are your notes neat and organized? Have you ever had trouble reading your own mathematics handwriting? (Be honest—I have.)

When any of these things happen, it's time to get organized. Here are a few suggestions:

- Write your notes and complete your homework assignments in a notebook with pockets (spiral or ring binder).
- Take class notes in this notebook, and then follow the notes with your completed homework assignment.
- When you receive graded papers or handouts, place them in the notebook pocket so that you will not lose them.
- Mark (possibly with an exclamation point) any note(s) that seem extra important to you.
- Mark (possibly with a question mark) any notes or homework that you are having trouble with.

- See your instructor or a math tutor to help you with the concepts or exercises that you are having trouble understanding.
- If you are having trouble reading your own handwriting, *slow down* and write your mathematics work clearly!

Exercises

1. Have you been completing your assignments on time?
2. Have you been correcting any exercises you may be having difficulty with?
3. If you are having trouble with a mathematical concept or correcting any homework exercises, have you visited your instructor, a tutor, or your campus math lab?
4. Are you taking lecture notes in your mathematics course? (By the way, these notes should include worked-out examples solved by your instructor.)
5. Is your mathematics course material (handouts, graded papers, lecture notes) organized?
6. If your answer to Exercise 5 is no, take a moment to review your course material. List at least two ways that you might organize it better.

Study Skills Builder 9
Organizing a Notebook

It's never too late to get organized. If you need ideas about organizing a notebook for your mathematics course, try some of these:

- Use a spiral or ring binder notebook with pockets and use it for mathematics only.
- Start each page by writing the book's section number you are working on at the top.
- When your instructor is lecturing, take notes. *Always* include any examples your instructor works for you.
- Place your worked-out homework exercises in your notebook immediately after the lecture notes from that section. This way, a section's worth of material is together.
- Homework exercises: Attempt and check all assigned homework.
- Place graded quizzes in the pockets of your notebook or a special section of your binder.

Exercises

Check your notebook organization by answering the following questions.

1. Do you have a spiral or ring binder notebook for your mathematics course only?
2. Have you ever had to flip through several sheets of notes and work in your mathematics notebook to determine what section's work you are in?
3. Are you now writing the textbook's section number at the top of each notebook page?
4. Have you ever lost or had trouble finding a graded quiz or test?
5. Are you now placing all your graded work in a dedicated place in your notebook?
6. Are you attempting all of your homework and placing all of your work in your notebook?
7. Are you checking and correcting your homework in your notebook? If not, why not?
8. Are you writing in your notebook the examples your instructor works for you in class?

Study Skills Builder 10

How Are Your Homework Assignments Going?

It is very important in mathematics to keep up with homework. Why? Many concepts build on each other. Often your understanding of a day's concepts depends on an understanding of the previous day's material.

Remember that completing your homework assignment involves a lot more than attempting a few of the problems assigned.

To complete a homework assignment, remember these four things:

- Attempt all of it.
- Check it.
- Correct it.
- If needed, ask questions about it.

Exercises

Take a moment to review your completed homework assignments. Answer the questions below based on this review.

1. Approximate the fraction of your homework you have attempted.
2. Approximate the fraction of your homework you have checked (if possible).
3. If you are able to check your homework, have you corrected it when errors have been found?
4. When working homework, if you do not understand a concept, what do you do?

MyMathLab and MathXL

Study Skills Builder 11

Tips for Turning in Your Homework on Time

It is very important to keep up with your mathematics homework assignments. Why? Many concepts in mathematics build upon each other.

Remember these four tips to help ensure that your work is completed on time:

- Know the assignments and due dates set by your instructor.
- Do not wait until the last minute to submit your homework.
- Set a goal to submit your homework 6–8 hours before the scheduled due date in case you have unexpected technology trouble.
- Schedule enough time to complete each assignment.

Following these tips will also help you avoid losing points for late or missed assignments.

Exercises

Take a moment to consider your work on your homework assignments to date and answer the following questions:

1. What percentage of your assignments have you turned in on time?
2. Why might it be a good idea to submit your homework 6–8 hours before the scheduled deadline?
3. If you have missed submitting any homework by the due date, list some of the reasons this occurred.
4. What steps do you plan to take in the future to ensure that your homework is submitted on time?

Study Skills Builder 12

Tips for Doing Your Homework Online

Practice is one of the main keys to success in any mathematics course. Did you know that MyMathLab/MathXL provides you with **immediate feedback** for each exercise? If you are incorrect, you are given hints to work the exercise correctly. You have **unlimited practice opportunities** and can rework any exercises you have trouble with until you master them, and submit homework assignments unlimited times before the deadline.

Remember these success tips when doing your homework online:

- Attempt all assigned exercises.
- Write down (neatly) your step-by-step work for each exercise before entering your answer.
- Use the immediate feedback provided by the program to help you check and correct your work for each exercise.
- Rework any exercises you have trouble with until you master them.

- Work through your homework assignment as many times as necessary until you are satisfied.

Exercises

Take a moment to think about your homework assignments to date and answer the following:

1. Have you attempted all assigned exercises?
2. Of the exercises attempted, have you also written out your work before entering your answer so that you can check it?
3. Are you familiar with how to enter answers using the MathXL player so that you avoid answer entry–type errors?
4. List some ways the immediate feedback and practice supports have helped you with your homework. If you have not used these supports, how do you plan to use them with the given success tips on your next assignment?

Study Skills Builder 13

Organizing Your Work

Have you ever used any readily available paper (such as the back of a flyer, another course assignment, Post-it notes, etc.) to work out homework exercises before entering the answer in MathXL? To save time, have you ever entered answers directly into MathXL without working the exercises on paper? When it's time to study, have you ever been unable to find your completed work or read and follow your own mathematics handwriting?

When any of these things happen, it's time to get organized. Here are some suggestions:

- Write your step-by-step work for each homework exercise (neatly) on lined, loose-leaf paper and keep this in a 3-ring binder.
- Refer to your step-by-step work when you receive feedback that your answer is incorrect in MathXL. Double-check against the steps and hints provided by the program and correct your work accordingly.
- Keep your written homework with your class notes for that section.

- Identify any exercises you are having trouble with and ask questions about them.
- Keep all graded quizzes and tests in this binder as well to study later.

If you follow these suggestions, you and your instructor or tutor will be able to follow your steps and correct any mistakes. You will have a written copy of your work to refer to later to ask questions and study for tests.

Exercises

1. Why is it important to write out your step-by-step work to homework exercises and keep a hard copy of all work submitted online?
2. If you have gotten an incorrect answer, are you able to follow your steps and find your error?
3. If you were asked today to review your previous homework assignments and first test, could you find them? If not, list some ways you might organize your work better.

Study Skills Builder 14

Getting Help with Your Homework Assignments

Many helpful resources are available to you through MathXL to help you work through any homework exercises you may have trouble with. It is important for you to know what these resources are and when and how to use them.

Let's review these features, found in the homework exercises:

- **Help Me Solve This**—provides step-by-step help for the exercise you are working. You must work an additional exercise of the same type (without this help) before you can get credit for having worked it correctly.

- **View an Example**—allows you to view a correctly worked exercise similar to the one you are having trouble with. You can go back to your original exercise and work it on your own.

- **E-Book**—allows you to read examples from your text and find similar exercises.

- **Video****—your text author, Elayn Martin-Gay, works an exercise similar to the one you need help with. **Not all exercises have an accompanying video clip.

- **Ask My Instructor**—allows you to email your instructor for help with an exercise.

Exercises

1. How does the "Help Me Solve This" feature work?

2. If the "View an Example" feature is used, is it necessary to work an additional problem before continuing the assignment?

3. When might be a good time to use the "Video" feature? Do all exercises have an accompanying video clip?

4. Which of the features above have you used? List those you found the most helpful to you.

5. If you haven't used the features discussed, list those you plan to try on your next homework assignment.

Study Skills Builder 15

Tips for Preparing for an Exam

Did you know that you can rework your previous homework assignments in MyMathLab and MathXL? This is a great way to prepare for tests. To do this, open a previous homework assignment and click "similar exercise." This will generate new exercises similar to the homework you have submitted. You can then rework the exercises and assignments until you feel confident that you understand them.

To prepare for an exam, follow these tips:

- Review your written work for your previous homework assignments along with your class notes.

- Identify any exercises or topics that you have questions on or have difficulty understanding.

- Rework your previous assignments in MyMathLab and MathXL until you fully understand them and can do them without help.

- Get help for any topics you feel unsure of or for which you have questions.

Exercises

1. Are your current homework assignments up to date and is your written work for them organized in a binder or notebook? If the answer is no, it's time to get organized. For tips on this, see Study Skills Builder 13—Organizing Your Work.

2. How many days in advance of an exam do you usually start studying?

3. List some ways you think that practicing previous homework assignments can help you prepare for your test.

4. List two or three resources you can use to get help for any topics you are unsure of or have questions on.

Good luck!

Study Skills Builder 16

How Well Do You Know the Resources Available to You in MyMathLab?

Many helpful resources are available to you in MyMathLab. Let's take a moment to locate and explore a few of them now. Go into your MyMathLab course and visit the multimedia library, tools for success, and E-book.

   Let's see what you found.

Exercises

1. List the resources available to you in the Multimedia Library.

2. List the resources available to you in the Tools for Success folder.

3. Where did you find the English/Spanish Audio Glossary?

4. Can you view videos from the E-book?

5. Did you find any resources you did not know about? If so, which ones?

6. Which resources have you used most often or found most helpful?

Additional Help Inside and Outside Your Textbook

Study Skills Builder 17

How Well Do You Know Your Textbook?

The following questions will help determine whether you are familiar with your textbook. For additional information, see Section 1.1 in this text.

1. What does the ● icon mean?

2. What does the ＼ icon mean?

3. What does the △ icon mean?

4. Where can you find a review for each chapter? What answers to this review can be found in the back of your text?

5. Each chapter contains an overview of the chapter along with examples. What is this feature called?

6. Each chapter contains a review of vocabulary. What is this feature called?

7. Practice exercises are contained in this text. What are they and how can they be used?

8. This text contains a student section in the back entitled Student Resources. List the contents of this section and how they might be helpful.

9. What exercise answers are available in this text? Where are they located?

Study Skills Builder 18

Are You Familiar with Your Textbook Supplements?

Below is a review of some of the student supplements available for additional study. Check to see whether you are using the ones most helpful to you.

- Chapter Test Prep Videos. These videos provide video clip solutions to the Chapter Test exercises in this text. You will find this extremely useful when studying for tests or exams.

- Interactive DVD Lecture Series. These are keyed to each section of the text. The material is presented by me, Elayn Martin-Gay, and I have placed a ⊙ by the exercises in the text that I have worked on the video.

- The *Student Solutions Manual.* This contains worked-out solutions to odd-numbered exercises as well as every exercise in the Integrated Reviews, Chapter Reviews, Chapter Tests, and Cumulative Reviews and every Practice exercise.

- Pearson Tutor Center. Mathematics questions may be phoned, faxed, or emailed to this center.

- MyMathLab is a text-specific online course. MathXL is an online homework, tutorial, and assessment system. Take a moment to determine whether these are available to you.

As usual, your instructor is your best source of information.

Exercises

Let's see how you are doing with textbook supplements.

1. Name one way the Lecture Videos can be helpful to you.

2. Name one way the Chapter Test Prep Video can help you prepare for a chapter test.

3. List any textbook supplements that you have found useful.

4. Have you located and visited a learning resource lab located on your campus?

5. List the textbook supplements that are currently housed in your campus's learning resource lab.

Study Skills Builder 19

Are You Getting All the Mathematics Help That You Need?

Remember that, in addition to your instructor, there are many places to get help with your mathematics course. For example:

- This text has an accompanying video lesson by the author for every section. There are also worked-out video solutions by the author to every Chapter Test exercise.

- The back of the book contains answers to odd-numbered exercises.

- A *Student Solutions Manual* is available that contains worked-out solutions to odd-numbered exercises as well as solutions to every exercise in the Integrated Reviews, Chapter Reviews, Chapter Tests, and Cumulative Reviews and every Practice exercise.

- Don't forget to check with your instructor for other local resources available to you, such as a tutor center.

Exercises

1. List items you find helpful in the text and all student supplements to this text.

2. List all the campus help that is available to you for this course.

3. List any help (besides the textbook) from Exercises 1 and 2 above that you are using.

4. List any help (besides the textbook) that you feel you should try.

5. Write a goal for yourself that includes trying everything you listed in Exercise 4 during the next week.

The Bigger Picture—Study Guide Outline

Simplifying Expressions and Solving Equations and Inequalities

I. Simplifying Expressions

A. Real Numbers

1. Add: (Sec. 1.5)

$$-1.7 + (-0.21) = -1.91 \quad \text{Adding like signs.}$$
Add absolute values. Attach common sign.

$$-7 + 3 = -4 \quad \text{Adding different signs.}$$
Subtract absolute values. Attach the sign of the number with the larger absolute value.

2. Subtract: Add the first number to the opposite of the second number. (Sec. 1.6)

$$17 - 25 = 17 + (-25) = -8$$

3. Multiply or divide: Multiply or divide the two numbers as usual. If the signs are the same, the answer is positive. If the signs are different, the answer is negative. (Sec. 1.7)

$$-10 \cdot 3 = -30, \quad -81 \div (-3) = 27$$

B. Exponents (Secs. 5.1 and 5.5)

$$x^7 \cdot x^5 = x^{12}; \ (x^7)^5 = x^{35}; \ \frac{x^7}{x^5} = x^2; \ x^0 = 1; \ 8^{-2} = \frac{1}{8^2} = \frac{1}{64}$$

C. Polynomials

1. Add: Combine like terms. (Sec. 5.2)

$$(3y^2 + 6y + 7) + (9y^2 - 11y - 15) = 3y^2 + 6y + 7 + 9y^2 - 11y - 15$$
$$= 12y^2 - 5y - 8$$

2. Subtract: Change the sign of the terms of the polynomial being subtracted, then add. (Sec. 5.2)

$$(3y^2 + 6y + 7) - (9y^2 - 11y - 15) = 3y^2 + 6y + 7 - 9y^2 + 11y + 15$$
$$= -6y^2 + 17y + 22$$

3. Multiply: Multiply each term of one polynomial by each term of the other polynomial. (Secs. 5.3 and 5.4)

$$(x + 5)(2x^2 - 3x + 4) = x(2x^2 - 3x + 4) + 5(2x^2 - 3x + 4)$$
$$= 2x^3 - 3x^2 + 4x + 10x^2 - 15x + 20$$
$$= 2x^3 + 7x^2 - 11x + 20$$

4. Divide: (Sec. 5.6)

   a. To divide by a monomial, divide each term of the polynomial by the monomial.

$$\frac{8x^2 + 2x - 6}{2x} = \frac{8x^2}{2x} + \frac{2x}{2x} - \frac{6}{2x} = 4x + 1 - \frac{3}{x}$$

b. To divide by a polynomial other than a monomial, use long division.

$$2x + 5 \overline{\smash{)}2x^2 - 7x + 10} \quad\quad x - 6 + \dfrac{40}{2x + 5}$$

$$\underline{2x^2 + 5x}$$
$$-12x + 10$$
$$\underline{+12x + 30}$$
$$40$$

D. Factoring Polynomials

See the Chapter 6 Integrated Review for steps.

$$3x^4 - 78x^2 + 75 = 3(x^4 - 26x^2 + 25) \quad \text{Factor out GCF—always first step.}$$
$$= 3(x^2 - 25)(x^2 - 1) \quad \text{Factor trinomial.}$$
$$= 3(x + 5)(x - 5)(x + 1)(x - 1) \quad \text{Factor further—each}$$
$$\text{difference of squares.}$$

E. Rational Expressions

1. Simplify: Factor the numerator and denominator. Then divide out factors of 1 by dividing out common factors in the numerator and denominator. (Sec. 7.1)

$$\frac{x^2 - 9}{7x^2 - 21x} = \frac{(x + 3)(x - 3)}{7x(x - 3)} = \frac{x + 3}{7x}$$

2. Multiply: Multiply numerators, then multiply denominators. (Sec. 7.2)

$$\frac{5z}{2z^2 - 9z - 18} \cdot \frac{22z + 33}{10z} = \frac{5 \cdot z}{(2z + 3)(z - 6)} \cdot \frac{11(2z + 3)}{2 \cdot 5 \cdot z} = \frac{11}{2(z - 6)}$$

3. Divide: First fraction times the reciprocal of the second fraction. (Sec. 7.2)

$$\frac{14}{x + 5} \div \frac{x + 1}{2} = \frac{14}{x + 5} \cdot \frac{2}{x + 1} = \frac{28}{(x + 5)(x + 1)}$$

4. Add or subtract: Must have same denominator. If not, find the LCD and write each fraction as an equivalent fraction with the LCD as denominator. (Sec. 7.4)

$$\frac{9}{10} - \frac{x + 1}{x + 5} = \frac{9(x + 5)}{10(x + 5)} - \frac{10(x + 1)}{10(x + 5)}$$
$$= \frac{9x + 45 - 10x - 10}{10(x + 5)} = \frac{-x + 35}{10(x + 5)}$$

F. Radicals

1. Simplify square roots: If possible, factor the radicand so that one factor is a perfect square. Then use the product rule and simplify. (Sec. 10.3)

$$\sqrt{75} = \sqrt{25 \cdot 3} = \sqrt{25} \cdot \sqrt{3} = 5\sqrt{3}$$

2. Add or subtract: Only like radicals (same index and radicand) can be added or subtracted. (Sec. 10.4)

$$8\sqrt{10} - \sqrt{40} + \sqrt{5} = 8\sqrt{10} - 2\sqrt{10} + \sqrt{5} = 6\sqrt{10} + \sqrt{5}$$

3. Multiply or divide: $\sqrt{a} \cdot \sqrt{b} = \sqrt{ab}; \dfrac{\sqrt{a}}{\sqrt{b}} = \sqrt{\dfrac{a}{b}}$. (Sec. 10.4)

$$\sqrt{11} \cdot \sqrt{3} = \sqrt{33}; \frac{\sqrt{140}}{\sqrt{7}} = \sqrt{\frac{140}{7}} = \sqrt{20} = \sqrt{4 \cdot 5} = 2\sqrt{5}$$

4. Rationalizing the denominator: (Sec. 10.5)

a. If denominator is one term,

$$\frac{5}{\sqrt{11}} = \frac{5 \cdot \sqrt{11}}{\sqrt{11} \cdot \sqrt{11}} = \frac{5\sqrt{11}}{11}$$

b. If denominator is two terms, multiply by 1 in the form of $\dfrac{\text{conjugate of denominator}}{\text{conjugate of denominator}}$.

$$\frac{13}{3 + \sqrt{2}} = \frac{13}{3 + \sqrt{2}} \cdot \frac{3 - \sqrt{2}}{3 - \sqrt{2}} = \frac{13(3 - \sqrt{2})}{9 - 2} = \frac{13(3 - \sqrt{2})}{7}$$

II. Solving Equations

A. Linear Equations: (Sec. 2.3)

$$5(x - 2) = \frac{4(2x + 1)}{3}$$

$$3 \cdot 5(x - 2) = \cancel{3} \cdot \frac{4(2x + 1)}{\cancel{3}}$$

$$15x - 30 = 8x + 4$$

$$7x = 34$$

$$x = \frac{34}{7}$$

B. Quadratic and Higher-Degree Equations (Secs. 6.6, 11.1, 11.2, 11.3)

$$2x^2 - 7x = 9 \qquad\qquad 2x^2 + x - 2 = 0$$

$$2x^2 - 7x - 9 = 0 \qquad\qquad a = 2, \ b = 1, \ c = -2$$

$$(2x - 9)(x + 1) = 0 \qquad\qquad x = \frac{-1 \pm \sqrt{1^2 - 4(2)(-2)}}{2 \cdot 2}$$

$$2x - 9 = 0 \quad \text{or} \quad x + 1 = 0 \qquad\qquad x = \frac{-1 \pm \sqrt{17}}{4}$$

$$x = \frac{9}{2} \quad \text{or} \qquad x = -1$$

C. Equations with Rational Expressions (Sec. 7.5)

$$\frac{7}{x - 1} + \frac{3}{x + 1} = \frac{x + 3}{x^2 - 1}$$

$$\cancel{(x - 1)}(x + 1) \cdot \frac{7}{\cancel{x - 1}} + (x - 1)\cancel{(x + 1)} \cdot \frac{3}{\cancel{x + 1}}$$

$$= \cancel{(x - 1)}\cancel{(x + 1)} \cdot \frac{x + 3}{\cancel{(x - 1)}\cancel{(x + 1)}}$$

$$7(x + 1) + 3(x - 1) = x + 3$$

$$7x + 7 + 3x - 3 = x + 3$$

$$9x = -1$$

$$x = -\frac{1}{9}$$

D. Proportions: An equation with two ratios equal. Set cross products equal, then solve. Make sure the proposed solution does not make the denominator 0. (Sec. 7.6)

$$\frac{5}{x} = \frac{9}{2x - 3}$$

$$5(2x - 3) = 9 \cdot x \qquad \text{Set cross products equal.}$$

$$10x - 15 = 9x \qquad \text{Multiply.}$$

$$x = 15 \qquad \text{Write equation with variable terms on one side and constants on the other.}$$

E. Absolute Value Equations (Sec. 9.2)

$$|3x - 1| = 8$$

$3x - 1 = 8$ or $3x - 1 = -8$

$3x = 9$ or $3x = -7$

$x = 3$ or $x = -\dfrac{7}{3}$

$$|x - 5| = |x + 1|$$

$x - 5 = x + 1$ or $x - 5 = -(x + 1)$

$\underbrace{-5 = 1}$ or $x - 5 = -x - 1$

No solution   or $2x = 4$

$x = 2$

F. Equations with Radicals (Sec. 10.6)

$$\sqrt{5x + 10} - 2 = x$$
$$\sqrt{5x + 10} = x + 2$$
$$(\sqrt{5x + 10})^2 = (x + 2)^2$$
$$5x + 10 = x^2 + 4x + 4$$
$$0 = x^2 - x - 6$$
$$0 = (x - 3)(x + 2)$$

$x - 3 = 0$ or $x + 2 = 0$

$x = 3$ or $x = -2$

Both solutions check.

G. Exponential Equations (Secs. 12.3, 12.8)

$$9^x = 27^{x+1}$$
$$(3^2)^x = (3^3)^{x+1}$$
$$3^{2x} = 3^{3x+3}$$
$$2x = 3x + 3$$
$$-3 = x$$

$$5^x = 7$$
$$\log 5^x = \log 7$$
$$x \log 5 = \log 7$$
$$x = \dfrac{\log 7}{\log 5}$$

H. Logarithmic Equations (Sec. 12.8)

$$\log 7 + \log(x + 3) = \log 5$$
$$\log 7(x + 3) = \log 5$$
$$7(x + 3) = 5$$
$$7x + 21 = 5$$
$$7x = -16$$
$$x = -\dfrac{16}{7}$$

III. Solving Inequalities

A. Linear Inequalities (Sec. 2.8)

$$-3(x + 2) \geq 6$$
$$-3x - 6 \geq 6$$
$$-3x \geq 12$$
$$\dfrac{-3x}{-3} \leq \dfrac{12}{-3}$$
$$x \leq -4 \quad \text{or} \quad (-\infty, -4]$$

B. Compound Inequalities (Sec. 9.1)

$x \leq 3$ *and* $x < -7$

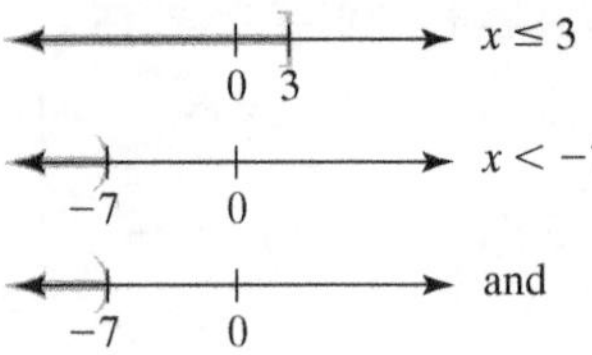

$$x \leq 3$$

$$x < -7$$

and

$$(-\infty, -7)$$

$x \leq 3$ *or* $x < -7$

$$x \leq 3$$

$$x < -7$$

or

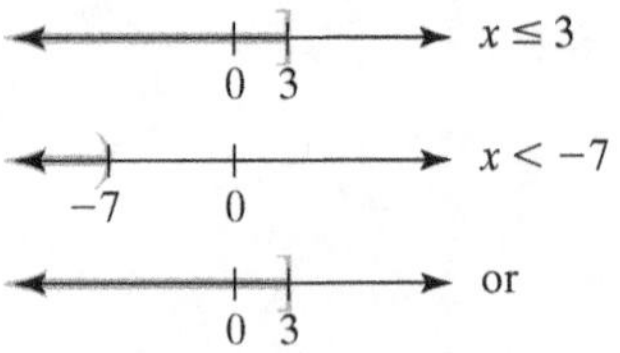

$$(-\infty, 3]$$

C. Absolute Value Inequalities (Sec. 9.3)

$$|x - 5| - 8 < -2$$
$$|x - 5| < 6$$
$$-6 < x - 5 < 6$$
$$-1 < x < 11$$
$$(-1, 11)$$

$$|2x + 1| \geq 17$$
$$2x + 1 \geq 17 \quad \text{or} \quad 2x + 1 \leq -17$$
$$2x \geq 16 \quad \text{or} \qquad 2x \leq -18$$
$$x \geq 8 \quad \text{or} \qquad x \leq -9$$
$$(-\infty, -9] \cup [8, \infty)$$

D. Nonlinear Inequalities (Sec. 11.4)

$$x^2 - x < 6$$
$$x^2 - x - 6 < 0$$
$$(x - 3)(x + 2) < 0$$

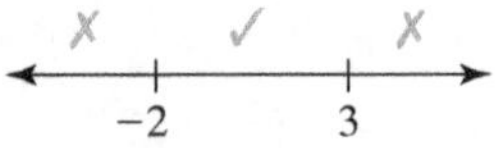

$$(-2, 3)$$

$$\frac{x - 5}{x + 1} \geq 0$$

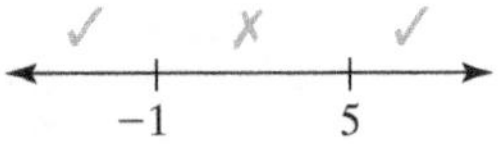

$$(-\infty, -1) \cup [5, \infty)$$

Evaluate.

1. $6[5 + 2(3 - 8) - 3]$

2. -3^4

3. 4^{-3}

4. $\dfrac{1}{2} - \dfrac{5}{6}$

Perform the indicated operations and simplify if possible.

5. $5x^3 + x^2 + 5x - 2 - (8x^3 - 4x^2 + x - 7)$

6. $(4x - 2)^2$

7. $(3x + 7)(x^2 + 5x + 2)$

Factor.

8. $y^2 - 8y - 48$

9. $9x^3 + 39x^2 + 12x$

10. $180 - 5x^2$

11. $3a^2 + 3ab - 7a - 7b$

12. $8y^3 - 64$

Simplify. Write answer with positive exponents only.

13. $\left(\dfrac{x^2 y^3}{x^3 y^{-4}}\right)^2$

Solve each equation or inequality. Write inequality answers using interval notation.

14. $-4(a + 1) - 3a = -7(2a - 3)$

15. $3x - 5 \geq 7x + 3$

16. $x(x + 6) = 7$

Graph the following.

17. $5x - 7y = 10$

18. $x - 3 = 0$

Find the slope of each line.

19. Through $(6, -5)$ and $(-1, 2)$

20. $-3x + y = 5$

Write equations of the following lines. Write each equation in standard form.

21. Through $(2, -5)$ and $(1, 3)$

22. Through $(-5, -1)$ and parallel to $x = 7$

Solve each system of equations.

23. $\begin{cases} \dfrac{1}{2}x + 2y = -\dfrac{15}{4} \\ 4x = -y \end{cases}$

24. $\begin{cases} 4x - 6y = 7 \\ -2x + 3y = 0 \end{cases}$

25. Divide by long division: $\dfrac{27x^3 - 8}{3x + 2}$

Answer the questions about functions.

26. If $h(x) = x^3 - x$, find

   a. $h(-1)$

   b. $h(0)$

   c. $h(4)$

27. Identify the x- and y-intercepts. Then find the domain and range of the function graphed.

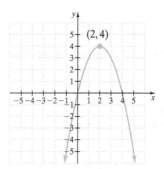

Solve each application.

28. Some states have a single area code for the entire state. Two such states have area codes where one is double the other. If the sum of these integers is 1203, find the two area codes.

29. Two trains leave Los Angeles simultaneously traveling on the same track in opposite directions at speeds of 50 and 64 mph. How long will it take before they are 285 miles apart?

30. Find the amount of a 12% saline solution a lab assistant should add to 80 cc (cubic centimeters) of a 22% saline solution in order to have a 16% solution.

31. Find the domain of the rational function

$$g(x) = \dfrac{9x^2 - 9}{x^2 + 4x + 3}.$$

Perform the indicated operations and simplify if possible.

32. $\dfrac{15x}{2x + 5} - \dfrac{6 - 4x}{2x + 5}$

33. $\dfrac{x^2 - 9}{x^2 - 3x} \div \dfrac{xy + 5x + 3y + 15}{2x + 10}$

34. $\dfrac{5a}{a^2 - a - 6} - \dfrac{2}{a - 3}$

35. $\dfrac{5 - \dfrac{1}{y^2}}{\dfrac{1}{y} + \dfrac{2}{y^2}}$

Solve each equation.

36. $\dfrac{4}{y} - \dfrac{5}{3} = -\dfrac{1}{5}$

37. $\dfrac{5}{y + 1} = \dfrac{4}{y + 2}$

38. $\dfrac{a}{a - 3} = \dfrac{3}{a - 3} - \dfrac{3}{2}$

Solve.

39. One number plus five times its reciprocal is equal to six. Find the number.

Simplify. If needed, write answers with positive exponents only.

40. $\sqrt{216}$

41. $\left(\dfrac{1}{125}\right)^{-1/3}$

42. $\left(\dfrac{64c^{4/3}}{a^{-2/3}b^{5/6}}\right)^{1/2}$

Perform the indicated operations and simplify if possible.

43. $\sqrt{125x^3} - 3\sqrt{20x^3}$

44. $(\sqrt{5} + 5)(\sqrt{5} - 5)$

Solve each equation or inequality. Write inequality solutions using interval notation.

45. $|6x - 5| - 3 = -2$

46. $-3 < 2(x - 3) \le 4$

47. $|3x + 1| > 5$

48. $y^2 - 3y = 5$

49. $x = \sqrt{x - 2} + 2$

50. $2x^2 - 7x > 15$

Graph the following.

51. $y > -4x$

52. $g(x) = -|x + 2| - 1$. Also, find the domain and range of this function.

53. $h(x) = x^2 - 4x + 4$. Label the vertex and any intercepts.

54. $f(x) = \begin{cases} -\dfrac{1}{2}x & \text{if } x \le 0 \\ 2x - 3 & \text{if } x > 0 \end{cases}$. Also, find the domain and range of this function.

Write equations of the following lines. Write each equation using function notation.

55. Through $(4, -2)$ and $(6, -3)$

56. Through $(-1, 2)$ and perpendicular to $3x - y = 4$

Find the distance or midpoint.

57. Find the distance between the points $(-6, 3)$ and $(-8, -7)$.

58. Find the midpoint of the line segment whose endpoints are $(-2, -5)$ and $(-6, 12)$.

Rationalize each denominator. Assume that variables represent positive numbers.

59. $\sqrt{\dfrac{9}{y}}$

60. $\dfrac{4 - \sqrt{x}}{4 + 2\sqrt{x}}$

Solve.

61. Suppose that W is inversely proportional to V. If $W = 20$ when $V = 12$, find W when $V = 15$.

62. Given the diagram shown, approximate to the nearest foot how many feet of walking distance a person saves by cutting across the lawn instead of walking on the sidewalk.

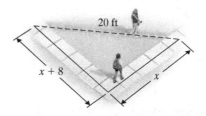

63. A stone is thrown upward from a bridge. The stone's height in feet, $s(t)$, above the water t seconds after the stone is thrown is a function given by the equation

$$s(t) = -16t^2 + 32t + 256$$

   a. Find the maximum height of the stone.

   b. Find the time it takes the stone to hit the water. Round the answer to two decimal places.

COMPLEX NUMBERS: CHAPTER 10

Perform the indicated operation and simplify. Write the result in the form $a + bi$.

64. $-\sqrt{-8}$

65. $(12 - 6i) - (12 - 3i)$

66. $(4 + 3i)^2$

67. $\dfrac{1 + 4i}{1 - i}$

INVERSE, EXPONENTIAL, AND LOGARITHMIC FUNCTIONS: CHAPTER 12

68. If $g(x) = x - 7$ and $h(x) = x^2 - 6x + 5$, find $(g \circ h)(x)$.

69. Determine whether $f(x) = 6 - 2x$ is a one-to-one function. If it is, find its inverse.

70. Use properties of logarithms to write the expression as a single logarithm.

$$\log_5 x + 3\log_5 x - \log_5(x + 1)$$

Solve. Give exact solutions.

71. $8^{x-1} = \dfrac{1}{64}$

72. $3^{2x+5} = 4$ Give an exact solution and a 4-decimal-place approximation.

73. $\log_8(3x - 2) = 2$

74. $\log_4(x + 1) - \log_4(x - 2) = 3$

75. $\ln\sqrt{e} = x$

76. Graph $y = \left(\dfrac{1}{2}\right)^x + 1$

77. The prairie dog population of the Grand Forks area now stands at 57,000 animals. If the population is growing at a rate of 2.6% annually, how many prairie dogs will there be in that area 5 years from now?

CONIC SECTIONS: CHAPTER 13

Sketch the graph of each equation.

78. $x^2 - y^2 = 36$

79. $16x^2 + 9y^2 = 144$

80. $x^2 + y^2 + 6x = 16$

81. Solve the system: $\begin{cases} x^2 + y^2 = 26 \\ x^2 - 2y^2 = 23 \end{cases}$

SEQUENCES, SERIES, AND THE BINOMIAL THEOREM: CHAPTER 14

82. Find the first five terms of the sequence $a_n = \dfrac{(-1)^n}{n + 4}$.

83. Find the partial sum S_5 of the sequence $a_n = 5(2)^{n-1}$.

84. Find S_∞ of the sequence $\dfrac{3}{2}, -\dfrac{3}{4}, \dfrac{3}{8}, \ldots$

85. Find $\displaystyle\sum_{i=1}^{4} i(i - 2)$

86. Expand: $(2x + y)^5$

Answers to Selected Exercises

CHAPTER 1 REVIEW OF REAL NUMBERS

Section 1.2
Practice Exercises

1. a. $<$ **b.** $>$ **c.** $<$ **2. a.** True **b.** False **c.** True **d.** True **3. a.** $3 < 8$ **b.** $15 \geq 9$ **c.** $6 \neq 7$ **4.** -10 **5. a.** 25 **b.** 25 **c.** $25, -15, -99$ **d.** $25, \frac{7}{3}, -15, -\frac{3}{4}, -3.7, 8.8, -99$ **e.** $\sqrt{5}$ **f.** $25, \frac{7}{3}, -15, -\frac{3}{4}, \sqrt{5}, -3.7, 8.8, -99$ **6. a.** $<$ **b.** $>$ **c.** $=$ **7. a.** 8 **b.** 9 **c.** 2.5 **d.** $\frac{5}{11}$ **e.** $\sqrt{3}$ **8. a.** $=$ **b.** $>$ **c.** $<$ **d.** $>$ **e.** $<$

Vocabulary, Readiness & Video Check 1.2

1. whole **3.** inequality **5.** real **7.** irrational **9.** To form a true statement: $0 < 7$. **11.** 0 belongs to the whole numbers, the integers, the rational numbers, and the real numbers; because 0 is a rational number, it cannot also be an irrational number

Exercise Set 1.2

1. $>$ **3.** $=$ **5.** $<$ **7.** $<$ **9.** $32 < 212$ **11.** $30 \leq 45$ **13.** true **15.** false **17.** false **19.** true **21.** false **23.** $8 < 12$ **25.** $5 \geq 4$ **27.** $15 \neq -2$ **29.** $14,494; -282$ **31.** $-28,000$ **33.** $350; -126$ **35.** whole, integers, rational, real **37.** integers, rational, real **39.** natural, whole, integers, rational, real **41.** rational, real **43.** irrational, real **45.** false **47.** true **49.** true **51.** true **53.** false **55.** $>$ **57.** $>$ **59.** $<$ **61.** $<$ **63.** $>$ **65.** $=$ **67.** $<$ **69.** $<$ **71.** 2009 **73.** 2009, 2010 **75.** 280 million $<$ 281 million **77.** 49 million $>$ 16 million **79.** 38 million pounds less, or -38 million **81.** $-0.04 > -26.7$ **83.** sun **85.** sun **87.** $20 \leq 25$ **89.** $6 > 0$ **91.** $-12 < -10$ **93.** answers may vary

Section 1.3
Practice Exercises

1. a. $2 \cdot 2 \cdot 3 \cdot 3$ **b.** $2 \cdot 2 \cdot 2 \cdot 5 \cdot 5$ **2. a.** $\frac{7}{8}$ **b.** $\frac{16}{3}$ **c.** $\frac{7}{25}$ **3.** $\frac{7}{24}$ **4. a.** $\frac{27}{16}$ **b.** $\frac{1}{36}$ **c.** $\frac{5}{2}$ **5. a.** 1 **b.** $\frac{6}{5}$ **c.** $\frac{4}{5}$ **d.** $\frac{1}{2}$ **6.** $\frac{14}{21}$ **7. a.** $\frac{46}{77}$ **b.** $\frac{1}{14}$ **c.** $\frac{1}{2}$ **8.** $22\frac{11}{15}$ **9.** $40\frac{5}{6}$

Vocabulary, Readiness & Video Check 1.3

1. fraction **3.** product **5.** factors, product **7.** equivalent **9.** The division operation changes to multiplication and the second fraction $\frac{1}{20}$ changes to its reciprocal $\frac{20}{1}$. **11.** The number $4\frac{7}{6}$ is not in proper mixed number form as the fraction part, $\frac{7}{6}$, should not be an improper fraction.

Exercise Set 1.3

1. $\frac{3}{8}$ **3.** $\frac{5}{7}$ **5.** $3 \cdot 11$ **7.** $2 \cdot 7 \cdot 7$ **9.** $2 \cdot 2 \cdot 5$ **11.** $3 \cdot 5 \cdot 5$ **13.** $3 \cdot 3 \cdot 5$ **15.** $\frac{1}{2}$ **17.** $\frac{2}{3}$ **19.** $\frac{3}{7}$ **21.** $\frac{3}{5}$ **23.** $\frac{30}{61}$ **25.** $\frac{3}{8}$ **27.** $\frac{1}{2}$ **29.** $\frac{6}{7}$ **31.** 15 **33.** $\frac{1}{6}$ **35.** $\frac{25}{27}$ **37.** $\frac{11}{20}$ sq mi **39.** $\frac{7}{36}$ sq ft **41.** $\frac{3}{5}$ **43.** 1 **45.** $\frac{1}{3}$ **47.** $\frac{9}{35}$ **49.** $\frac{21}{30}$ **51.** $\frac{4}{18}$ **53.** $\frac{16}{20}$ **55.** $\frac{23}{21}$ **57.** $\frac{11}{60}$ **59.** $\frac{5}{66}$ **61.** $\frac{7}{5}$ **63.** $\frac{1}{5}$ **65.** $\frac{3}{8}$ **67.** $\frac{1}{9}$ **69.** $18\frac{20}{27}$ **71.** $2\frac{28}{29}$ **73.** $48\frac{1}{15}$ **75.** $7\frac{1}{12}$ **77.** $\frac{5}{7}$ **79.** $\frac{65}{21}$ **81.** $\frac{2}{5}$ **83.** $\frac{10}{9}$ **85.** $\frac{17}{3}$ **87.** 37 **89.** $\frac{5}{66}$ **91.** $\frac{1}{5}$ **93.** $5\frac{1}{6}$ **95.** $\frac{17}{18}$ **97.** $55\frac{1}{4}$ ft **99.** answers may vary **101.** $3\frac{3}{8}$ mi **103.** $\frac{21}{100}$ **105.** multiplexes **107.** incorrect; $\frac{12}{24} = \frac{2 \cdot 2 \cdot 3}{2 \cdot 2 \cdot 2 \cdot 3} = \frac{1}{2}$ **109.** incorrect; $\frac{2}{7} + \frac{9}{7} = \frac{11}{7}$

Section 1.4
Practice Exercises

1. a. 1 **b.** 25 **c.** $\frac{1}{100}$ **d.** 9 **e.** $\frac{8}{125}$ **2. a.** 33 **b.** 11 **c.** $\frac{32}{9}$ or $3\frac{5}{9}$ **d.** 36 **e.** $\frac{3}{16}$ **3.** $\frac{31}{11}$ **4.** 4 **5.** $\frac{9}{22}$ **6. a.** 9 **b.** $\frac{8}{15}$ **c.** $\frac{19}{10}$ **d.** 33 **7.** No **8. a.** $6x$ **b.** $x - 8$ **c.** $x \cdot 9$ or $9x$ **d.** $2x + 3$ **e.** $7 + x$ **9. a.** $x + 7 = 13$ **b.** $x - 2 = 11$ **c.** $2x + 9 \neq 25$ **d.** $5(11) \geq x$

Graphing Calculator Explorations 1.4

1. 625 **3.** 59,049 **5.** 30 **7.** 9857 **9.** 2376

Vocabulary, Readiness & Video Check 1.4

1. base; exponent **3.** variable **5.** equation **7.** solving **9.** The replacement value for z is not used because it's not needed–there is no variable z in the given algebraic expression. **11.** We translate phrases to mathematical expressions and sentences to mathematical equations.

Exercise Set 1.4

1. 243 **3.** 27 **5.** 1 **7.** 5 **9.** 49 **11.** $\frac{16}{81}$ **13.** $\frac{1}{125}$ **15.** 1.44 **17.** 0.000064 **19.** 17 **21.** 20 **23.** 10 **25.** 21

27. 45 **29.** 0 **31.** 30 **33.** 2 **35.** $\frac{7}{18}$ **37.** $\frac{27}{10}$ **39.** $\frac{7}{5}$ **41.** 32 **43.** $\frac{23}{27}$ **45. a.** 64 **b.** 43 **c.** 19 **d.** 22 **47.** 9

49. 1 **51.** 1 **53.** 11 **55.** 8 **57.** 45 **59.** 27 **61.** 132 **63.** $\frac{37}{18}$ **65.** 16; 64; 144; 256 **67.** yes **69.** no **71.** no **73.** yes

75. no **77.** $x + 15$ **79.** $x - 5$ **81.** $\frac{x}{4}$ **83.** $3x + 22$ **85.** $1 + 2 = 9 \div 3$ **87.** $3 \neq 4 \div 2$ **89.** $5 + x = 20$ **91.** $7.6x = 17$

93. $13 - 3x = 13$ **95.** multiply **97.** subtract **99.** no; answers may vary **101.** 14 in., 12 sq in. **103.** 14 in., 9.01 sq in. **105.** Rectangles with the same perimeter can have different areas. **107.** $(20 - 4) \cdot 4 \div 2$ **109. a.** expression **b.** equation **c.** equation **d.** expression **e.** expression **111.** answers may vary **113.** answers may vary, for example, $-2(5) - 1$ **115.** 12,000 sq ft **117.** 51 mph

Section 1.5
Practice Exercises

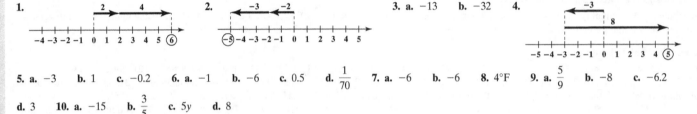

1. **2.** **3. a.** -13 **b.** -32 **4.**

5. a. -3 **b.** 1 **c.** -0.2 **6. a.** -1 **b.** -6 **c.** 0.5 **d.** $\frac{1}{70}$ **7. a.** -6 **b.** -6 **8.** 4°F **9. a.** $\frac{5}{9}$ **b.** -8 **c.** -6.2

d. 3 **10. a.** -15 **b.** $\frac{3}{5}$ **c.** $5y$ **d.** 8

Vocabulary, Readiness & Video Check 1.5
1. opposites **3.** n **5.** absolute values **7.** Negative temperatures; the high temperature for the day was -6°F

Exercise Set 1.5

1. 9 **3.** -14 **5.** 1 **7.** -12 **9.** -5 **11.** -12 **13.** -4 **15.** 7 **17.** -2 **19.** 0 **21.** -19 **23.** 31 **25.** -47

27. -2.1 **29.** -8 **31.** 38 **33.** -13.1 **35.** $\frac{2}{8} = \frac{1}{4}$ **37.** $-\frac{3}{16}$ **39.** $-\frac{13}{10}$ **41.** -8 **43.** -59 **45.** -9 **47.** 5 **49.** 11

51. -18 **53.** 19 **55.** -0.7 **57.** $-6°$ **59.** 146 ft **61.** $-\$6.9$ million **63.** -16 **65.** -6 **67.** 2 **69.** 0 **71.** -6 **73.** -2

75. 0 **77.** $-\frac{2}{3}$ **79.** yes **81.** no **83.** July **85.** October **87.** 4.7°F **89.** -3 **91.** -22 **93.** negative **95.** positive **97.** true

99. false **101.** answers may vary **103.** answers may vary

Section 1.6
Practice Exercises

1. a. -13 **b.** -7 **c.** 12 **d.** -2 **2. a.** 10.9 **b.** $-\frac{1}{2}$ **c.** $-\frac{19}{20}$ **3.** -7 **4. a.** -6 **b.** 6.1 **5. a.** -20 **b.** 13 **6. a.** 2

b. 13 **7.** $\$357$ **8. a.** 28° **b.** 137°

Vocabulary, Readiness & Video Check 1.6
1. $7 - x$ **3.** $x - 7$ **5.** $7 - x$ **7.** $-10 - (-14)$; d **9.** addition; opposite **11.** There's a minus sign in the numerator and the replacement value is negative (notice parentheses are used around the replacement value), and it's always good to be careful when working with negative signs. **13.** In Example 9, you have two supplementary angles and know the measure of one of them. From the definition, you know that two supplementary angles must sum to 180°. Therefore you can subtract the known angle measure from 180° to get the measure of the other angle.

Exercise Set 1.6

1. -10 **3.** -5 **5.** 19 **7.** $\frac{1}{6}$ **9.** 2 **11.** -11 **13.** 11 **15.** 5 **17.** 37 **19.** -6.4 **21.** -71 **23.** 0 **25.** 4.1

27. $\frac{2}{11}$ **29.** $-\frac{11}{12}$ **31.** 8.92 **33.** 13 **35.** -5 **37.** -1 **39.** -23 **41.** -26 **43.** -24 **45.** 3 **47.** -45 **49.** -4

51. 13 **53.** 6 **55.** 9 **57.** -9 **59.** -7 **61.** $\frac{7}{5}$ **63.** 21 **65.** $\frac{1}{4}$ **67.** 100°F **69.** 265°F **71.** 35,653 ft **73.** -308 ft

75. 19,852 ft **77.** 130° **79.** 30° **81.** no **83.** no **85.** yes **87.** $-5 + x$ **89.** $-20 - x$ **91.** $-4.4°; 2.6°; 12°; 23.5°; 15.3°$ **93.** May **95.** answers may vary **97.** 16 **99.** -20 **101.** true; answers may vary **103.** false; answers may vary **105.** negative, $-30,387$

Integrated Review

1. negative **2.** negative **3.** positive **4.** 0 **5.** positive **6.** 0 **7.** positive **8.** positive **9.** $-\frac{1}{7}; \frac{1}{7}$ **10.** $\frac{12}{5}; \frac{12}{5}$ **11.** 3; 3

12. $-\frac{9}{11}; \frac{9}{11}$ **13.** -42 **14.** 10 **15.** 2 **16.** -18 **17.** -7 **18.** -39 **19.** -2 **20.** -9 **21.** -3.4 **22.** -9.8 **23.** $-\frac{25}{28}$

24. $-\frac{5}{24}$ **25.** -4 **26.** -24 **27.** 6 **28.** 20 **29.** 6 **30.** 61 **31.** -6 **32.** -16 **33.** -19 **34.** -13 **35.** -4 **36.** -1

37. $\frac{13}{20}$ **38.** $-\frac{29}{40}$ **39.** 4 **40.** 9 **41.** -1 **42.** -3 **43.** 8 **44.** 10 **45.** 47 **46.** $\frac{2}{3}$

Section 1.7
Practice Exercises

1. a. -40 **b.** 12 **c.** -54 **2. a.** -30 **b.** 24 **c.** 0 **d.** 26 **3. a.** -0.046 **b.** $-\dfrac{4}{15}$ **c.** 14 **4. a.** 36 **b.** -36 **c.** -64

d. -64 **5. a.** $\dfrac{3}{8}$ **b.** $\dfrac{1}{15}$ **c.** $-\dfrac{7}{2}$ **d.** $-\dfrac{1}{5}$ **6. a.** -8 **b.** -4 **c.** 5 **7. a.** 3 **b.** -16 **c.** $-\dfrac{6}{5}$ **d.** $-\dfrac{1}{18}$ **8. a.** 0

b. undefined   **c.** undefined   **9. a.** $-\dfrac{84}{5}$ **b.** 11 **10. a.** -9 **b.** 33 **c.** $\dfrac{5}{3}$ **11.** -52

Graphing Calculator Explorations 1.7

1. 38 **3.** -441 **5.** $163.\overline{3}$ **7.** $54{,}499$ **9.** $15{,}625$

Vocabulary, Readiness & Video Check 1.7

1. $0; 0$ **3.** positive   **5.** negative   **7.** positive   **9.** The parentheses, or lack of them, determine the base of the expression. In Example 6, $(-2)^4$, the base is -2 and all of -2 is raised to 4. In Example 7, -2^4, the base is 2 and only 2 is raised to 4.   **11.** Yes; because division of real numbers is defined in terms of multiplication.   **13.** The football team lost 4 yards on each play and a loss of yardage is represented by a negative number.

Exercise Set 1.7

1. -24 **3.** -2 **5.** 50 **7.** -12 **9.** 0 **11.** -18 **13.** $\dfrac{3}{10}$ **15.** $\dfrac{2}{3}$ **17.** -7 **19.** 0.14 **21.** -800 **23.** -28 **25.** 25

27. $-\dfrac{8}{27}$ **29.** -121 **31.** $-\dfrac{1}{4}$ **33.** -30 **35.** 23 **37.** -7 **39.** true   **41.** false   **43.** 16 **45.** -1 **47.** 25 **49.** -49

51. $\dfrac{1}{9}$ **53.** $\dfrac{3}{2}$ **55.** $-\dfrac{1}{14}$ **57.** $-\dfrac{11}{3}$ **59.** $\dfrac{1}{0.2}$ **61.** -6.3 **63.** -9 **65.** 4 **67.** -4 **69.** 0 **71.** -5 **73.** undefined

75. 3 **77.** -15 **79.** $-\dfrac{18}{7}$ **81.** $\dfrac{20}{27}$ **83.** -1 **85.** $-\dfrac{9}{2}$ **87.** -4 **89.** 16 **91.** -3 **93.** $-\dfrac{16}{7}$ **95.** 2 **97.** $\dfrac{6}{5}$ **99.** -5

101. $\dfrac{3}{2}$ **103.** -21 **105.** 41 **107.** -134 **109.** 3 **111.** 0 **113.** $-71 \cdot x$ or $-71x$ **115.** $-16 - x$ **117.** $-29 + x$ **119.** $\dfrac{x}{-33}$

or $x \div (-33)$ **121.** $3 \cdot (-4) = -12$; a loss of 12 yd   **123.** $5(-20) = -100$; a depth of 100 ft   **125.** yes   **127.** no   **129.** yes   **131.** $-162°F$

133. answers may vary   **135.** $1, -1$ **137.** positive   **139.** not possible   **141.** negative   **143.** $-2 + \dfrac{-15}{3}$; -7 **145.** $2[-5 + (-3)]$; -16

Section 1.8
Practice Exercises

1. a. $8 \cdot x$ **b.** $17 + x$ **2. a.** $2 + (9 + 7)$ **b.** $(-4 \cdot 2) \cdot 7$ **3. a.** $x + 14$ **b.** $-30x$ **4. a.** $5x - 5y$ **b.** $-24 - 12t$
c. $6x - 8y - 2z$ **d.** $-3 + y$ **e.** $-x + 7 - 2s$ **f.** $x + 11$ **5. a.** $5(w + 3)$ **b.** $9(w + z)$ **6. a.** commutative property of multiplication   **b.** associative property of addition   **c.** identity element for addition   **d.** multiplicative inverse property   **e.** commutative property of addition   **f.** additive inverse property   **g.** commutative and associative properties of multiplication

Vocabulary, Readiness & Video Check 1.8

1. commutative property of addition   **3.** distributive property   **5.** associative property of addition   **7.** opposites or additive inverses
9. 2 is outside the parentheses, so the point is made that you should only distribute the -9 to the terms within the parentheses and not also to the 2.

Exercise Set 1.8

1. $16 + x$ **3.** $y \cdot (-4)$ **5.** yx **7.** $13 + 2x$ **9.** $x \cdot (yz)$ **11.** $(2 + a) + b$ **13.** $(4a) \cdot b$ **15.** $a + (b + c)$ **17.** $17 + b$
19. $24y$ **21.** y **23.** $26 + a$ **25.** $-72x$ **27.** s **29.** $2 + x$ **31.** $4x + 4y$ **33.** $9x - 54$ **35.** $6x + 10$ **37.** $28x - 21$
39. $18 + 3x$ **41.** $-2y + 2z$ **43.** $-21y - 35$ **45.** $5x + 20m + 10$ **47.** $-4 + 8m - 4n$ **49.** $-5x - 2$ **51.** $-r + 3 + 7p$
53. $3x + 4$ **55.** $-x + 3y$ **57.** $6r + 8$ **59.** $-36x - 70$ **61.** $-16x - 25$ **63.** $4(1 + y)$ **65.** $11(x + y)$ **67.** $-1(5 + x)$
69. $30(a + b)$ **71.** commutative property of multiplication   **73.** associative property of addition   **75.** distributive property
77. associative property of multiplication   **79.** identity element of addition   **81.** distributive property   **83.** commutative and associative

properties of multiplication   **85.** $-8; \dfrac{1}{8}$ **87.** $-x; \dfrac{1}{x}$ **89.** $2x; -2x$ **91.** false   **93.** no   **95.** yes   **97.** yes   **99.** no

101. a. commutative property of addition   **b.** commutative property of addition   **c.** associative property of addition   **103.** answers may vary
105. answers may vary

Chapter 1 Vocabulary Check

1. inequality symbols   **2.** equation   **3.** absolute value   **4.** variable   **5.** opposites   **6.** numerator   **7.** solution   **8.** reciprocals
9. base; exponent   **10.** denominator   **11.** grouping symbols   **12.** set

Chapter 1 Review

1. $<$ **3.** $>$ **5.** $<$ **7.** $=$ **9.** $>$ **11.** $4 \geq -3$ **13.** $0.03 < 0.3$ **15. a.** $1, 3$ **b.** $0, 1, 3$ **c.** $-6, 0, 1, 3$

d. $-6, 0, 1, 1\dfrac{1}{2}, 3, 9.62$ **e.** π **f.** $-6, 0, 1, 1\dfrac{1}{2}, 3, \pi, 9.62$ **17.** Friday   **19.** $2 \cdot 2 \cdot 3 \cdot 3$ **21.** $\dfrac{12}{25}$ **23.** $\dfrac{13}{10}$ **25.** $9\dfrac{3}{8}$ **27.** 15

29. $\dfrac{7}{12}$ **31.** $A = 1\dfrac{1}{6}$ sq m; $P = 4\dfrac{5}{12}$ m   **33.** $14\dfrac{1}{8}$ lb   **35.** $18\dfrac{7}{16}$ lb   **37.** Baby E   **39.** c   **41.** $\dfrac{4}{49}$ **43.** 37 **45.** $\dfrac{18}{7}$

47. $20 - 12 = 2 \cdot 4$ **49.** 18 **51.** 5 **53.** $63°$ **55.** yes   **57.** 9 **59.** -2 **61.** -11 **63.** $-\dfrac{3}{16}$ **65.** -13.9 **67.** -14

69. 5 **71.** -19 **73.** a **75.** \$51 **77.** $-\dfrac{1}{6}$ **79.** -48 **81.** 3 **83.** undefined **85.** undefined **87.** -12 **89.** 9

91. $-7 \cdot x$ or $-7x$ **93.** $-20 - x$ **95.** commutative property of addition **97.** distributive property **99.** associative property of addition
101. distributive property **103.** multiplicative inverse property **105.** $5y - 10$ **107.** $-7 + x - 4z$ **109.** $-12z - 27$ **111.** $<$

113. -15.3 **115.** -80 **117.** $-\dfrac{1}{4}$ **119.** 16 **121.** -5 **123.** $-\dfrac{5}{6}$ **125.** $1\dfrac{3}{8}$ ft

Chapter 1 Test

1. $|-7| > 5$ **2.** $9 + 5 \geq 4$ **3.** -5 **4.** -11 **5.** -3 **6.** -39 **7.** 12 **8.** -2 **9.** undefined **10.** -8 **11.** $-\dfrac{1}{3}$ **12.** $4\dfrac{5}{8}$

13. 1.275 **14.** -32 **15.** -48 **16.** 3 **17.** 0 **18.** $>$ **19.** $>$ **20.** $<$ **21.** $=$ **22.** $2221 < 10{,}993$ **23. a.** 1, 7 **b.** 0, 1, 7

c. $-5, -1, 0, 1, 7$ **d.** $-5, -1, 0, \dfrac{1}{4}, 1, 7, 11.6$ **e.** $\sqrt{7}, 3\pi$ **f.** $-5, -1, 0, \dfrac{1}{4}, 1, 7, 11.6, \sqrt{7}, 3\pi$ **24.** 40 **25.** 12 **26.** 22 **27.** -1
28. associative property of addition **29.** commutative property of multiplication **30.** distributive property **31.** multiplicative inverse property
32. 9 **33.** -3 **34.** second down **35.** yes **36.** $17°$ **37.** \$650 million **38.** \$420

CHAPTER 2 EQUATIONS, INEQUALITIES, AND PROBLEM SOLVING

Section 2.1
Practice Exercises

1. a. 1 **b.** -7 **c.** $-\dfrac{1}{5}$ **d.** 43 **e.** -1 **2. a.** like terms **b.** unlike terms **c.** like terms **d.** like terms **3. a.** $8y$ **b.** $5x^2$

c. $5x + 5x^2$ **d.** $21y^2$ **4. a.** $11y - 5$ **b.** $5x - 6$ **c.** $-\dfrac{1}{4}t$ **d.** $12.2y + 13$ **e.** $5z - 3z^4$ **5. a.** $6x - 21$ **b.** $-5x + 2.5z + 25$

c. $-2x + y - z + 2$ **6. a.** $36x + 10$ **b.** $-11x + 1$ **c.** $-30x - 17$ **7.** $-5x + 4$ **8. a.** $2x + 3$ **b.** $x - 1$ **c.** $2x + 10$ **d.** $\dfrac{13}{2}x$

Vocabulary, Readiness & Video Check 2.1
1. expression; term **3.** numerical coefficient **5.** numerical coefficient **7.** Although these terms have exactly the same variables, the exponents on each are not exactly the same—the exponents on x differ in each term. **9.** -1

Exercise Set 2.1
1. -7 **3.** 1 **5.** 17 **7.** like **9.** unlike **11.** like **13.** $15y$ **15.** $13w$ **17.** $-7b - 9$ **19.** $-m - 6$ **21.** -8 **23.** $7.2x - 5.2$
25. $4x - 3$ **27.** $5x^2$ **29.** $1.3x + 3.5$ **31.** $5y - 20$ **33.** $-2x - 4$ **35.** $7d - 11$ **37.** $-10x + 15y - 30$ **39.** $-3x + 2y - 1$
41. $2x + 14$ **43.** $10x - 3$ **45.** $-4x - 9$ **47.** $-4m - 3$ **49.** $k - 6$ **51.** $-15x + 18$ **53.** 16 **55.** $x + 5$ **57.** $x + 2$

59. $2k + 10$ **61.** $-3x + 5$ **63.** -11 **65.** $3y + \dfrac{5}{6}$ **67.** $-22 + 24x$ **69.** $0.9m + 1$ **71.** $10 - 6x - 9y$ **73.** $-x - 38$ **75.** $5x - 7$

77. $2x - 4$ **79.** $2x + 7$ **81.** $\dfrac{3}{4}x + 12$ **83.** $-2 + 12x$ **85.** $8(x + 6)$ or $8x + 48$ **87.** $x - 10$ **89.** $7x - 7$ **91.** 2 **93.** -23

95. -25 **97.** $(18x - 2)$ ft **99.** balanced **101.** balanced **103.** answers may vary **105.** $(15x + 23)$ in. **107.** answers may vary
109. $5b^2c^3 + b^3c^2$ **111.** $5x^2 + 9x$ **113.** $-7x^2y$

Section 2.2
Practice Exercises
1. -8 **2.** -1.8 **3.** -10 **4.** 18 **5.** 20 **6.** -12 **7.** 65 **8.** -3 **9. a.** 7 **b.** $9 - x$ **c.** $(9 - x)$ ft **10.** $3x + 6$

Vocabulary, Readiness & Video Check 2.2
1. equation; expression **3.** solution **5.** addition **7.** multiplication **9.** true **11.** both sides **13.** addition property; multiplication property; answers may vary

Exercise Set 2.2
1. 3 **3.** -2 **5.** -14 **7.** 0.5 **9.** -3 **11.** -0.7 **13.** 3 **15.** 11 **17.** 0 **19.** -3 **21.** 16 **23.** -4 **25.** 0 **27.** 12
29. 10 **31.** -12 **33.** 3 **35.** -2 **37.** 0 **39.** answers may vary **41.** 10 **43.** -20 **45.** 0 **47.** -5 **49.** 0
51. $-\dfrac{3}{2}$ **53.** -21 **55.** $\dfrac{11}{2}$ **57.** 1 **59.** $-\dfrac{1}{4}$ **61.** 12 **63.** -30 **65.** $\dfrac{9}{10}$ **67.** -30 **69.** 2 **71.** -2 **73.** 23
75. $20 - p$ **77.** $(10 - x)$ ft **79.** $(180 - x)°$ **81.** $(n + 284)$ votes **83.** $(m - 60)$ ft **85.** $(n - 28{,}000)$ students **87.** $7x$ sq mi
89. $2x + 2$ **91.** $2x + 2$ **93.** $5x + 20$ **95.** $7x - 12$ **97.** 1 **99.** $>$ **101.** $=$ **103.** $(173 - 3x)°$ **105.** answers may vary

107. 4 **109.** answers may vary **111.** answers may vary **113.** -48 **115.** $\dfrac{700}{3}$ mg **117.** solution **119.** -2.95 **121.** 0.02

Section 2.3
Practice Exercises

1. 3 **2.** $\dfrac{21}{13}$ **3.** -15 **4.** 3 **5.** 0 **6.** no solution **7.** all real numbers

Graphing Calculator Explorations 2.3

1. solution   **3.** not a solution   **5.** solution

Vocabulary, Readiness & Video Check 2.3

1. equation   **3.** expression   **5.** expression   **7.** equation   **9.** 3; distributive property, addition property of equality, multiplication property of equality   **11.** The number of decimal places in each number helps you determine what power of 10 you can multiply through by so you are no longer dealing with decimals.

Exercise Set 2.3

1. -6 **3.** 3   **5.** 1   **7.** $\dfrac{3}{2}$ **9.** 0   **11.** -1 **13.** 4   **15.** -4 **17.** -3 **19.** 2   **21.** 50   **23.** 1   **25.** $\dfrac{7}{3}$ **27.** 0.2

29. all real numbers   **31.** no solution   **33.** no solution   **35.** all real numbers   **37.** 18   **39.** $\dfrac{19}{9}$ **41.** $\dfrac{14}{3}$ **43.** 13   **45.** 4

47. all real numbers   **49.** $-\dfrac{3}{5}$ **51.** -5 **53.** 10   **55.** no solution   **57.** 3   **59.** -17 **61.** -4 **63.** 3   **65.** all real numbers

67. $-8 - x$ **69.** $-3 + 2x$ **71.** $9(x + 20)$ **73.** $(6x - 8)$ m   **75. a.** all real numbers   **b.** answers may vary   **c.** answers may vary
77. A   **79.** B   **81.** C   **83.** answers may vary   **85. a.** $x + x + x + 2x + 2x = 28$ **b.** $x = 4$ **c.** $x = 4$ cm; $2x = 8$ cm   **87.** answers

may vary   **89.** 15.3   **91.** -0.2 **93.** $-\dfrac{7}{8}$ **95.** no solution

Integrated Review

1. 6   **2.** -17 **3.** 12   **4.** -26 **5.** -3 **6.** -1 **7.** $\dfrac{27}{2}$ **8.** $\dfrac{25}{2}$ **9.** 8   **10.** -64 **11.** 2   **12.** -3 **13.** no solution

14. no solution   **15.** -2 **16.** -2 **17.** $-\dfrac{5}{6}$ **18.** $\dfrac{1}{6}$ **19.** 1   **20.** 6   **21.** 4   **22.** 1   **23.** $\dfrac{9}{5}$ **24.** $-\dfrac{6}{5}$ **25.** all real numbers

26. all real numbers   **27.** 0   **28.** -1.6 **29.** $\dfrac{4}{19}$ **30.** $-\dfrac{5}{19}$ **31.** $\dfrac{7}{2}$ **32.** $-\dfrac{1}{4}$ **33.** 2   **34.** 2   **35.** no solution   **36.** no solution

37. $\dfrac{7}{6}$ **38.** $\dfrac{1}{15}$

Section 2.4
Practice Exercises

1. 9   **2.** 2   **3.** 9 in. and 36 in.   **4.** 29 Republican and 20 Democratic governors   **5.** $25°, 75°, 80°$ **6.** $46, 48, 50$

Vocabulary, Readiness & Video Check 2.4

1. $2x; 2x - 31$ **3.** $x + 5; 2(x + 5)$ **5.** $20 - y; \dfrac{20 - y}{3}$ or $(20 - y) \div 3$ **7.** in the statement of the application   **9.** That the 3 angle measures are consecutive even integers and that they sum to $180°$.

Exercise Set 2.4

1. $6x + 1 = 5x; -1$ **3.** $3x - 6 = 2x + 8; 14$ **5.** $2(x - 8) = 3(x + 3); -25$ **7.** $2(-2 + x) = x - \dfrac{1}{2}; \dfrac{7}{2}$ **9.** 3 in.; 6 in.; 16 in.

11. 1st piece: 5 in.; 2nd piece: 10 in.; 3rd piece: 25 in.   **13.** 7837 screens; 31,710; In 2010, 7837 screens were 3D.   **15.** 1st angle: $37.5°$;
2nd angle: $37.5°$; 3rd angle: $105°$ **17.** $3x + 3$ **19.** $x + 2; x + 4; 2x + 4$ **21.** $x + 1; x + 2; x + 3; 4x + 6$ **23.** $x + 2; x + 4; 2x + 6$

25. $234, 235$ **27.** Belgium: 32; France: 33; Spain: 34   **29.** Sahara: 3,500,000 sq mi; Gobi: 500,000 sq mi   **31.** 5 ft, 12 ft   **33.** $\dfrac{5}{4}$

35. Botswana: 32,000,000 carats; Angola: 8,000,000 carats   **37.** $58°, 60°, 62°$ **39.** South Korea: 14; Russia: 15; Austria: 16   **41.** -16 **43.** $43°, 137°$

45. 1   **47.** $\dfrac{3}{2}$ **49.** Maglev: 361 mph; TGV: 357.2 mph   **51.** $\dfrac{5}{2}$ **53.** California: 58; Montana: 56   **55.** $111°$ **57.** 1st piece: 3 ft; 2nd piece:

12 ft; 3rd piece: 15 ft   **59.** Eagles: *Their Greatest Hits, 1971–1975*   **61.** *Thriller*: $27 million; *The Wall*: $23 million   **63.** answers may vary
65. 34   **67.** 225π **69.** 15 ft by 24 ft   **71.** 5400 chirps per hour; 129,600 chirps per day; 47,304,000 chirps per year   **73.** answers may vary
75. answers may vary   **77.** c

Section 2.5
Practice Exercises

1. 116 sec or 1 min 56 sec   **2.** 9 ft   **3.** $46.4°F$ **4.** length: 28 in.; width: 5 in.   **5.** $r = \dfrac{I}{Pt}$ **6.** $s = \dfrac{H - 10a}{5a}$ **7.** $d = \dfrac{N - F}{n - 1}$

8. $B = \dfrac{2A - ab}{a}$

Vocabulary, Readiness & Video Check 2.5

1. relationships   **3.** To show that the process of solving this equation for x—dividing both sides by 5, the coefficient of x—is the same process used to solve a formula for a specific variable. Treat whatever is multiplied by that specific variable as the coefficient—the coefficient is all the factors except that specific variable.

Exercise Set 2.5

1. $h = 3$ **3.** $h = 3$ **5.** $h = 20$ **7.** $c = 12$ **9.** $r \approx 2.5$ **11.** $T = 3$ **13.** $h \approx 15$ **15.** $h = \dfrac{f}{5g}$ **17.** $w = \dfrac{V}{lh}$ **19.** $y = 7 - 3x$

21. $R = \dfrac{A - P}{PT}$ **23.** $A = \dfrac{3V}{h}$ **25.** $a = P - b - c$ **27.** $h = \dfrac{S - 2\pi r^2}{2\pi r}$ **29.** 120 ft   **31. a.** area: 103.5 sq ft; perimeter: 41 ft

b. baseboard: perimeter; carpet: area   **33. a.** area: 480 sq in.; perimeter: 120 in.   **b.** frame: perimeter; glass: area   **35.** −10°C   **37.** length: 78 ft; width: 52 ft   **39.** 18 ft, 36 ft, 48 ft   **41.** 55.2 mph   **43.** 96 piranhas   **45.** 61.5°F   **47.** 60 chirps per minute   **49.** increases   **51.** 2 bags   **53.** one 16-in. pizza   **55.** $x = 6$ m, $2.5x = 15$ m   **57.** 22 hr   **59.** 13 in.   **61.** 2.25 hr   **63.** 12,090 ft   **65.** 50°C   **67.** 332.6°F   **69.** 449 cu in.   **71.** 0.32   **73.** 2.00 or 2   **75.** 17%   **77.** 720%   **79.** multiplies the volume by 8; answers may vary   **81.** $53\frac{1}{3}$ **83.** $V = G(N - R)$ **85.** 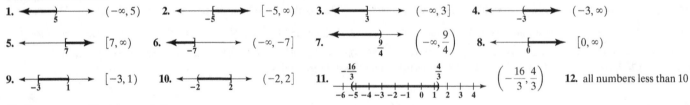 $\bigcirc = \dfrac{\blacksquare - \blacktriangle}{\blacksquare}$ **87.** 500 sec or $8\frac{1}{3}$ min   **89.** 608.33 ft   **91.** 4.42 min   **93.** $35\frac{11}{17}$ mph

Section 2.6
Practice Exercises
1. 62.5%   **2.** 360   **3. a.** 42%   **b.** 98%   **c.** 79.3 million dogs   **4.** discount: $408; new price: $72   **5.** 42.6%   **6.** 3554 screens   **7.** 2 liters of 5% eyewash; 4 liters of 2% eyewash

Vocabulary, Readiness & Video Check 2.6
1. no   **3.** yes   **5. a.** equals; =   **b.** multiplication; ·   **c.** Drop the percent symbol and move the decimal point two places to the left.   **7.** You must first find the actual amount of increase in price by subtracting the original price from the new price.

Exercise Set 2.6
1. 11.2   **3.** 55%   **5.** 180   **7.** 4%   **9.** 9990   **11.** discount: $1480; new price: $17,020   **13.** $46.58   **15.** 9.8%   **17.** 30%   **19.** $104   **21.** $42,500   **23.** 2 gal   **25.** 7 lb   **27.** 4.6   **29.** 50   **31.** 30%   **33.** 23%   **35.** 90,405   **37.** 59%; 5%; 26%; 2%; 99% due to rounding   **39.** decrease: $64; sale price: $192   **41.** 27.2%   **43.** 239 million   **45.** 300%   **47.** 400 oz   **49.** 66.7%   **51.** 120 employees   **53.** 361 college students   **55.** 400 oz   **57.** 854 thousand Scoville units   **59.** >   **61.** =   **63.** >   **65.** no; answers may vary   **67.** no; answers may vary   **69.** 9.6%   **71.** 26.9%; yes   **73.** 17.1%

Section 2.7
Practice Exercises
1. 2.2 hr   **2.** eastbound: 62 mph; westbound: 52 mph   **3.** 106 $5 bills; 59 $20 bills   **4.** $18,000 at 11.5%; $12,000 at 6%

Vocabulary, Readiness & Video Check 2.7
1.

	r ·	t =	d
bus	55	x	$55x$
car	50	$x + 3$	$50(x + 3)$

; $55x = 50(x + 3)$

3.

P ·	R ·	T =	I
x	0.06	1	$0.06x$
$36{,}000 - x$	0.04	1	$0.04(36{,}000 - x)$

; $0.06x = 0.04(36{,}000 - x)$

Exercise Set 2.7
1. $666\frac{2}{3}$ mi   **3.** 55 mph   **5.** $0.10y$ **7.** $0.05(x + 7)$ **9.** $20(4y)$ or $80y$ **11.** $50(35 - x)$ **13.** 12 $10 bills; 32 $5 bills   **15.** $11,500 at 8%; $13,500 at 9%   **17.** $7000 at 11% profit; $3000 at 4% loss   **19.** 187 adult tickets; 313 child tickets   **21.** 2 hr   **23.** $30,000 at 8%; $24,000 at 10%   **25.** 2 hr $37\frac{1}{2}$ min   **27.** 36 mph; 46 mph   **29.** 483 dimes; 161 nickels   **31.** 4 hr   **33.** 2.5 hr   **35.** $4500   **37.** 2.2 mph; 3.3 mph   **39.** 27.5 mi   **41.** −4   **43.** $\frac{9}{16}$ **45.** −4   **47.** 25 $100 bills; 71 $50 bills; 175 $20 bills   **49.** 25 skateboards   **51.** 800 books   **53.** answers may vary

Section 2.8
Practice Exercises
1. $(-\infty, 5)$ **2.** $[-5, \infty)$ **3.** $(-\infty, 3]$ **4.** $(-3, \infty)$ **5.** $[7, \infty)$ **6.** $(-\infty, -7]$ **7.** $\left(-\infty, \frac{9}{4}\right)$ **8.** $[0, \infty)$ **9.** $[-3, 1)$ **10.** $(-2, 2]$ **11.** $\left(-\frac{16}{3}, \frac{4}{3}\right)$ **12.** all numbers less than 10

13. Kasonga can afford at most 3 classes.

Vocabulary, Readiness & Video Check 2.8
1. expression   **3.** inequality   **5.** −5   **7.** The graph of Example 1 is shaded from −∞ to and including −1, as indicated by a bracket. To write interval notation, you write down what is shaded for the inequality from left to right. A parenthesis is always used with −∞, so from the graph, the interval notation is $(-\infty, -1]$.   **9.** You would divide the left, middle, and right by −3 instead of 3, which would reverse the directions of both inequality symbols.

Exercise Set 2.8
1. $x \geq 2$ **3.** $x < -5$ **5.** $(-\infty, -1]$ **7.** $\left(-\infty, \frac{1}{2}\right)$ **9.** $[5, \infty)$ **11.** $x < -3$, $(-\infty, -3)$ **13.** $x \geq -5$, $[-5, \infty)$ **15.** $x \geq -2$, $[2, \infty)$ **17.** $x > -3$, $(-3, \infty)$ **19.** $x \leq 1$, $(-\infty, 1]$ **21.** $x > -5$, $(-5, \infty)$ **23.** $x \leq -2$, $(-\infty, -2]$ **25.** $x \leq -8$, $(-\infty, -8]$

27. $x > 4$,   [graph] $(4, \infty)$ **29.** $x \geq 20$,   [graph] $[20, \infty)$ **31.** $x > 16$,   [graph] $(16, \infty)$

33. $x > -3$,   [graph] $(-3, \infty)$ **35.** $x \leq -\dfrac{2}{3}$,   [graph] $\left(-\infty, -\dfrac{2}{3}\right]$ **37.** $x > \dfrac{8}{3}$,   [graph] $\left(\dfrac{8}{3}, \infty\right)$

39. $x > -13$,   [graph] $(-13, \infty)$ **41.** $x < 0$,   [graph] $(-\infty, 0)$ **43.** $x \leq 0$,   [graph] $(-\infty, 0]$

45. $x > 3$,   [graph] $(3, \infty)$ **47.** $x > \dfrac{8}{3}$ [graph] $\left(\dfrac{8}{3}, \infty\right)$ **49.** [graph] $(-1, 3)$ **51.** [graph] $[0, 2)$

53. [graph] $(-1, 2)$ **55.** [graph] $[4, 5]$ **57.** [graph] $(1, 5]$ **59.** [graph] $(1, 4)$

61. [graph] $\left(0, \dfrac{14}{3}\right]$ **63.** all numbers greater than -10 **65.** 35 cm   **67.** at least 193   **69.** 86 people   **71.** at least 35 min

73. $-3 < x < 3$ **75.** 8   **77.** 1   **79.** $\dfrac{16}{49}$ **81.** $>$ **83.** $\geq$ **85.** when multiplying or dividing by a negative number

87. final exam score ≥ 78.5 **89.** answers may vary   **91.** answers may vary   **93.** $0.924 \leq d \leq 0.987$ **95.** [graph] $(1, \infty)$

97. [graph] $\left(-\infty, \dfrac{5}{8}\right)$

Chapter 2 Vocabulary Check

1. like terms   **2.** unlike terms   **3.** linear equation in one variable   **4.** linear inequality in one variable   **5.** compound inequalities   **6.** formula
7. numerical coefficient   **8.** equivalent equations   **9.** all real numbers   **10.** no solution   **11.** the same   **12.** reversed

Chapter 2 Review

1. $6x$ **3.** $4x - 2$ **5.** $3n - 18$ **7.** $-6x + 7$ **9.** $3x - 7$ **11.** 4   **13.** 6   **15.** 0   **17.** -23 **19.** 5; 5   **21.** b   **23.** b   **25.** -12
27. 0   **29.** 0.75   **31.** -6 **33.** -1 **35.** $-\dfrac{1}{5}$ **37.** $3x + 3$ **39.** -4 **41.** 2   **43.** no solution   **45.** $\dfrac{3}{4}$ **47.** 20   **49.** $\dfrac{23}{7}$

51. 102   **53.** 6665.5 in.   **55.** Kellogg: 35 plants; Keebler: 18 plants   **57.** 3   **59.** $w = 9$ **61.** $m = \dfrac{y - b}{x}$ **63.** $x = \dfrac{2y - 7}{5}$ **65.** $\pi = \dfrac{C}{D}$

67. 15 m   **69.** 1 hr 20 min   **71.** 20%   **73.** 110   **75.** mark-up: \$209; new price: \$2109   **77.** 40% solution: 10 gal; 10% solution: 20 gal
79. 18%   **81.** 966 customers   **83.** 32%   **85.** 50 km   **87.** 80 nickels   **89.** $(0, \infty)$ [graph]   **91.** $[0.5, 1.5)$ [graph]

93. $(-\infty, -4)$ [graph]   **95.** $(-\infty, 4]$ [graph]   **97.** $\left(-\dfrac{1}{2}, \dfrac{3}{4}\right)$ [graph]   **99.** $\left(-\infty, \dfrac{19}{3}\right]$ [graph]

101. \$2500   **103.** 4   **105.** $-\dfrac{3}{2}$ **107.** all real numbers   **109.** -13 **111.** $h = \dfrac{3V}{A}$ **113.** 160   **115.** $(9, \infty)$ [graph]
117. $(-\infty, 0]$ [graph]

Chapter 2 Test

1. $y - 10$ **2.** $5.9x + 1.2$ **3.** $-2x + 10$ **4.** $10y + 1$ **5.** -5 **6.** 8   **7.** $\dfrac{7}{10}$ **8.** 0   **9.** 27   **10.** 3   **11.** 0.25   **12.** $\dfrac{25}{7}$

13. no solution   **14.** $x = 6$ **15.** $h = \dfrac{V}{\pi r^2}$ **16.** $y = \dfrac{3x - 10}{4}$ **17.** $(-\infty, -2]$ [graph]   **18.** $(-\infty, 4)$ [graph]

19. $\left(-1, \dfrac{7}{3}\right)$ [graph]   **20.** $\left(\dfrac{2}{5}, \infty\right)$ [graph]   **21.** 21   **22.** 62 ft by 64 ft   **23.** 401, 802   **24.** \$8500 at 10%; \$17,000 at 12%

25. $2\dfrac{1}{2}$ hr   **26.** 552   **27.** 40%   **28.** 16%

Chapter 2 Cumulative Review

1. a. 11, 112   **b.** 0, 11, 112   **c.** $-3, -2, 0, 11, 112$ **d.** $-3, -2, -1.5, 0, \dfrac{1}{4}, 11, 112$ **e.** $\sqrt{2}$ **f.** all numbers in the given set; Sec. 1.2, Ex. 5

3. a. 4   **b.** 5   **c.** 0   **d.** $\dfrac{1}{2}$ **e.** 5.6; Sec. 1.2, Ex. 7   **5. a.** $2 \cdot 2 \cdot 2 \cdot 5$ **b.** $3 \cdot 3 \cdot 7$; Sec. 1.3, Ex. 1   **7.** $\dfrac{8}{20}$; Sec. 1.3, Ex. 6   **9.** 66; Sec. 1.4, Ex. 4

11. 2 is a solution; Sec. 1.4, Ex. 7   **13.** -3; Sec. 1.5, Ex. 2   **15.** 2; Sec. 1.5, Ex. 4   **17. a.** 10   **b.** $\dfrac{1}{2}$ **c.** $2x$ **d.** -6; Sec. 1.5, Ex. 10

19. a. 9.9   **b.** $-\dfrac{4}{5}$ **c.** $\dfrac{2}{15}$; Sec. 1.6, Ex. 2   **21. a.** $52°$ **b.** $118°$; Sec. 1.6, Ex. 8   **23. a.** -0.06 **b.** $-\dfrac{7}{15}$ **c.** 16; Sec. 1.7, Ex. 3

25. a. 6   **b.** -12 **c.** $-\dfrac{8}{15}$ **d.** $-\dfrac{1}{6}$; Sec. 1.7, Ex. 7   **27. a.** $5 + x$ **b.** $x \cdot 3$; Sec. 1.8, Ex. 1   **29. a.** $8(2 + x)$ **b.** $7(s + t)$; Sec. 1.8, Ex. 5

31. $-2x - 1$; Sec. 2.1, Ex. 7   **33.** -1.6; Sec. 2.2, Ex. 2   **35.** 8; Sec. 2.2, Ex. 4   **37.** 140; Sec. 2.2, Ex. 7   **39.** 2; Sec. 2.3, Ex. 1   **41.** 10; Sec. 2.4, Ex. 2
43. $\dfrac{V}{wh} = l$; Sec. 2.5, Ex. 5   **45.** $(-\infty, -10]$ [graph]; Sec. 2.8, Ex. 2

APPENDIX A   OPERATIONS ON DECIMALS/PERCENT, DECIMAL, AND FRACTION TABLE

1. 17.08   **3.** 12.804   **5.** 110.96   **7.** 2.4   **9.** 28.43   **11.** 227.5   **13.** 2.7   **15.** 49.2339   **17.** 80   **19.** 0.07612   **21.** 4.56   **23.** 648.46
25. 767.83   **27.** 12.062   **29.** 61.48   **31.** 7.7   **33.** 863.37   **35.** 22.579   **37.** 363.15   **39.** 7.007

APPENDIX B   REVIEW OF ALGEBRA TOPICS

B.1 Practice Exercises

1. -4 **2.** $\dfrac{5}{6}$ **3.** $-\dfrac{3}{4}$ **4.** $\dfrac{5}{4}$ **5.** $-\dfrac{1}{8}, 2$

Exercise Set B.1

1. $-3, -8$ **3.** -2 **5.** $\dfrac{1}{4}, -\dfrac{2}{3}$ **7.** $1, 9$ **9.** 0 **11.** 5 **13.** $\dfrac{3}{5}, -1$ **15.** no solution   **17.** $\dfrac{1}{8}$ **19.** 0 **21.** $6, -3$ **23.** all real numbers
25. $\dfrac{2}{5}, -\dfrac{1}{2}$ **27.** $\dfrac{3}{4}, -\dfrac{1}{2}$ **29.** 29 **31.** -8 **33.** $-\dfrac{1}{3}, 0$ **35.** $-\dfrac{7}{8}$ **37.** $\dfrac{31}{4}$ **39.** 1 **41.** $-7, 4$ **43.** $4, 6$ **45.** $-\dfrac{1}{2}$
47. a. incorrect **b.** correct **c.** correct **d.** incorrect   **49.** $K = -11$ **51.** $K = 24$ **53.** -4.86 **55.** 1.53

B.2 Practice Exercises

1. a. $3x + 6$ **b.** $6x - 1$ **2.** $3x + 18.1$ **3.** $14, 34, 70$ **4.** $\$450$

Vocabulary & Readiness Check B.2

1. $>$ **3.** $=$ **5.** $31, 32, 33, 34$ **7.** $18, 20, 22$ **9.** $y, y + 1, y + 2$ **11.** $p, p + 1, p + 2, p + 3$

Exercise Set B.2

1. $4y$ **3.** $3z + 3$ **5.** $(65x + 30)$ cents   **7.** $10x + 3$ **9.** $2x + 14$ **11.** -5 **13.** $45, 225, 145$ **15.** approximately 1612.41 million acres
17. 7747 earthquakes   **19.** 1275 shoppers   **21.** 23%   **23.** 417 employees   **25.** $29°, 35°, 116°$ **27.** 28 m, 36 m, 38 m
29. 18 in., 18 in., 27 in., 36 in.   **31.** $75, 76, 77$ **33.** Fallon's ZIP code is 89406; Fernley's ZIP code is 89408; Gardnerville Ranchos' ZIP code is 89410
35. 55 million; 97 million; 138 million   **37.** biomedical engineer: 12 thousand; skin care specialist: 15 thousand; physician assistant: 29 thousand
39. B767-300ER: 207 seats; B737-200: 119 seats; F-100: 87 seats   **41.** $\$430.00$ **43.** $\$446,028$ **45.** 1,800,000 people   **47.** $40°, 140°$
49. $64°, 32°, 84°$ **51.** square: 18 cm; triangle: 24 cm   **53.** $76, 78, 80$ **55.** Darlington: 61,000; Daytona: 159,000   **57.** Tokyo: 36.67 million; New York: 19.43 million; Mexico City: 19.46 million   **59.** 40.5 ft; 202.5 ft; 240 ft   **61.** incandescent: 1500 bulb hours; fluorescent: 100,000 bulb hours; halogen: 4000 bulb hours   **63.** Milwaukee Brewers: 77 wins; Houston Astros: 76 wins; Chicago Cubs: 75 wins   **65.** Guy's Tower: 469 ft; Queen Mary Hospital: 449 ft; Galter Pavilion: 402 ft

B.3 Practice Exercises

1.   **a.** Quadrant IV   **b.** y-axis   **c.** Quadrant II   **d.** x-axis   **e.** Quadrant III   **f.** Quadrant I

2. $y = -3x - 2$ **3.**

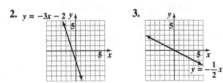

Exercise Set B.3

1. $(5, 2)$ **3.** $(3, 0)$ **5.** $(-5, -2)$ **7.** $(-1, 0)$ **9.** Quadrant I   **11.** Quadrant II   **13.** Quadrant III
15. y-axis   **17.** Quadrant III   **19.** x-axis   **21.** Quadrant IV   **23.** x-axis   **25.** Quadrant III
27.   **29.**   **31.**   **33.**   **35.** 1 **37.** -4 **39.** $1, 3$ **41.** $g(-1) = -2$

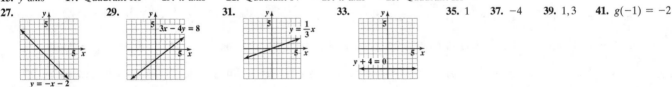

B.4 Practice Exercises

1. a. $3xy(4x - 1)$ **b.** $(7x + 2)(7x - 2)$ **c.** $(5x - 3)(x + 1)$ **d.** $(x^2 + 2)(3 + x)$ **e.** $(2x + 5)^2$ **f.** cannot be factored
2. a. $(4x + y)(16x^2 - 4xy + y^2)$ **b.** $7y^2(x + 3y)(x - 3y)$ **c.** $3(x + 2 + b)(x + 2 - b)$ **d.** $x^2 y(xy + 3)(x^2 y^2 - 3xy + 9)$
e. $(x + 7 + 9y)(x + 7 - 9y)$

Exercise Set B.4

1. $2y^2 + 2y - 11$ **3.** $x^2 - 7x + 7$ **5.** $25x^2 - 30x + 9$ **7.** $2x^3 - 4x^2 + 5x - 5 + \dfrac{8}{x + 2}$ **9.** $(x - 4 + y)(x - 4 - y)$

11. $x(x - 1)(x^2 + x + 1)$ **13.** $2xy(7x - 1)$ **15.** $4(x + 2)(x - 2)$ **17.** $(3x - 11)(x + 1)$ **19.** $4(x + 3)(x - 1)$ **21.** $(2x + 9)^2$

23. $(2x + 5y)(4x^2 - 10xy + 25y^2)$ **25.** $8x^2(2y - 1)(4y^2 + 2y + 1)$ **27.** $(x + 5 + y)(x^2 + 10x + 25 - xy - 5y + y^2)$ **29.** $(5a - 6)^2$

31. $7x(x - 9)$ **33.** $(b - 6)(a + 7)$ **35.** $(x^2 + 1)(x + 1)(x - 1)$ **37.** $(5x - 11)(2x + 3)$ **39.** $5a^3b(b^2 - 10)$ **41.** prime

43. $10x(x - 10)(x - 11)$ **45.** $a^3b(4b - 3)(16b^2 + 12b + 9)$ **47.** $2(x - 3)(x^2 + 3x + 9)$ **49.** $(3y - 5)(y^4 + 2)$

51. $100(z + 1)(z^2 - z + 1)$ **53.** $(2b - 9)^2$ **55.** $(y - 4)(y - 5)$ **57.** $A = 9 - 4x^2 = (3 + 2x)(3 - 2x)$

B.5 Practice Exercises

1. a. $\dfrac{2n + 1}{n(n - 1)}$ **b.** $-x^2$ **2. a.** $-\dfrac{y^3}{21(y + 3)}$ **b.** $\dfrac{7x + 2}{x + 2}$ **3. a.** $\dfrac{20p + 3}{5p^4q}$ **b.** $\dfrac{5y^2 + 19y - 12}{(y + 3)(y - 3)}$ **c.** 3 **4.** 1

Exercise Set B.5

1. $\dfrac{1}{2}$ **3.** $\dfrac{1 + 2x}{8}$ **5.** $\dfrac{2(x - 4)}{(x + 2)(x - 1)}$ **7.** 4 **9.** -5 **11.** $\dfrac{2x + 5}{x(x - 3)}$ **13.** -2 **15.** $\dfrac{(a + 3)(a + 1)}{a + 2}$ **17.** $-\dfrac{1}{5}$

19. $\dfrac{4a + 1}{(3a + 1)(3a - 1)}$ **21.** $-1, \dfrac{3}{2}$ **23.** $\dfrac{3}{x + 1}$ **25.** -1 **27. a.** $\dfrac{x}{5} - \dfrac{x}{4} + \dfrac{1}{10}$ **b.** Write each rational expression term so that the denominator

is the LCD, 20.   **c.** $\dfrac{-x + 2}{20}$ **29.** b   **31.** d   **33.** d

APPENDIX C   AN INTRODUCTION TO USING A GRAPHING UTILITY

The Viewing Window and Interpreting Window Settings Exercise Set

1. yes   **3.** no   **5.** answers may vary   **7.** answers may vary   **9.** answers may vary

11. Xmin $= -12$ Ymin $= -12$ **13.** Xmin $= -9$ Ymin $= -12$ **15.** Xmin $= -10$ Ymin $= -25$ **17.** Xmin $= -10$ Ymin $= -30$
    Xmax $= 12$ Ymax $= 12$ Xmax $= 9$ Ymax $= 12$ Xmax $= 10$ Ymax $= 25$ Xmax $= 10$ Ymax $= 30$
    Xscl $= 3$ Yscl $= 3$ Xscl $= 1$ Yscl $= 2$ Xscl $= 2$ Yscl $= 5$ Xscl $= 1$ Yscl $= 3$
19. Xmin $= -20$ Ymin $= -30$
    Xmax $= 30$ Ymax $= 50$
    Xscl $= 5$ Yscl $= 10$

Graphing Equations and Square Viewing Window Exercise Set

1. Setting B   **3.** Setting B   **5.** Setting B

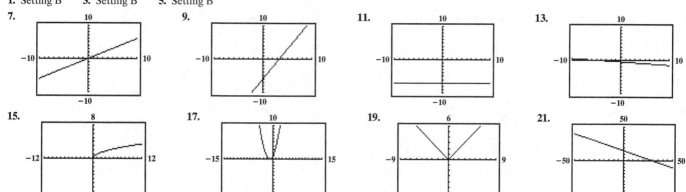

APPENDIX D   SOLVING SYSTEMS OF EQUATIONS BY MATRICES

Practice Exercises

1. $(2, -1)$ **2.** $\{\ \}$ or $\varnothing$ **3.** $(-1, 1, 2)$

Exercise Set

1. $(2, -1)$ **3.** $(-4, 2)$ **5.** $\{\ \}$ or $\varnothing$ **7.** $\{(x, y) \mid 3x - 3y = 9\}$ **9.** $(-2, 5, -2)$ **11.** $(1, -2, 3)$ **13.** $(4, -3)$ **15.** $(2, 1, -1)$

17. $(9, 9)$ **19.** $\{\ \}$ or $\varnothing$ **21.** $\{\ \}$ or $\varnothing$ **23.** $(1, -4, 3)$ **25.** c

APPENDIX E   SOLVING SYSTEMS OF EQUATIONS BY DETERMINANTS

1. 26   **3.** −19   **5.** 0   **7.** (1, 2)   **9.** $\{(x, y) \mid 3x + y = 1\}$ **11.** (9, 9)   **13.** 8   **15.** 0   **17.** 54   **19.** (−2, 0, 5)   **21.** (6, −2, 4)

23. 16   **25.** 15   **27.** $\dfrac{13}{6}$ **29.** 0   **31.** 56   **33.** (−3, −2)   **35.** { } or ∅   **37.** (−2, 3, −1)   **39.** (3, 4)   **41.** (−2, 1)

43. $\{(x, y, z) \mid x - 2y + z = -3\}$ **45.** (0, 2, −1)   **47.** 5   **49.** 0; answers may vary   **51.** $\begin{matrix} + & - & + & - \\ - & + & - & + \\ + & - & + & - \\ - & + & - & + \end{matrix}$ **53.** −125   **55.** 24

APPENDIX F   MEAN, MEDIAN, AND MODE

1. mean: 29, median: 28, no mode   **3.** mean: 8.1, median: 8.2, mode: 8.2   **5.** mean: 0.6, median: 0.6, mode: 0.2 and 0.6
7. mean: 370.9, median: 313.5, no mode   **9.** 1214.8 ft   **11.** 1117 ft   **13.** 6.8   **15.** 6.9   **17.** 85.5   **19.** 73   **21.** 70 and 71
23. 9   **25.** 21, 21, 24

APPENDIX G   REVIEW OF ANGLES, LINES, AND SPECIAL TRIANGLES

1. 71°   **3.** 19.2°   **5.** $78\dfrac{3}{4}°$ **7.** 30°   **9.** 149.8°   **11.** $100\dfrac{1}{2}°$ **13.** $m\angle 1 = m\angle 5 = m\angle 7 = 110°; m\angle 2 = m\angle 3 = m\angle 4 = m\angle 6 = 70°$

15. 90°   **17.** 90°   **19.** 90°   **21.** 45°, 90°   **23.** 73°, 90°   **25.** $50\dfrac{1}{4}°$, 90°   **27.** $x = 6$ **29.** $x = 4.5$ **31.** 10   **33.** 12

PRACTICE FINAL EXAM

1. −48   **2.** −81   **3.** $\dfrac{1}{64}$ **4.** $-\dfrac{1}{3}$ **5.** $-3x^3 + 5x^2 + 4x + 5$ **6.** $16x^2 - 16x + 4$ **7.** $3x^3 + 22x^2 + 41x + 14$ **8.** $(y - 12)(y + 4)$

9. $3x(3x + 1)(x + 4)$ **10.** $5(6 + x)(6 - x)$ **11.** $(a + b)(3a - 7)$ **12.** $8(y - 2)(y^2 + 2y + 4)$ **13.** $\dfrac{y^{14}}{x^2}$ **14.** $\dfrac{25}{7}$ **15.** $(-\infty, -2]$

16. −7, 1   **17.** 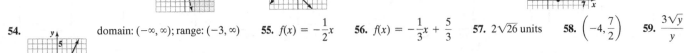   **18.**   **19.** $m = -1$ **20.** $m = 3$ **21.** $8x + y = 11$ **22.** $x = -5$ **23.** $\left(\dfrac{1}{2}, -2\right)$

24. no solution; { } or ∅   **25.** $9x^2 - 6x + 4 - \dfrac{16}{3x + 2}$ **26. a.** 0   **b.** 0   **c.** 60   **27.** x-intercepts: (0, 0), (4, 0); y-intercept: (0, 0);

domain: $(-\infty, \infty)$; range: $(-\infty, 4]$ **28.** 401, 802   **29.** $2\dfrac{1}{2}$ hr   **30.** 120 cc   **31.** $\{x \mid x \text{ is a real number}, x \neq -1, x \neq -3\}$ **32.** $\dfrac{19x - 6}{2x + 5}$

33. $\dfrac{2(x + 5)}{x(y + 5)}$ **34.** $\dfrac{3a - 4}{(a - 3)(a + 2)}$ **35.** $\dfrac{5y^2 - 1}{y + 2}$ **36.** $\dfrac{30}{11}$ **37.** −6   **38.** no solution   **39.** 5 or 1   **40.** $6\sqrt{6}$ **41.** 5

42. $\dfrac{8a^{1/3}c^{2/3}}{b^{5/12}}$ **43.** $-x\sqrt{5x}$ **44.** −20   **45.** 1, $\dfrac{2}{3}$ **46.** $\left(\dfrac{3}{2}, 5\right]$ **47.** $(-\infty, -2) \cup \left(\dfrac{4}{3}, \infty\right)$ **48.** $\dfrac{3 \pm \sqrt{29}}{2}$ or $\dfrac{3}{2} \pm \dfrac{\sqrt{29}}{2}$ **49.** 2, 3

50. $\left(-\infty, -\dfrac{3}{2}\right) \cup (5, \infty)$ **51.**   **52.**   domain: $(-\infty, \infty)$; range: $(-\infty, -1]$ **53.**

54.   domain: $(-\infty, \infty)$; range: $(-3, \infty)$ **55.** $f(x) = -\dfrac{1}{2}x$ **56.** $f(x) = -\dfrac{1}{3}x + \dfrac{5}{3}$ **57.** $2\sqrt{26}$ units   **58.** $\left(-4, \dfrac{7}{2}\right)$ **59.** $\dfrac{3\sqrt{y}}{y}$

60. $\dfrac{8 - 6\sqrt{x} + x}{8 - 2x}$ **61.** 16   **62.** 7 ft   **63. a.** 272 ft   **b.** 5.12 sec   **64.** $0 - 2i\sqrt{2}$ **65.** $0 - 3i$ **66.** $7 + 24i$ **67.** $-\dfrac{3}{2} + \dfrac{5}{2}i$

68. $(g \circ h)(x) = x^2 - 6x - 2$ **69.** one-to-one; $f^{-1}(x) = \dfrac{-x + 6}{2}$ **70.** $\log_5 \dfrac{x^4}{x + 1}$ **71.** −1   **72.** $\dfrac{1}{2}\left(\dfrac{\log 4}{\log 3} - 5\right); -1.8691$ **73.** 22

74. $\dfrac{43}{21}$ **75.** $\dfrac{1}{2}$ **76.**   **77.** 64,805 prairie dogs   **78.** 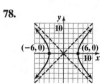   **79.**   **80.**

81. $(-5, -1), (-5, 1), (5, -1), (5, 1)$ **82.** $-\dfrac{1}{5}, \dfrac{1}{6}, -\dfrac{1}{7}, \dfrac{1}{8}, -\dfrac{1}{9}$ **83.** 155   **84.** 1   **85.** 10   **86.** $32x^5 + 80x^4y + 80x^3y^2 + 40x^2y^3 + 10xy^4 + y^5$

Index

The following chapters were taken from
Geometry: Fundamental Concepts and Applications.

Area and Perimeter

While the Greeks were responsible for a rigorous, systematic approach to geometry, it is generally assumed that the Egyptians were the first to use geometry for practical reasons. The earliest writing on geometry came from the Egyptians in about 1700 B.C. One factor that motivated the Egyptians to use geometry was the desire to divide land between people.

The image in the margin is of a large piece of land divided into several parts by roads. How much land is in each of the sections is an important question that can be answered using the techniques found in this section.

■ Perimeter

The **perimeter** of a polygon is the distance around the sides. This can be found by adding the lengths of its sides. Because it represents a distance, perimeter has a linear unit attached, such as feet, meters, centimeters, miles, and so on.

> **EXAMPLE 7-1**   The Perimeter of a Pentagon
>
> Find the perimeter of the pentagon below.

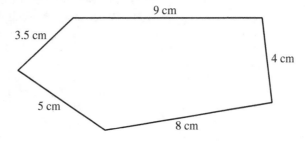

◆ **SOLUTION**

In geometry, the variable P usually represents perimeter. So, in this case $P = 9 \text{ cm} + 4 \text{ cm} + 8 \text{ cm} + 5 \text{ cm} + 3.5 \text{ cm} = 29.5 \text{ cm}$.   ◆

Since a rectangle has opposite sides that are congruent, the perimeter of a rectangle can be expressed by the formula $P = 2w + 2\ell$. Note the illustration in the margin.

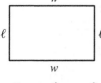

$$P = w + \ell + w + \ell$$
$$= 2w + 2\ell$$

> **EXAMPLE 7-2**   Working with the Rectangle Perimeter Formula
>
> The perimeter of a rectangle is 75.8 feet. If the width of the rectangle is 18.5 feet, what is the length?

◆ **SOLUTION**

We have been given that $P = 75.8$ ft and $w = 18.5$ ft.

$w = 18.5$ ft

$\ell = ?$ | $P = 75.8$ ft | $\ell = ?$

$w = 18.5$ ft

If we substitute these values into the formula $P = 2w + 2\ell$, we get the equation $75.8 = 2(18.5) + 2\ell$. Now we can solve for ℓ.

$$75.8 = 2(18.5) + 2\ell$$
$$75.8 = 37 + 2\ell$$
$$38.8 = 2\ell$$
$$19.4 = \ell$$

So the length is 19.4 feet. Finally, we do a quick check to make sure these measurements add to give the correct perimeter: $2(18.5) + 2(19.4) = 37 + 38.8 = 75.8.$✓ ◆

In certain cases, you may not know a side length and have to find it before you can find the perimeter, as in this next application.

EXAMPLE 7-3   The Cost of Fencing

A business wants to have their lot fenced in. The lot is pictured below. If fencing costs $13.50 per foot, what will the total cost be?

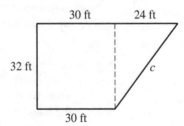

54 ft

32 ft

?

30 ft

◆ **SOLUTION**

The lot is in the shape of a trapezoid, but we don't know one of the side lengths. To find this length, notice that the lot could be partitioned into a triangle and a rectangle.

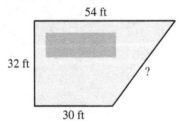

30 ft   24 ft

32 ft

c

30 ft

Thinking of the trapezoid this way makes the missing length the hypotenuse of a right triangle. We have labeled it c and can find its length using the Pythagorean Theorem:

$$c^2 = 24^2 + 32^2$$
$$c^2 = 1600$$
$$c = 40$$

So the entire perimeter is $P = 54 + 40 + 30 + 32 = 156$ ft. Since the cost per foot is $13.50, we multiply $13.50 \cdot 156 = 2106$. So the total cost would be $2106. ◆

Area

The **area** of any two-dimensional object measures the amount of flat space it takes up. To take such a measurement, you would need to use square units. One square unit is the amount of space taken up by a square that has sides of length 1 unit. Here are two examples.

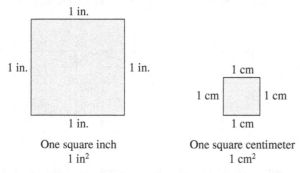

One square inch
1 in^2

One square centimeter
1 cm^2

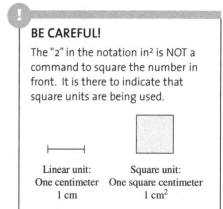

BE CAREFUL!

The "2" in the notation in² is NOT a command to square the number in front. It is there to indicate that square units are being used.

Linear unit:
One centimeter
1 cm

Square unit:
One square centimeter
1 cm²

The total amount of space in a house would be given in square feet (ft^2). If you measure the area of an entire state, you would probably use square miles (mi^2) or square kilometers (km^2). The state of California, for example, is 158,706 mi^2.

To better illustrate the concept of area, suppose we wanted to know how much space is taken up by the object in the margin. One way to accomplish this would be to impose a grid onto the figure, as shown below.

In this case, the units are square centimeters (cm^2). Every square on the grid represents one square centimeter. Now we can just count the total number of square centimeters covered by the object, noting that some of the sections only take up half a square. So the total area of the object is $A = 4 \cdot \frac{1}{2} \text{ cm}^2 + 9 \cdot 1 \text{ cm}^2 = 2 \text{ cm}^2 + 9 \text{ cm}^2 = 11 \text{ cm}^2$.

This technique is most effective in finding the area of a rectangle, and even leads to a general formula for finding the area of a rectangle given its length and width. Consider the rectangle below. We have divided the length and width into 1-inch pieces. Notice that this creates squares that have side lengths of 1 inch, so each square is 1 square inch (1 in^2). Notice also that each of the eight vertical strips has six squares, so the total area is $8 \cdot 6 = 48 \text{ in}^2$. This is true in general. That is, to find the area of a rectangle, we multiply its length and width.

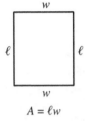

$A = \ell w$

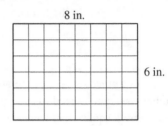

8 in.

6 in.

While this technique illustrates the concept of area well, it will not work for all objects.

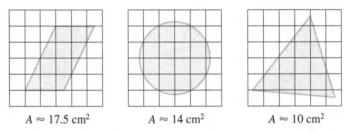

$A \approx 17.5 \text{ cm}^2$ $A \approx 14 \text{ cm}^2$ $A \approx 10 \text{ cm}^2$

Notice in these figures, having the grid allows us only to *approximate* the area of each object and not get an exact value. Fortunately, formulas can be derived for the areas of the popular shapes that we use in this book. As we will see, the justification for these formulas is based on the formula for the area of a rectangle: $A = \ell \cdot w$.

◼ Derived Area Formulas

Let's run through the derivation of the formulas for the area of some popular shapes.

Parallelogram: $A = b \cdot h$

Take a parallelogram and cut it into two parts along its perpendicular height (labeled h). If you reorient the two resulting pieces, you can create a rectangle that looks like the second figure below. This shows that the area of a parallelogram is $A = b \cdot h$, where b is the length of its base and h is its perpendicular height.

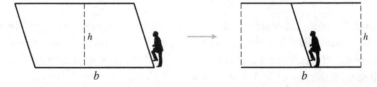

b b

Triangle: $A = \frac{1}{2} \cdot b \cdot h$

If we make a copy of the triangle, we can reorient the copy so that the two make a parallelogram. As shown, the area of a parallelogram is $A =$ base $\cdot$ height. But we only want half of that since our parallelogram is made out of two congruent triangles. So, for a triangle: $A = \frac{1}{2} \cdot b \cdot h$.

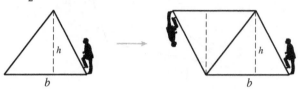

Trapezoid: $A = \frac{1}{2}h(B + b)$

If we take a copy of the trapezoid and rearrange it, we can make a parallelogram. While this is indeed a parallelogram, its base and height are actually $B + b$ and h, respectively. So the entire area of the figure to the right is $A = h \cdot (B + b)$. We only want half this area, so for a trapezoid: $A = \frac{1}{2}h(B + b)$.

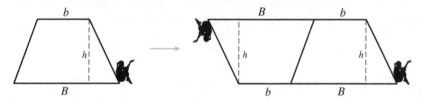

The area formulas for a rectangle, parallelogram, triangle, and trapezoid should be committed to memory.

EXAMPLE 7-4   The Area of a Parallelogram

Find the perimeter and area of the following parallelogram.

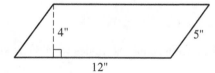

◆ **SOLUTION**

The trick here is knowing which measurement to use for which calculation and knowing which units are appropriate in each case.

- The perimeter is the distance around the object, so it doesn't involve the perpendicular height at all: $P = 12 + 5 + 12 + 5 = 34$ in. Notice the unit is inches.

- The formula for the area of a parallelogram is $A = bh$, where h is the perpendicular height, so $b = 12$ and $h = 4$. So $A = bh = 12 \cdot 4 = 48$ in². Notice the unit is square inches.   ◆

EXAMPLE 7-5   The Perimeter and Area of a Triangle

Find the perimeter and area of the following triangle.

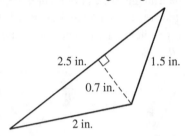

◆ SOLUTION

• Finding the perimeter is straightforward:

$$P = 1.5 + 2.5 + 2 = 6 \text{ in.}$$

• For the area, we note that even though the perpendicular height is not oriented straight up and down the way we are used to seeing it, it is still the perpendicular height. Since the perpendicular height is always perpendicular to the base, $h = 0.7$ in. and $b = 2.5$ in. So, for the area, $A = \frac{1}{2} \cdot 2.5 \cdot 0.7 = 0.875 \text{ in}^2$.   ◆

EXAMPLE 7-6   Working with an Area Formula

Find the smaller base of the trapezoid, given that the area is 45 ft^2.

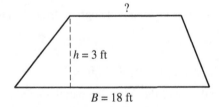

◆ SOLUTION

Given the area of 45 square feet and the values we already know, the area formula $A = \frac{1}{2}h(B + b)$ becomes

$$45 = \frac{1}{2} \cdot 3 \cdot (18 + b)$$
$$90 = 3(18 + b) \qquad \textit{clear fractions}$$
$$30 = 18 + b \qquad \textit{divide by 3}$$
$$b = 12 \qquad \textit{subtract 18}$$

So the smaller base is 12 feet. We can make a quick substitution of this value back into the area formula to make sure we get an area of 45 square feet:

$$A = \frac{1}{2}h(B + b) = \frac{1}{2} \cdot 3 \cdot (18 + 12) = \frac{1}{2} \cdot 3 \cdot 30 = \frac{1}{2} \cdot 90 = 45\checkmark$$ ◆

More Complex Shapes

Some figures are composed of different shapes joined together. The technique used in such situations is to separate the object into smaller pieces whose areas are easy to find. Consider the figure below and suppose we want to find the area of the shaded region. We show the figure before it is divided and then again after it is divided, the idea being that

Shaded Area = Area of a Triangle + Area of a Trapezoid − Area of a Rectangle.

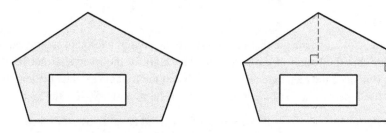

This technique is particularly useful in applications, as we will see in the next example.

EXAMPLE 7-7   Bricking a Patio

A mason is being hired to cover the patio area below with brick. The rectangle in the center represents the customer's grill area, which doesn't need to be covered. If the mason charges $7.50 per square foot for labor and materials, what will the total charge be?

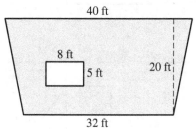

◆ SOLUTION

To find the charge, we have to find the total area to be covered. We can use the equation

$$\text{Total Area} = \text{Area of Trapezoid} - \text{Area of Rectangle}$$
$$\text{Total Area} = \tfrac{1}{2} \cdot h(B + b) - \ell \cdot w$$
$$= \tfrac{1}{2} \cdot 20(40 + 32) - 8 \cdot 5$$
$$= 10(72) - 40 = 720 - 40 = 680$$

A total of 680 square feet is to be covered with brick. At $7.50 per square foot, the total charge will be $7.50 · 680 = $5100. ◆

EXAMPLE 7-8   The Area of a Complex Shape

Find the shaded area in the following figure.

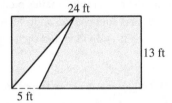

◆ SOLUTION

The figure shows a rectangle that needs to have the area of a triangle subtracted out of it. Notice that the length of the perpendicular height of the triangle is not labeled explicitly. But since the rectangle is 13 feet high and the triangle extends the length of it, we can use a perpendicular height of 13 feet for the triangle. So, for the area:

$$A = \ell \cdot w - \frac{1}{2} \cdot b \cdot h = 24 \cdot 13 - \frac{1}{2} \cdot 5 \cdot 13 = 312 - 32.5 = 279.5 \text{ ft}^2.$$ ◆

EXAMPLE 7-9   Finding Missing Values

Find the area and perimeter of the figure below.

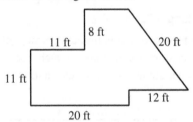

◆ SOLUTION

First, we divide the building into familiar geometric shapes.

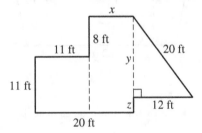

Notice, however, we don't know a few of the lengths, so we have labeled them with variables. We begin by finding these missing values.

• Find x: Since the total length is 20 feet and the left rectangle is 11 feet wide, we have

$$11 + x = 20$$
$$x = 9$$

• Find y: The length y is the height of our triangular piece and is a little more challenging to find. Notice that y is the only missing piece of a right triangle. By the Pythagorean Theorem:

$$y^2 + 12^2 = 20^2$$
$$y^2 = 256$$
$$y = 16$$

- Find z: Knowing y makes z easy to find since, from looking at the left sides, we see the height of the figure is $11 + 8 = 19$ ft.

$$y + z = 19$$
$$16 + z = 19$$
$$z = 3 \text{ ft}$$

So the figure can now be redrawn with all the needed measurements.

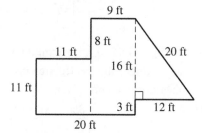

To find the perimeter, we add the side lengths that make up the original figure:

$$11 + 11 + 8 + 9 + 20 + 12 + 3 + 20 = 94$$

So the perimeter is 94 feet.

For area, we use the equation

Total Area = Area of Square + Area of Rectangle + Area of Triangle

$$\text{Total Area} = s^2 + \ell w + \frac{1}{2}bh$$
$$= 11^2 + 19 \cdot 9 + \frac{1}{2} \cdot 16 \cdot 12$$
$$= 121 + 171 + 96 = 388$$

Therefore, the total area is 388 ft^2.

We redrew the figure two times in this problem to help illustrate the process. When you do these problems in the homework, you may not even have to draw the figure over at all; just so long as you can imagine it being divided in a way that lets you find the area.

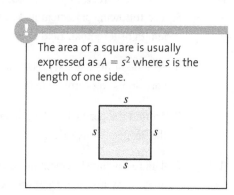

The area of a square is usually expressed as $A = s^2$ where s is the length of one side.

Section 7 | Exercises

For exercises 1–4, use the terms from the **Vocabulary Checklist** *to fill in the blanks.*

VOCABULARY CHECKLIST:

linear unit	perimeter
square unit	area

1. The total amount of space taken up by a house would be measured using a(n) _____.

2. If I say the distance around my rectangular yard is 176 feet, I have given the _____ of the yard.

3. The _____ of the state of Texas is 268,581 square miles.

4. The kilometer is an example of a _____.

For exercises 5–8, answer TRUE or FALSE.

T | F 5. The following statement makes sense: "The total length of a football field is 100 square yards."

T | F 6. Any two-dimensional object can have a corresponding formula that will give its area.

T | F 7. To find the perimeter of an object, you just take the product of its sides.

T | F 8. The following statement makes sense: "The total area of my house is 1540 square feet."

9. **Using a Grid to Approximate Area.** Use the grid to help approximate the shaded area inside. Assume the grid measures the units given.

Square centimeters

10. **Using a Grid to Approximate Area.** Use the grid to help approximate the shaded area inside. Assume the grid measures the units given.

Square feet

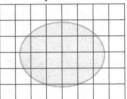

11. **Using a Grid to Approximate Area.** Use the grid to help approximate the shaded area inside. Assume the grid measures the units given.

Square kilometers

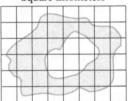

12. Find the area and perimeter of the square.

20 in.

13. Find the area and perimeter of the square.

4.5 ft

14. Find the area and perimeter of the square.

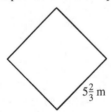

$5\frac{2}{3}$ m

15. Find the area and perimeter of the rectangle.

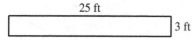

25 ft

3 ft

16. Find the area and perimeter of the rectangle.

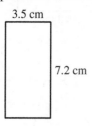

3.5 cm

7.2 cm

17. Find the area and perimeter of the rectangle.

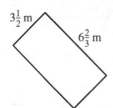

$3\frac{1}{2}$ m

$6\frac{2}{3}$ m

18. Find the area and perimeter.

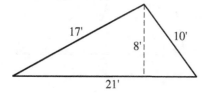

17'

10'

8'

21'

19. Find the area and perimeter.

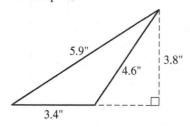

5.9"

3.8"

4.6"

3.4"

20. Find the area and perimeter.

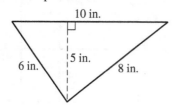

10 in.

6 in.

5 in.

8 in.

21. Find the area and perimeter.

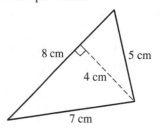

8 cm

5 cm

4 cm

7 cm

22. Find the area and perimeter of the parallelogram.

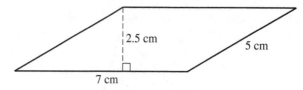

2.5 cm

5 cm

7 cm

23. Find the area and perimeter of the parallelogram.

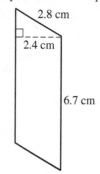

2.8 cm

2.4 cm

6.7 cm

24. Find the area and perimeter of the parallelogram.

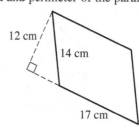

12 cm

14 cm

17 cm

25. Find the area and perimeter of the trapezoid.

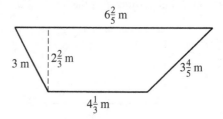

$6\frac{2}{5}$ m

3 m

$2\frac{2}{3}$ m

$3\frac{4}{5}$ m

$4\frac{1}{3}$ m

26. Find the area of the trapezoid.

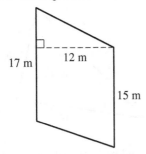

27. Find the area and perimeter of the trapezoid.

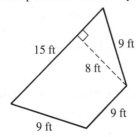

28. Find the area and perimeter. Assume all the angles are right angles.

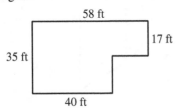

29. Find the area.

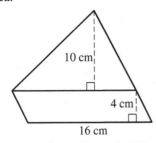

30. Find the area and perimeter of the trapezoid.

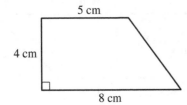

31. Find the area and perimeter.

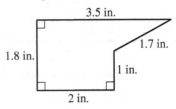

32. Find the area.

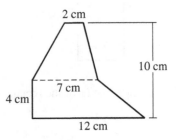

33. Find the area.

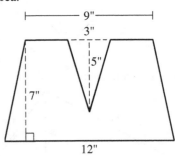

34. Find the shaded area.

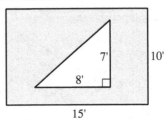

35. Find the shaded area.

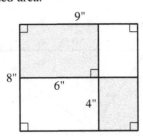

Below are maps of North Dakota, Tennessee, Nevada, and Utah. Notice the scales on the maps that represents either 80 miles or 100 miles. Use an appropriate formula to approximate each state's area and perimeter.

36. **North Dakota**

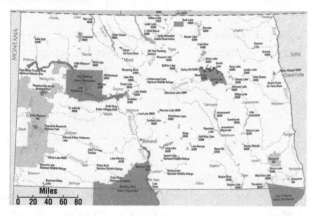

37. **Tennessee**

38. **Nevada**

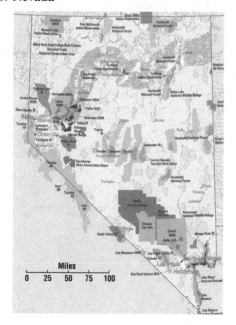

39. **Utah**

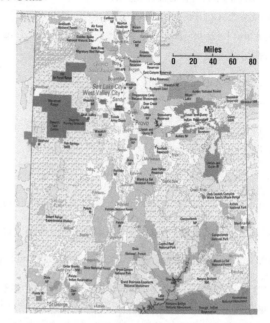

40. A triangle has a base of 4.8 inches. Its height is three times as long as its base. What is the area of the triangle?

41. A certain rectangle has a perimeter of 32 meters. Its length is 5 meters less than twice its width. What are the dimensions of the rectangle?

42. A trapezoid has a height of 6 inches. Its smaller base is 3 inches more than twice its height. Its larger base is four times its height. Find the area of the trapezoid.

43. A certain isosceles triangle has a perimeter of 42 inches. The unequal side is one-third the length of the equal sides' length. What is the length of each side?

44. **Isosceles Triangles.** In an isosceles triangle the angles opposite congruent sides are equal. Furthermore, the height of the triangle drawn from the vertex opposite the unequal side bisects the unequal side. This information is summarized in the figure below.

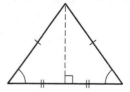

If an isosceles triangle has two sides that are 5 centimeters and a base that is 6 centimeters, find the height of the triangle and its area. (*Hint:* You will need the Pythagorean Theorem.)

45. Sketch any rectangle that has an area of 36 square centimeters.

46. Sketch and label any parallelogram that has an area of 24 square inches.

47. Sketch any rectangle that has a perimeter of 24 inches.

48. Sketch any rectangle that has an area of 72 square meters.

49. Sketch any parallelogram that has a perimeter of 25 feet.

50. Sketch any trapezoid that has an area of 54 square inches.

51. **Pricing Hardwood Floors.** The Smiths are considering getting hardwood floors in their living room. The room is rectangular with dimensions 25 feet by 32 feet. If hardwood floors cost $12.25 per square foot, how much will it cost the Smiths to have their living room covered?

52. **The Cost of a Billboard.** A standard billboard has dimensions 12 feet by 8 feet. A graphics company charges $9.50 per square foot to print the billboard posters. What is the typical charge for a billboard?

53. **Custom Framing.** A custom frame shop charges $2.75 per square inch to frame a picture. If Holly wants a rectangular picture with dimensions 13 inches by 9 inches framed, how much will it cost?

54. **Artistic Murals.** Vincent charges $75 per square foot to do murals. A client wants a mural drawn in an area the shape of an isosceles triangle with a base of 8 feet and a height of 10 feet. What will Vincent charge to paint the mural?

55. **Fertilizing a Garden.** A rectangular garden of dimensions 70 feet by 95 feet needs to be completely covered with fertilizer. If one bag of fertilizer costs $15 and covers 350 square feet, how many bags will be needed and what will the total cost be?

56. **Land for a Park.** The government wants to set aside a rectangular piece of land as a national park. The land is on a thin strip with parallel boundary lines that are a distance of 3 miles apart. If the idea is to set aside 35 square miles of land, how many miles long should the strip be?

57. **Establishing a Garden.** Holly has established an area with the following dimensions as a flower garden.

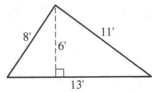

A small rock retaining wall around the perimeter will cost $5 per linear foot. Fertilizer will cost $2 per square foot. How much will it cost to build the retaining wall and fertilize the garden?

58. **Fencing an Area of Land.** If it costs $7.50 per linear foot for fencing, how much will it cost to fence in the following yard?

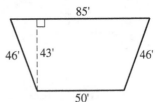

59. **Laying a Driveway.** A company charges $55 per square yard to pour, set, and smooth concrete. Roger has the following design in mind for a driveway. What will the company charge him to lay concrete for the driveway?

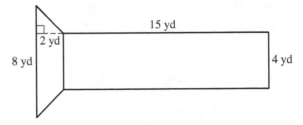

60. **Carpeting a Room.** Given that carpet costs $3.50 per square foot, how much would it cost to carpet the following area?

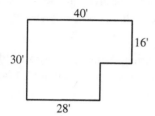

61. **Landscaping.** A well-renowned landscaper charges $8 per square yard of green in the area he is hired to develop, and you are wondering if you can afford him. Your yard has the shape shown next. The rectangles shown in the yard represent your house and a utility building in back. What will the landscaper charge you for a visit in which he cares for the whole yard?

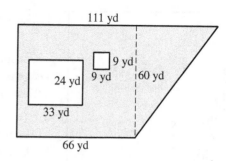

62. **Finding a Perimeter.** Suppose you want to build a fence around the yard illustrated in exercise 61. Find the perimeter of the entire yard. Express your answer in yards. (*Hint:* You will need to use the Pythagorean Theorem.)

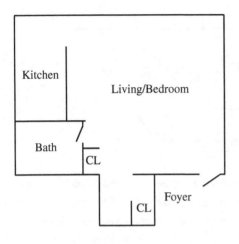

| ## Your Dream House

Congratulations! You are about to design your dream home! In the process, you will keep track of the measurements involved with this type of plan.

Here are some guidelines for the project:

1. The example in the margin sure is boring. A dream house should at least involve triangles and trapezoids; maybe even circles (see Section 8). Make sure to use at least two shapes other than rectangles.

2. Your house should have *at least* the following:
   - a kitchen
   - two bedrooms
   - one bathroom
   - two closets

   Then, feel free to give yourself a recreation room, a three-car garage, an indoor basketball court; whatever you want.

3. The length should all be to scale. That is, you could use 1 inch to represent 5 feet. Or, if you know you want a really big house, let 1 centimeter represent 5 feet. However you scale the work, make sure the measurements are accurate and proportional.

4. Label the length of every wall.

5. For each room, use a formula from this section (or Section 8 if you feel ambitious) to find and label its area in square feet.

6. To the side of the blueprint, include the following information:
   - the total perimeter of the house
   - the total area of the house
   - the total cost of having your house built (use $90 per square foot)

8

Circles

The circle represents a definite shift in our study. All the objects we have studied so far share a characteristic that can be summed up in one word: "straightness." A circle's lack of "straightness" is its defining characteristic.

The oldest wheel ever discovered in an archeological excavation dates back to about 6,000 years and was found in what was ancient Mesopotamia (now parts of Iraq, Syria, and Turkey.

▨ Definitions and Terminology

A **circle** is the set of all points *in a plane* that lie at a specific distance from a given point called the **center.** All line segments that have one endpoint at that center point and the other on the circle are the same length. Each of these segments is called a **radius** (r) of the circle. The plural form of the word radius is radii, so we say that all radii of the same circle have the same length. The word *radius* also refers to the length of a radius.

A line segment drawn from one side of the circle to the other that passes through the center of the circle is called a **diameter** (d). All diameters of the same circle have the same length. The word *diameter* also refers to the length of such a line segment. The length of the diameter is two times the length of the radius, so $d = 2 \cdot r$.

Here are some other terms we will use in exploring the properties of circles, along with a figure that illustrates all the terms:

- A **chord** is any line segment with its endpoints on the circle. So every diameter is a chord, but not all chords are diameters.

- A **tangent line** is a line that touches the circle at only one point. A **tangent segment** or **tangent ray** is one that, if extended, would create a tangent line.

- A **secant** is a line that touches the circle twice.

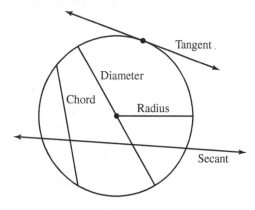

EXAMPLE 8-1   Using Terminology

Consider the circle below and do the exercises that follow.

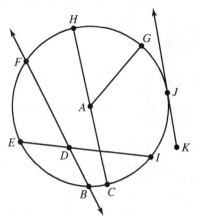

a. How many radii are shown? Name them.

b. Name a diameter for the circle.

c. Name a chord for the circle.

d. Name a secant for the circle.

e. Name a tangent for the circle and indicate what type of tangent it is.

f. If $HC = 18$, what is the radius of the circle?

g. If $AG = 4.5$, what is the diameter of the circle?

h. If $\overline{HG}$ were drawn, would it be a chord, secant, or tangent?

◆ **SOLUTION**

a. There are three radii given: $\overline{AG}$, $\overline{AC}$, and $\overline{AH}$. Notice that two of these form a diameter together.

b. The diameter is given by $\overline{HC}$.

c. The chord is given by $\overline{EI}$.

d. The secant is given by $\overleftrightarrow{FB}$.

e. The tangent is given by the ray $\overrightarrow{KJ}$, so it is a tangent ray.

f. Since $\overline{HC}$ is a diameter, the radius is half its length, so the radius $r = 9$.

g. Since $\overline{AG}$ is a radius, the diameter is twice its length, so the diameter $d = 9$.

h. If $\overline{HG}$ were drawn it would be a chord since it would be a line segment that has its endpoints on the circle.   ◆

There are several theorems pertaining to these objects that are easy to prove. Here are some examples:

1. **Theorem:** *A tangent to a circle is perpendicular to exactly one radius and exactly one diameter.*

2. **Theorem:** *If two distinct tangent segments share an endpoint and each has their second endpoint on the circle, then they are congruent.*

3. **Theorem:** *A radius that is perpendicular to a chord bisects that chord.*

EXAMPLE 8-2   Illustrating Theorems

Sketch figures that illustrate the first two theorems mentioned above.

◆ SOLUTION

1. **Theorem:** *A tangent to a circle is perpendicular to exactly one radius and exactly one diameter.*

This theorem involves a tangent, a radius, and a diameter, so the illustration must involve these objects. The tangent could be a line, ray, or segment, but we'll use a line to illustrate.

2. **Theorem:** *If two distinct tangent segments share an endpoint and each has their second endpoint on the circle, then they are congruent.*

We begin by drawing a point on the exterior of the circle and forming two tangent segments to the circle from that point. And since the theorem is saying that the two resulting tangent segments are congruent, we mark them with tick marks.

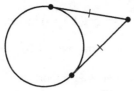

The illustration of the third theorem is left to you as an exercise.   ◆

While we present and explore this information in a very abstract way, circles and the objects related to them are practical for a number of sciences, including engineering and astronomy. The figure below gives a geometric explanation for the occurrence of a major and minor lunar eclipse. Notice that the figure involves circle tangent rays.

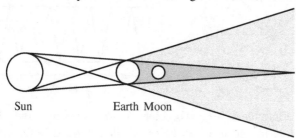

Sun   Earth Moon

Archimedes is the Greek mathematician attributed with the first close approximation of *pi* (π) using regular polygons.

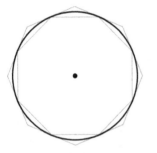

The value of π to eight decimal places is π = 3.14159265.

Circumference and Area

It is often useful to know the distance around a circle. The concept behind this is the same as for the perimeter of a polygon. But a circle is not a polygon, so we use the term *circumference* instead of perimeter: the **circumference** of a circle is the total distance around the circle.

The question of how the radius or diameter and the circumference of a circle are related was a puzzle for thousands of years. The Greek mathematician Archimedes (287 B.C.−212 B.C.) tried to find out how they are related by drawing polygons inside and outside a circle and finding the perimeter of the polygons. When he used polygons with more and more sides, the perimeters of the polygons became closer to the circumference of the circle.

Eventually, it was discovered that if we can accurately measure both the circumference C and the diameter d of a circle, then C divided by d always results in the same number. This number is called π (spelled pi). π is an irrational number, meaning it never terminates or repeats. π is usually approximated to two decimal places ($π \approx 3.14$) or as the fraction $\frac{22}{7}$. So we have $\frac{C}{d} = π$, or $C = π \cdot d$. Since the diameter is twice as long as the radius, we can also say $C = 2πr$. This is the most commonly used formula.

> **EXAMPLE 8-3**   The Circumference of a Circle

If a circle has a radius of 12 inches, find its circumference. Give an answer that includes π, then use $π \approx 3.14$ to get an approximation to the nearest hundredth.

♦ **SOLUTION**

The circumference can be calculated as

$$C = 2π(12) = 24π \approx 24(3.14) \text{ inches} = 75.36 \text{ inches}.$$

The answer $24π$ is called the exact form, and 75.36 is an approximate answer.   ♦

The **area** enclosed by a circle is another important quantity to consider. Archimedes used his polygon method on this problem too and discovered that the area of the inside or outside polygons was a little more than 3 times the square of the radius of the circle. The exact formula is $A = πr^2$.

The best way to explore this formula is to notice that if we slice a circle into several pieces it can be approximated by a rectangle.

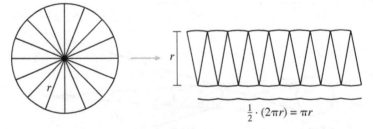

$$\tfrac{1}{2} \cdot (2πr) = πr$$

In this case the formula $A = \ell \cdot w$ becomes $A = r \cdot πr = πr^2$. And while the figure above is not a true rectangle, it can be shown that if we slice the circle into even smaller pieces the figure gets closer to a rectangle.

In case you have a hard time believing this approach, there is an easy way to show that it is reasonable. To start, we draw a circle of radius r, circumscribe a square around it, and draw four radii to make four squares total. The area of the circle is obviously less than the total area of the four squares, which is $r^2 + r^2 + r^2 + r^2 = 4r^2$. Since it looks like the four white areas make a total of about one square, then the area of the circle would be close to $4r^2 - r^2 = 3r^2$. Since $\pi \approx 3.14$, the formula $A = \pi r^2$ is at least close. But, in fact, it is exact.

EXAMPLE 8–4   The Circumference and Area of a Circle

If a circle has a radius of 10 meters, find its circumference and area. Use $\pi \approx 3.14$.

◆ SOLUTION

Circumference: $C = 2\pi r = 2\pi (10) = 20\pi \approx 62.8$ m
Area: $A = \pi r^2 = \pi(10)^2 = 100\pi \approx 314$ m^2

The ancient Egyptians were content when measurements were *close* to being correct. They would, for example, have no problem with using a square to approximate the area of a circle.

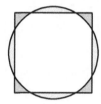

EXAMPLE 8–5   Interesting Result for Agriculture

An agriculture specialist has a square plot of land to plant on. The square plot is 72 yards on each side, but the crop will be planted in a circle. Which of the following will provide more crop area?

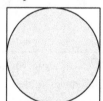

Plant one circular crop that is as large as possible.

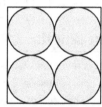

Plant four smaller equally sized crop circles as large as possible.

The reasoning here is that the dark and light shaded regions balance each other out.

The Greeks were more concerned with proving the *exact* value of areas of geometric objects.

◆ SOLUTION

Let's find the total area in each situation.

• One large circle: Since the square has a side length of 72 yards, the largest circle that could go in it would have a radius of 36 yards. This means the total area would be

$$A = \pi r^2 = \pi(36)^2 \approx 3.14 \cdot 1296 = 4069.44 \text{ yd}^2.$$

• Four smaller equal circles: The length of the square is two diameters of the circles. This means the diameter of one circle is 36 yards. So the radius of one circle is 18 yards. The area of one of the small circles is

$$A = \pi(18)^2 \approx 3.14 \cdot 324 = 1017.36 \text{ yd}^2.$$

Since there are four such circles, we multiply this area by 4:

$$1017.36 \text{ yd}^2 \times 4 = 4069.44 \text{ yd}^2.$$

So either decision produces the same area.   ◆

EXAMPLE 8-6   The Perimeter of a Complex Shape

A **semicircle** is half of a circle. The following figure contains a semicircle. Find the area and perimeter. Use $\pi \approx 3.14$.

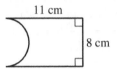

11 cm

8 cm

◆ **SOLUTION**

This example involves what looks like a rectangle, except that one side has been replaced by a semicircle.

- Perimeter: Notice that the diameter of the circle is the length of the rectangle, or 8 cm. So the perimeter can be found by adding the three sides of the rectangle and half the circumference of the circle:

$$P = 11 + 8 + 11 + \frac{1}{2} \cdot 2 \cdot \pi \cdot 4 \approx 30 + 12.56 = 42.56 \text{ cm}$$

- Area: We can find the area of the rectangle and then subtract out the area of the semi-circle, which is half the area of a normal circle:

$$A = \ell \cdot w - \frac{1}{2} \cdot \pi \cdot r^2 \approx 8 \cdot 11 - 0.5 \cdot 3.14 \cdot 4^2 = 88 - 25.12 = 62.88 \text{ cm}^2 \quad ◆$$

Sectors and Arc Length

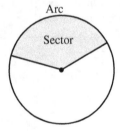

Arc

Sector

A **sector** of a circle is a region enclosed between two radii. An **arc** is a part of the actual circle between two points on the circle. The angle formed by the two radii is called a **central angle.** The area of a sector depends on the angle formed by the two radii. If the radii happen to meet in a right angle or 90°, then the area of the sector is one-fourth of the area of the circle, since 90° corresponds to one-fourth of a complete circle: 360°. If the radii create a 60° angle, then six such sectors would fit inside the circle, so the area of each is one-sixth of the area of the circle. This idea of proportionality leads to a general formula for the area of a sector. We can also use the same idea to find the length of the corresponding arc. We summarize the information and results below.

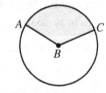

Here, the shaded area is one-fourth the total area, or $A = \frac{1}{4}\pi r^2$.

Here, the shaded area is one-sixth the total area, or $A = \frac{1}{6}\pi r^2$.

In general, the shaded area in a *sector* is $A = \dfrac{m\angle ABC}{360°} \cdot \pi r^2$

The length of the arc would be one-fourth the total circumference, or $s = \frac{1}{4} \cdot 2\pi r$.

The length of the arc would be one-sixth the total circumference, or $s = \frac{1}{6} \cdot 2\pi r$.

In general, the length of the *arc* is $s = \dfrac{m\angle ABC}{360°} \cdot 2\pi r$

EXAMPLE 8-7   Finding the Area of a Sector and Arc Length

A circle has a radius of 12 cm. Suppose that a sector of the circle is formed by a central angle of 40°. Find the area of the sector and the arc length. Use $\pi \approx 3.14$ and round to the nearest hundredth.

◆ SOLUTION

The area of the sector is $A = \dfrac{40°}{360°} \cdot \pi \cdot 12^2 = \dfrac{1}{9} \cdot \pi \cdot 144 = 16\pi \text{ cm}^2 \approx 50.24 \text{ cm}^2.$

The length of the arc is $s = \dfrac{40°}{360°} \cdot 2 \cdot \pi \cdot 12 = \dfrac{1}{9} \cdot \pi \cdot 24 = \dfrac{8}{3}\pi \text{ cm} \approx 8.37 \text{ cm}.$ ◆

EXAMPLE 8-8   Making Snow

A snow maker/blower used by a ski resort fans back and forth throwing snow over a distance of 70 feet. If the blower sweeps out an angle that is 80°, how much area is covered by the blower?

◆ SOLUTION

We use the formula for the area of a sector.

$$A = \frac{m\angle ACB}{360°} \cdot \text{Area of Circle} = \frac{80}{360} \cdot \pi r^2 \approx \frac{2}{9} \cdot 3.14 \cdot 70^2 = 3419.11 \text{ ft}^2$$

So the snow blower covers a total of 3419.11 ft^2.   ◆

Section 8 | Exercises

For exercises 1–6, use the terms from the **Vocabulary Checklist** *to fill in the blanks.*

> **VOCABULARY CHECKLIST:**
>
> circle   pi (π)
>
> radius   circumference
>
> diameter   semicircle
>
> tangent   sector
>
> secant   arc
>
> chord   central angle

1. A part of a circle is called a(n) _____.

2. For a circle, the idea of perimeter (total distance around) is expressed by the term _____.

3. Drawing a line segment from the center of a circle to a point on the circle creates a(n) _____.

4. Two radii and the arc that connects their endpoints create an area called a(n) _____.

5. A(n) _____ can be a line segment, ray, or line, as long as its corresponding line touches the circle only once.

6. A chord that passes through the center of a circle is called a _____.

For exercises 7–10, answer TRUE or FALSE.

T | F   7. The number π is exactly 3.14.

T | F   8. While they have the same property with regard to the circle, a secant is a line and a chord is a line segment.

T | F   9. It is possible for a line to be both a secant and a tangent to a circle.

T | F 10. The circumference of a circle is exactly half the diameter.

11. Give the diameter of a circle that has the indicated radius.

    a. 6 feet

    b. $3\frac{2}{5}$ in.

    c. 5.8 miles

    d. $(b + 5)$ cm

    e. $(7x)$ meters

12. Give the radius of a circle with the indicated diameter.

    a. 10 meters

    b. $7\frac{2}{5}$ yd

    c. 16.8 km

    d. $(2x - 8)$ cm

    e. $(7x)$ meters

13. The circle below has its center at point *C*. What line segment(s) represent a radius and what line segment(s) represent a diameter?

14. The circle below has its center at point *A*. Without naming them, how many diameters are given in the following circle? How many radii?

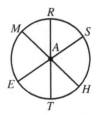

15. Without naming them, how many diameters are given in the following circle? How many radii?

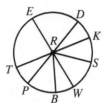

16. Name every object in the following figure and indicate what it is in relation to the circle.

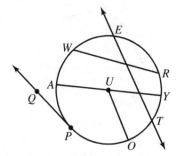

17. Draw a circle and label it so that the following objects are created:

   • radius $\overline{AS}$

   • diameter $\overline{GS}$

   • tangent ray $\overrightarrow{FG}$

   • secant $\overleftrightarrow{RT}$

   • chord $\overline{WQ}$

18. In Example 8-2 we illustrated two of three theorems about various objects pertaining to a circle. Sketch a diagram to illustrate the third theorem mentioned preceding Example 8-2.

19. In the circle below, name each central angle and give its measure. Assume $\overline{HT}$ is a diameter.

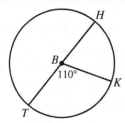

20. In the circle below, name each central angle and give its measure.

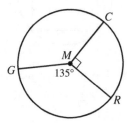

21. Find the area and circumference of the circle. Leave π in your answer.

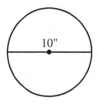

22. If a circle has a diameter of 6 centimeters, find its circumference and its area. Use $\pi \approx 3.14$ to approximate your answer.

23. If a circle has a radius of 7 feet, find its circumference and its area. Use $\pi \approx \frac{22}{7}$ to approximate your answer.

24. **Geometry Rocks!** A standard compact disc has a diameter of $4\frac{1}{2}$ inches. Find its circumference. Use $\pi \approx \frac{22}{7}$ to approximate your answer.

25. Find the area and circumference of the circle below. Leave π in your answer.

26. **No Fly Zone.** No planes are allowed to fly within three miles of a military base. How many square miles are covered by the "no fly" zone? Use $\pi \approx 3.14$.

27. Find the radius of a circle that has a circumference of 12π meters.

28. Find the area of a circle that has a circumference of 22π inches.

29. Using $\pi \approx 3.14$, find the radius of a circle whose circumference is 94.2 miles.

30. Find the radius of a circle that has an area of 49π in^2.

31. Find the radius of a circle that has an area of 25π yd^2.

32. Using $\pi \approx 3.14$, find the radius of a circle whose area is 200.96 square feet.

33. Find the radius of a circle whose circumference in linear units is equal to its area in square units.

34. **A Semicircular Table.** Find the area and perimeter of the semicircular tabletop below, given that it has a radius of 3 feet. Use $\pi \approx 3.14$.

35. **Measurements of a Window.** The window below is made of a rectangle and a semicircle. Find the area of the window. Also, if trim is to be used to frame the interior and exterior of the window as indicated, how much trim will be needed? Use $\pi \approx 3.14$.

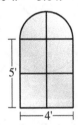

36. Find the area and perimeter of the following figure (assume it is made of semicircles). Use $\pi \approx 3.14$.

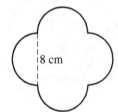

37. Find the area of the shaded region. Use $\pi \approx 3.14$. Assume that the longest side of the triangle is a diameter.

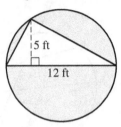

38. Find the area of the shaded region. Use $\pi \approx 3.14$.

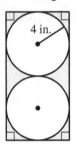

39. Find the area of the shaded region given that the circular part is a semicircle. Use $\pi \approx 3.14$. You will need the Pythagorean Theorem.

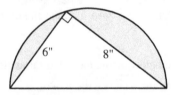

40. Find the area of the shaded region, given that the figure inside the circle is a square. Use $\pi \approx 3.14$ and round to the nearest hundredth if necessary. *Hints:* Remember, the diagonals of a circle form perpendicular line segments. You will need the Pythagorean Theorem.

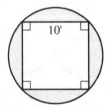

41. **Pizza Time.** Which is the better purchase: one 13-inch diameter pizza for $12.95 or two 9-inch pizzas for $12.49? Use $\pi \approx 3.14$.

42. **Seconds.** If you wanted to make two mini pizzas equivalent in area to one 10-inch diameter pizza, what should the diameter of the mini pizzas be? Round to the nearest inch.

43. **Geometry in Art.** Vincent Burkhead creates mandalas from common everyday pictures. For each of the following mandalas, find the measure of the central angle made by one "slice" of the mandala.

Jasmine

Symphony

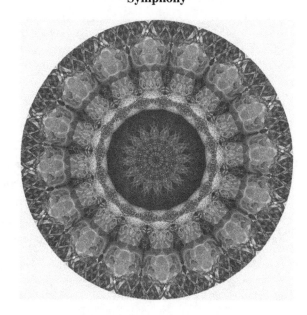

44. A sector of a circle is formed by a central angle of 50°. The radius of the circle is 18 inches. What is the area of the sector? Use $\pi \approx 3.14$.

45. Suppose an arc of a circle corresponds to a central angle of 70°. The diameter of the circle is 3 feet. What is the length of the arc? Use $\pi \approx 3.14$.

46. **Sprinkler System.** A sprinkler system rotates 80°, throwing water over a distance of 15 yards. How many square yards of lawn will the sprinkler water? Use $\pi \approx \frac{22}{7}$.

47. If the length of an arc is 12π feet and the radius is 24 feet, find the measure of the central angle.

48. If the length of an arc is 18π meters and the central angle measures 75°, find the radius of the circle.

49. If the length of an arc is 10π cm and the central angle measures 15°, find the length of the radius.

50. If the length of an arc is 15π inches and the radius of the circle is 45 inches, find the measure of the central angle.

51. If the area of a sector of a circle is 20π square inches and the radius $r = 10$ in., find the measure of the central angle.

52. If the area of a sector is 6π m² and the radius is 12 m, find the measure of the central angle.

53. If the area of a sector of a circle is 90π cm² and the measure of the central angle is 100°, find the radius.

54. If the area of a sector of a circle is 288π yd² and the measure of the central angle is 80°, find the radius.

55. **Geometry and Algebra.** The circumference of the circle below is 8π units. Find x.

56. **Geometry and Algebra.** The circumference of the circle below is 132 units. Find t. Use $\pi \approx \frac{22}{7}$.

57. **Geometry and Algebra.** The area of the circle below is 64π square units. Find x.

58. **Geometry and Algebra.** The area of the circle below is 616 square units. Find b. Use $\pi \approx \frac{22}{7}$.

59. **Corner Rug.** This is a corner rug that has the shape of a quarter circle. Find its area and perimeter, given the radius is 3 feet. Use $\pi \approx 3.14$.

60. **Garden Path.** A circular garden, 20 feet in diameter, has a path around it that is three feet wide. Find the area of the path. Use $\pi \approx 3.14$.

61. **Garden Path.** Here is another circular garden surrounded by a path. The area of the big circle is 144π square yards. The radius of the inner circle is $(x + 5)$ yards, and the width of the path is $(x - 3)$ yards. Find the width of the path. Also find the area of the path.

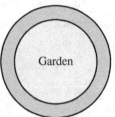

Exercises 62 and 63 require the use of the Pythagorean Theorem in order to find the area.

62. This "ice cream cone" shape is a semicircle on top of an isosceles triangle. Find the area and the perimeter of the shape. Use $\pi \approx 3.14$.

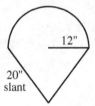

63. This "ice cream cup" shape is a semicircle on top of an isosceles trapezoid. Find the area and perimeter. Use $\pi \approx 3.14$.

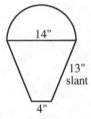

64. **The Orbit of Planet Earth.** The planet Earth is 93 million miles from the sun. How much distance does the Earth travel in four months? Use $\pi \approx 3.14$. *Hint:* If four months is one-third of a year, how many degrees does the Earth travel in that time? Now use the formula for arc length.

65. **Road Trip!** The radius of the moon at its equator is approximately 1080 miles. To the nearest hour, how long would it take to drive around the moon at its equator if you traveled at 60 miles an hour? Use $\pi \approx 3.14$. *Hint:* Use *distance* = *rate* · *time* and solve for *time*.

66. A circle has a radius of 6 inches. If the circle doubles in radius, how is its circumference affected? How is its area affected?

67. A circle has a radius of 10 feet. If the circle doubles in radius, how is its circumference affected? How is its area affected?

CONSTRUCTION

68. **Ruler and Compass. Concentric circles** are two or more circles that have the same center. Use a compass and/or ruler to create three concentric circles so that the radius of the inner circle is 1 centimeter and each circle after that has a radius that is twice the one before it.

69. **Ruler, Protractor, and Compass.** A **circumscribed circle** is a circle that has been drawn around a polygon such that all the polygon's vertices are points on the circle. The figure here shows a circle *circumscribed* around a square.

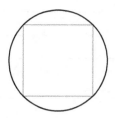

Use a ruler, protractor, and compass to create a circle circumscribed around a square of side length 3 cm. The following theorem will help.

Theorem: *A circle can always be circumscribed around a square. Further, the diagonals of the square are diameters of the circle.*

70. **Straightedge and Compass.** Here is a theorem that addresses the issue of circumscribing a circle around a triangle.

Theorem: *A circle can always be circumscribed around a triangle. Further, if the perpendicular bisectors of each side of a triangle are extended, their point of intersection is the center of the triangle's corresponding circumscribed circle.*

Use a straightedge to draw any acute triangle. Use the theorem above to circumscribe a circle around the triangle. *Hint:* To draw the perpendicular bisectors, you will need the construction technique discussed in the Construction Example in Section 1. According to the theorem above, the perpendicular bisectors should intersect at one point. That point is the center of the triangle's corresponding circumscribed circle.

Repeat the exercise with any obtuse triangle.

| Geometry Project 8 | Proofs in Geometry |

It's time once again to look at how to prove some of the ideas we have encountered in the last few sections. You may want to review the techniques used for proofs in the projects at the ends of Sections 2 and 3. The proofs you will do in this project involve theorems from other sections of this book. These proofs have been saved until now because we prove a result about tangent line segments to circles

Project Exercises | Writing Geometry Proofs

1. **Theorem:** *The diagonals of a parallelogram bisect each other.*

Here is a proof for this theorem. The statements have been provided. For each statement, provide a justification.

Prove: $AM = MD$, given that the points A, B, C, and D are for a parallelogram.

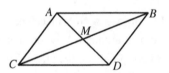

Statement	Justification
$AB = CD$	?
$\overline{AB}$ is parallel to $\overline{CD}$	?
$m\angle MAB = m\angle MDC$ $m\angle MBA = m\angle MCD$	?
$\triangle AMB \cong \triangle CMD$	?
$AM = MD$	?

2. **Theorem:** *Drawing the diagonal of a parallelogram creates two congruent triangles.*

Use the two-column system to prove this theorem. *Strategy hint:* As always, draw a picture to illustrate. You will have to use the *alternate interior angles theorem* and the *ASA theorem*.

3. **Theorem:** *If two distinct tangent segments share an endpoint and each has their second endpoint on the circle, then they are congruent.*

Use the two-column system to prove this theorem. *Setup and strategy hint:* This theorem was stated in Example 8-2 and is illustrated with the following figure. This figure illustrates what you are trying to prove.

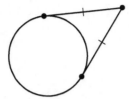

Set up the proof of the theorem using the following figure.

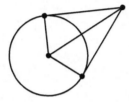

Label points on the figure for reference and try to prove that the figure contains two congruent triangles. This will require a congruence theorem and use of a theorem about circle tangents that appears in the same example as the theorem you are proving (Example 8-2).

Volume and Surface Area

In this section we explore three-dimensional objects, their volume, and their surface area. Here are some examples of volume and surface area that may help you connect with the ideas.

- The newest iPod shuffle can hold up to 240 songs but only has a volume of 0.5 cubic inches.

- The volume of all the Earth's oceans combined is about 1,370,000,000 cubic kilometers.

- The volume of a typical elephant is about 5 cubic meters, while the volume of a typical human is only about 3 cubic feet.

- Because of its spongy nature, the surface area of a human lung is approximately the same as the area of a tennis court.

- The surface area of an apple is usually around 40 square inches.

In geometry, a three-dimensional object is usually referred to as a **solid**. The **volume** of a solid measures the amount of space it takes up. Volume is measured in cubic units. **Surface area** measures the area taken up by the surface of the object. Surface area is measured in square units. Now would be a good time to review the units used for perimeter, area, surface area, and volume. We will use inches in this example, but the same idea can be applied to any linear unit of measure: feet, meters, miles, and so on.

Unit Type	Linear unit	Square unit	Cubic unit
Example (Notation)	Inch (in.)	Square inch (in^2)	Cubic inch (in^3)
What It Looks Like			
What It Measures	Perimeter	Area and surface area	Volume

Here are all the solids we will study in this section.

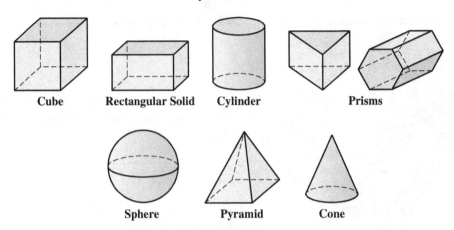

All these figures have formulas that can be used to find their volume and surface area. There are also some concepts we will discuss that are helpful in exploring volume and surface area.

Volume Formulas for Cubes, Rectangular Solids, Cylinders, and Prisms

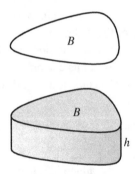

Before we give formulas to calculate volumes, we want to discuss a general concept that will help in understanding the calculations. Suppose we start with a two-dimensional object such as the one in the margin. While it would be difficult to find the area of this object, the area does exist. We will call that area B = the area of the object.

Now suppose we take the same object and create a solid by projecting it upward, so that the result looks like the solid in the margin. We have given the object a height (indicated by the variable h). There is a fascinating and very useful relationship between the two-dimensional object's area and the corresponding solid's volume:

$$\text{Volume} = \text{Area of Base} \cdot \text{Height} = B \cdot h$$

This principle can be applied to any of the following shapes.

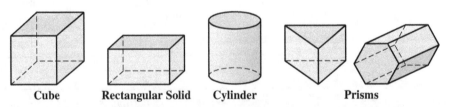

Since all these figures have sides that form right angles with the base, they are called **right.** The cylinder above is a right cylinder, and the prisms are right prisms. Not all solids are right. If the lateral side does not form a right angle, the solid is called **oblique.**

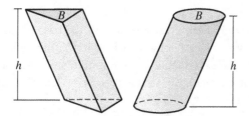

Notice that for these objects, h represents the *perpendicular height* of the object. This measurement, and not the actual length of the side, is used to find volume. The good news is that the formula, Volume = Area of Base · Height = $B \cdot h$, still applies to these oblique solids.

Remember, the value of B is actually an area. In fact, in this section the variable B will always represent the area of the base of a solid. The way the value of B is calculated will vary from object to object. For instance, if the base of a solid is a rectangle (as with a box), then the formula for calculating the area of the base would be $B = \ell \cdot w$. If the base is a circle (as with a cylinder), then $B = \pi r^2$.

EXAMPLE 9–1   The Volume of a Triangular Prism

Find the volume of the triangular prism below.

◆ SOLUTION

As its name indicates, the base of this prism is a triangle. So, to find the area of the base we use $B = \frac{1}{2}bh = \frac{1}{2} \cdot 8 \cdot 5 = 20$ in^2.

So the volume of the solid is found by $V = B \cdot h = 20 \cdot 3 = 60$ in^3. Note that we switch to cubic inches since we are measuring volume. Also notice that we used the variable h = height twice in the same problem: first as the height of a triangle, then as the height of a solid. Be careful about keeping these straight.   ◆

EXAMPLE 9–2   The Volume of an Oblique Hexagonal Prism

The object below is called a hexagonal prism (because its base is a hexagon). As indicated, its base has an area of 32 in^2, its perpendicular height is 7.5 in., and its lateral height is 9.3 in. Find its volume.

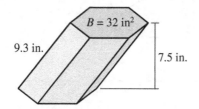

◆ SOLUTION

Since we have already been given the area of the base of this solid, the volume can be found quickly by using the formula $V = B \cdot h$. The trick here is that we need to make sure we use the *perpendicular height* of the prism and not the *lateral height* (the actual length of the side). So, in this case, $h = 7.5$. That means the volume is $V = 32 \cdot 7.5 = 240$ in^3. ◆

Here is a more practical example that can be done without the aid of a diagram.

EXAMPLE 9–3   Guitar Picks

A company called Tortoise makes the best bass guitar picks in the world; their shape and flexibility are perfect. Each pick has a base area of 0.9 square inches. If a pick is 0.08 inches thick, how much plastic is used to make one pick? How many picks could be made with 500 cubic inches of plastic?

◆ SOLUTION

The value of B is the area of the base, so $B = 0.9$ in^2. The value of h represents the height of the object, so $h = 0.08$ in. So the volume is simply $V = 0.9 \cdot 0.08 = 0.072$ in^3. Note we switched to cubic units since we are dealing with volume.

Now to find out how many picks could be made from 500 cubic inches of plastic. We want to divide 500 cubic inches of plastic into picks that are 0.072 cubic inches each; we have $500 \div 0.072 = 6944.4 \approx 6944$ picks. ◆

As mentioned before, this process leads to simple volume formulas for rectangular solids, cylinders, and prisms. We will summarize these formulas at the end of the section, but you are encouraged to take an intuitive approach in finding these volumes using the method outlined here, and not rely so much on the formulas. For some solids, however, this technique will not work. For the sphere, the pyramid, and the cone, we rely on the formulas summarized below. In these formulas, the variable B still represents the area of the base of the object, and h still represents the perpendicular height. Let's look at the sphere in more detail.

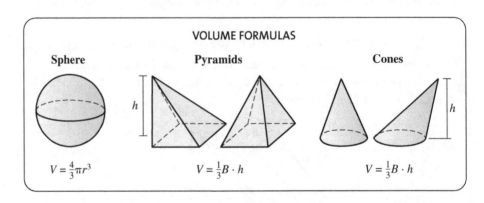

VOLUME FORMULAS

Sphere	Pyramids	Cones
$V = \frac{4}{3}\pi r^3$	$V = \frac{1}{3}B \cdot h$	$V = \frac{1}{3}B \cdot h$

The Sphere

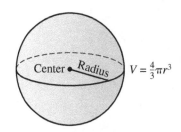

$$V = \tfrac{4}{3}\pi r^3$$

My best math teacher, David Trogdan, used to say, "A sphere is just a circle on steroids." The message in this humorous quote is that the definition and properties of a sphere are identical to those of a circle applied to three dimensions. Recall the definition for a circle: A **circle** is the set of all points *in a given plane* that are a given distance from a center point. A **sphere,** on the other hand, is the set of all points in *any* direction that are a fixed distance from a center point. The distance from the center to the points on the sphere is still called the **radius,** and the center point is still called the **center.**

The volume of a sphere can be found using the formula $V = \tfrac{4}{3}\pi r^3$, where r is the radius of the sphere. Notice that the only value needed to determine the volume of the sphere is the radius (similar to the area of a circle).

EXAMPLE 9-4   The Volume of the Earth

By around 200 B.C. the Greeks had already used properties of angles to figure out that the radius of the Earth is approximately 4000 miles (although their unit of measure was not miles). What is the approximate volume of the Earth? Use $\pi \approx 3.14$ and express your answer in scientific notation.

◆ **SOLUTION**

This problem is a straightforward application of the formula for the volume of a sphere:

$$V = \tfrac{4}{3}\pi r^3 \approx \tfrac{4}{3}(3.14)(4000)^3 = 4.19(6.4 \times 10^{10}) = 26.82 \times 10^{10} = 2.682 \times 10^{11} \text{ mi}^3$$

So the volume of the Earth is approximately 2.68×10^{11} cubic miles.   ◆

Cones and Pyramids

Since cones and pyramids are identified by their base and height, each one has a corresponding box, prism, or cylinder that encompasses it. Notice in the formulas for cones and pyramids, the volume is exactly one-third the volume of a prism or cylinder. This can be helpful in working problems if you don't want to have to memorize formulas; you can find the volume of the corresponding cylinder or prism and then multiply by $\tfrac{1}{3}$.

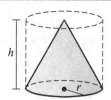

The relationship between these two objects is always the same, and can be expressed as follows:

$$V_{\text{cone}} = \tfrac{1}{3} \cdot V_{\text{cylinder}}$$

This relationship is also true for a pyramid and the corresponding prism.

EXAMPLE 9-5   The Volume of an Egyptian Pyramid

The Great Pyramid of Giza in Egypt is one of the Seven Wonders of the World. Its base is a square with an impressive side length of 230 meters. The height of the pyramid is 150 meters. What is its volume?

◆ **SOLUTION**

The base is a square, so its area can be found by $B = s^2 = 230^2 = 52{,}900 \text{ m}^2$. Now we use the formula given earlier: $V = \tfrac{1}{3} \cdot B \cdot h = \tfrac{1}{3} \cdot 52{,}900 \cdot 150 = 2{,}645{,}000$. The volume is $2{,}645{,}000 \text{ m}^3$. To give you an idea of how large that is, the volume of the Empire State Building is just over 1 million cubic meters.   ◆

EXAMPLE 9-6   The Volume of an Oblique Cone

Find the volume of the object below.

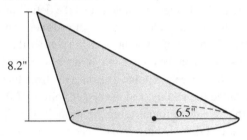

8.2"

6.5"

SUMMARY OF VOLUME FORMULAS

OBJECT	FORMULA FOR VOLUME
Cube	$V = s^3$
Rectangular Solid	$V = \ell \cdot w \cdot h$
Cylinder	$V = B \cdot h = \pi r^2 \cdot h$
Cone	$V = \frac{1}{3}B \cdot h = \frac{1}{3}\pi r^2 h$
Prism	$V = B \cdot h$
Pyramid	$V = \frac{1}{3}B \cdot h$
Sphere	$V = \frac{4}{3}\pi r^3$

◆ **SOLUTION**

The base of this cone is a circle, so the area of the base can be found using the formula $B = \pi r^2 \approx 3.14 \cdot 42.25 = 132.67$ in^2. Note that we used $\pi \approx 3.14$, and rounded to the nearest hundredth. Now we can use the formula

$$V = \frac{1}{3} \cdot B \cdot h = \frac{1}{3} \cdot 132.67 \cdot 8.2 = 362.63.$$

So the volume is 362.63 in^3.   ◆

A summary of all the volume formulas discussed in this section is in the table in the margin.

Note that the specific formulas for B = Area of Base are left out for the prism and pyramid because the base for each could be any polygon (rectangle, triangle, etc.).

Surface Area

Surface area gives the amount of two-dimensional space taken up by the surface of a three-dimensional object. So, for example, if someone wanted to find the surface area of the Earth, they would actually be looking for the flat area of the shape shown in the margin. This is a rather unusual shape to find the area of. Fortunately, the sphere and the cone have formulas for finding surface area, and other objects do not require a formula as we will now explore. Let's look at how we could take a right prism, right cylinder, or right pyramid and find their surface area. *Note:* We will not look at oblique solids in this discussion on surface area.

In order to find the surface area of a triangular prism, you will have to find the area of two triangles and three rectangles. For a cylinder, you must find the area of two circles and one rectangle. Finding the surface area of a rectangular pyramid is tricky; you have to be able to find measurements on its triangular sides. Be careful to distinguish between the height of the pyramid itself and the height(s) of its triangular sides (these are called **lateral heights**). Lateral height is necessary for the surface area of a cone as well. Here are the formulas for the surface area of a sphere and a right cone.

$$\text{Sphere: } S = 4\pi r^2$$
$$\text{Right cone: } S = \pi \cdot r \cdot \ell + \pi \cdot r^2$$

In the formula for the surface area of a right cone, the variable ℓ represents the lateral height of the cone, as opposed to the perpendicular height:

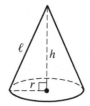

$$h = \text{perpendicular height}$$
$$r = \text{radius}$$
$$\ell = \text{lateral height}$$

Finding the lateral height may require the use of the Pythagorean Theorem.

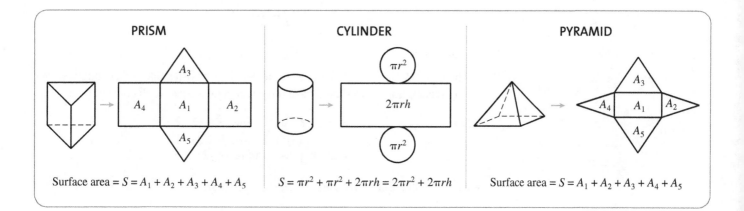

PRISM	CYLINDER	PYRAMID

Surface area $= S = A_1 + A_2 + A_3 + A_4 + A_5$ $S = \pi r^2 + \pi r^2 + 2\pi rh = 2\pi r^2 + 2\pi rh$ Surface area $= S = A_1 + A_2 + A_3 + A_4 + A_5$

EXAMPLE 9-7   **The Surface Area of a Cone**

Find the surface area of the cone below.

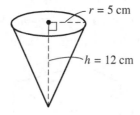

$r = 5$ cm

$h = 12$ cm

◆ SOLUTION

Notice that the lateral height is not already given. Fortunately, it is the hypotenuse of a right triangle. This is always the case for lateral height. So, as mentioned above, we need only use the Pythagorean Theorem to find it.

$$\ell^2 = 5^2 + 12^2 \Rightarrow \ell^2 = 169 \Rightarrow \ell = 13$$

Now we can finish finding the surface area easily using the formula given.

$$S = \pi \cdot r \cdot \ell + \pi \cdot r^2$$
$$= \pi \cdot 5 \cdot 13 + \pi(5)^2$$
$$= 65\pi + 25\pi = 90\pi \approx 90(3.14) = 282.6$$

So the cone as a geometric solid has a surface area of 282.6 square centimeters.   ◆

EXAMPLE 9-8   Packaging Food

A company that makes ice cream cones needs to arrange shipping the cones to stores. They have selected a packaging shown below. How many square inches of cardboard will be used to make each package?

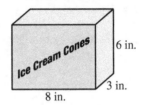

◆ SOLUTION

The box has six faces. Each one is a rectangle. Opposite sides of the box are congruent rectangles, so we should have three rectangular areas each counted twice:

$$S = 2 \cdot \ell \cdot w + 2 \cdot w \cdot h + 2 \cdot \ell \cdot h$$
$$= 2(3)(8) + 2(8)(6) + 2(3)(6)$$
$$= 48 + 96 + 36 = 180$$

Each box will require 180 square inches of cardboard.   ◆

So we see that in some cases finding surface area is easiest by using a formula, and in some cases it can be approached by finding the area of each of the object's sides. This next example illustrates how we can approach trying to find the surface area of a prism.

EXAMPLE 9-9   The Surface Area of an Irregular Prism

Find the surface area of the following prism, given that its base has an area of 50 in^2.

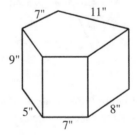

◆ SOLUTION

We know that the base is 50 in^2, so we just have to find the areas of the five rectangles that make up its lateral sides. Note that the length of each of these rectangles is 9 in., and we are given their widths. So the area of all these rectangles combined is given by the sum $5 \cdot 9 + 7 \cdot 9 + 8 \cdot 9 + 11 \cdot 9 + 7 \cdot 9 = 45 + 63 + 72 + 99 + 63 = 342$. The area of the lateral sides is 342 in^2. Now we can add the area of the base in twice to get the total surface area: $342 + 50 + 50 = 432$. The total surface area of the prism is 432 in^2.   ◆

Notice in this last example that when we found the area of the five rectangles involved, this could have been done by finding the perimeter of the base and multiplying by the height. That is, $(5 + 7 + 8 + 11 + 7) \cdot 9 = 38 \cdot 9 = 342$. This works because the lateral sides of the prism could be thought of as one big rectangle.

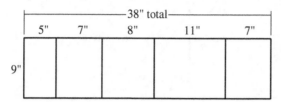

This idea leads to a formula that can be used to help find the surface area of any prism. If we take the perimeter of the base and multiply by the perpendicular height, we get the area of the lateral sides. Then we just add the area of the base two times. The formula looks like this:

Surface Area of a Prism $= S = 2 \cdot B + P \cdot h$, where
B = area of the base, P = perimeter of the base, and h = height of the prism

Finally, we show an example from which no useful formula can efficiently be derived; the point being that even if we don't have a formula we can often work out the surface area using our knowledge of two-dimensional geometry.

EXAMPLE 9–10   Using the Pythagorean Theorem to Help Find the Surface Area of a Pyramid

The following pyramid has a square base. Find the total surface area of the pyramid. Round to the nearest tenth if necessary.

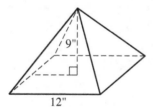

◆ **SOLUTION**

We are trying to find a flat area that looks like this:

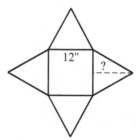

The one problem we have is that we don't know the height of the triangle. The number 9" refers to the height of the pyramid, not the height of its triangular, lateral side.

SUMMARY OF SURFACE AREA FORMULAS	
OBJECT	FORMULA FOR SURFACE AREA
Box	$S = 2\ell w + 2\ell h + 2hw$
Cylinder	$S = 2\pi r^2 + 2\pi rh$
Cone	$S = \pi \cdot r \cdot \ell + \pi \cdot r^2$, where ℓ = lateral height
Sphere	$S = 4\pi r^2$
Prism	$S = 2B + Ph$, where B = area of base and P = perimeter of base

Fortunately, however, the height of the lateral side is the hypotenuse of a right triangle whose legs are the height of the pyramid and half the length of its base. So we find this missing measurement in the calculation below, rounding to the nearest tenth as instructed.

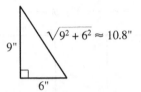

So 10.8" is the height of the lateral side of the pyramid. The surface area then becomes the sum of the square base and four times the area of the triangular lateral face:

$$S = s^2 + 4 \cdot \left(\frac{1}{2} \cdot b \cdot h\right) = 12^2 + 4 \cdot \left(\frac{1}{2} \cdot 12 \cdot 10.8\right) = 144 + 4 \cdot 64.8 = 403.2$$

The surface area of the pyramid is 403.2 in². ◆

Section 9 | Exercises

For exercises 1–4, use the terms from the **Vocabulary Checklist** *to fill in the blanks.*

VOCABULARY CHECKLIST:

linear unit	volume
square unit	surface area
cubic unit	sphere
solid	

1. The _____ of a three-dimensional object is measured using a square unit.

2. If the definition of a circle is applied in all directions instead of just points in a plane, the result is a _____.

3. The volume of a three-dimensional object is measured using a(n) _____.

4. The perpendicular height of a three-dimensional object is measured using a(n) _____.

For exercises 5–8, answer TRUE or FALSE.

T | F   5. The amount of liquid that can be held by a soda can would be measured using cubic units.

T | F   6. In geometry, any three-dimensional object is referred to as a solid.

T | F   7. The following statement makes sense: "The total capacity of my new refrigerator is 95 cubic feet."

T | F   8. The following statement makes sense: "The surface area of the moon is 38.7 million kilometers."

In exercises 9–19, sketch the indicated figure and, if appropriate, use variables to label the measurements that would be required to find its volume.

9. A right cylinder.

10. A right cone.

11. An oblique cylinder.

12. An oblique pyramid.

13. A sphere.

14. An oblique prism.

15. An oblique cone.

16. An oblique pentagonal prism.

17. A right hexagonal prism.

18. A right solid that cannot be labeled by any name.

19. An oblique solid that cannot be labeled by any name.

20. Find the volume and surface area of the cube.

4 in.

21. Find the volume and surface area of the cube.

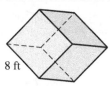

8 ft

22. Find the volume and surface area of the rectangular solid.

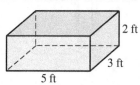

2 ft
3 ft
5 ft

23. Find the volume and surface area of the rectangular solid.

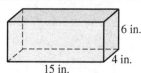

6 in.
4 in.
15 in.

24. Find the volume and surface area of the cylinder. Leave π in your answer.

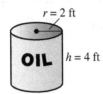

r = 2 ft

OIL   h = 4 ft

25. Find the volume and surface area of the cylinder. Use π ≈ 3.14.

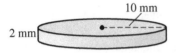

10 mm

2 mm

26. Find the volume of the prism.

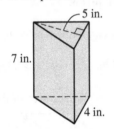

5 in.

7 in.

4 in.

27. Find the volume and surface area of the right prism.

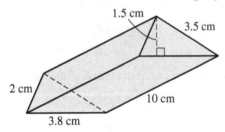

1.5 cm

3.5 cm

2 cm

10 cm

3.8 cm

28. Find the volume.

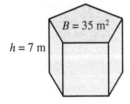

B = 35 m²

h = 7 m

29. Find the volume.

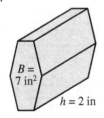

B = 7 in²

h = 2 in

30. Find the volume of the following pyramid, given that its base is rectangular.

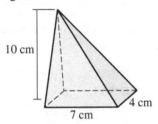

10 cm

4 cm

7 cm

31. Find the volume of the following pyramid, given that its base is rectangular.

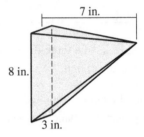

7 in.

8 in.

3 in.

32. Find the volume and surface area of the cone. Use π ≈ 3.14 and round to the nearest hundredth if necessary.

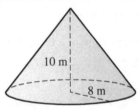

10 m

8 m

33. Find the volume and surface area of the cone. Use π ≈ 3.14 and round to the nearest hundredth if necessary.

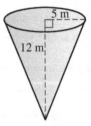

5 m

12 m

34. Find the volume and surface area. Leave π in your answer.

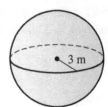

3 m

35. Find the volume and surface area. Use $\pi \approx 3.14$.

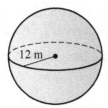

12 m

36. Find the volume. Use $\pi \approx 3.14$.

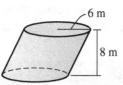

6 m

8 m

37. Find the volume. Leave π in your answer.

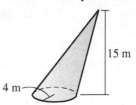

15 m

4 m

38. Find the volume and surface area of the following prism, given that the base has an area of 14 in^2.

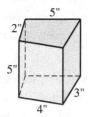

5"

2"

5"

3"

4"

39. The following shape is an oblique trapezoidal prism. Find its volume.

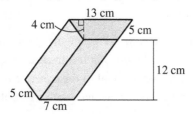

13 cm

4 cm

5 cm

12 cm

5 cm

7 cm

40. Find the volume of the pyramid.

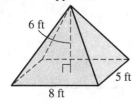

6 ft

5 ft

8 ft

41. Find the surface area of the pyramid. You will need to use the Pythagorean Theorem to find its lateral height.

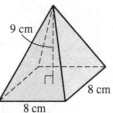

9 cm

8 cm

8 cm

42. Repeat exercise 41 for the following pyramid.

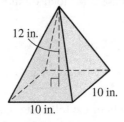

12 in.

10 in.

10 in.

43. Find the volume.

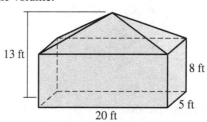

13 ft

8 ft

5 ft

20 ft

44. Find the volume. Round to the nearest hundredth if necessary. (*Hint:* Note the right angle.)

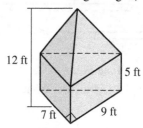

12 ft

5 ft

7 ft

9 ft

45. Find the volume and surface area. Use $\pi \approx 3.14$.

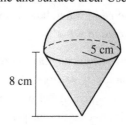

5 cm

8 cm

46. Find the volume. Use $\pi \approx 3.14$.

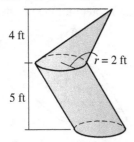

47. The following picture is of a hexagonal pyramid. What is the area of the base if the total volume is 18 cm³?

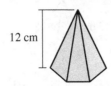

48. What is the height of the following oblique cylinder, given that its total volume is 252π yd³?

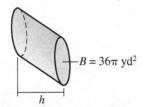

49. **Laying a Foundation.** Wayne needs to lay a concrete foundation with the following dimensions. If one bag of cement makes 2.5 cubic feet of concrete, how many bags will Wayne need to complete the job?

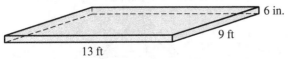

50. A box is twice as long as it is wide, three times as high as it is long. Its width is 4 inches. What is the volume and surface area of the box?

51. **How Much Water Covers the Earth?** The Earth has a diameter of approximately 8000 miles. Given that 70% of the Earth is covered in water, how many square miles of the Earth is covered in water?

52. **Packaging Pens.** A company that makes pens has sheets of cardboard that are 38 square inches. The company wants to use all 38 square inches of cardboard for each box to ship its pens in. Because of the pens, the width must be

$\frac{1}{2}$ inch and the height must be 5 inches. What should the length of each box be so that all the cardboard is used? *Hint:* Start with the formula for the surface area of a box.

53. **Measurements of a Basketball.** A standard basketball has a radius of about 4.5 inches. What is its volume and surface area?

54. **Piling Sand.** A processor cleans sand that will be made into glass and piles it in a cone. If the pile has a diameter of 10 feet and a height of 6 feet, what is its volume? Use $\pi \approx 3.14$.

55. Suppose, as in the previous exercise, that a processor is dumping sand into a pile. Given that the pile stays at a constant height of 21 feet, what must the radius be for the volume to be 1028 cubic feet? Use $\pi \approx \frac{22}{7}$.

56. **Storing Oil.** A cylindrical oil drum has a radius of 1 ft and a height of 3 ft. If 1 cubic foot contains about 7.5 gallons, about how many gallons are in one oil drum? Use $\pi \approx 3.14$.

57. **Medicine Capsules.** A pharmaceutical company is designing medicine capsules. The capsules are cylinders with half spheres on each end. If the length of the cylinder is 12 mm and the radius is 2 mm, how many cubic mm of medication can one capsule hold? Round your answer to the nearest tenth.

58. **Pouring Concrete.** In the rectangular patio area below, concrete needs to be filled in the entire area, excluding the flower bed and the pool. If the concrete is to be poured 6 inches deep, how many cubic feet of concrete will be needed? Use $\pi \approx 3.14$.

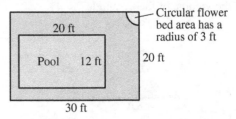

Geometry Project 9 | Approximating Volumes

For this project you will choose three items and approximate their volume and/or surface area by making certain assumptions and using formulas for familiar shapes. At least one of the items should be an item for which the volume is known (like a drink bottle) so you can see how accurate your approximation is.

For example, you may choose a 2.5 gallon water container like the one shown. Its volume could be approximated using just a rectangular box. Or, for accuracy, you could use several shapes, including boxes, half-cylinders, and triangular prisms, adding and subtracting out volumes as needed. The surface area could be closely approximated using several two-dimensional shapes like rectangles and trapezoids. Our assumption here is that these shapes can be used even though the edges of the container are smooth and rounded. Be creative and resourceful. See if you can find a challenge. Here are some conversions that will help you in seeing how accurate you are.

UNIT	CUBIC INCHES	CUBIC CENTIMETERS
1 gallon	231.0	3785.4
1 liter	61.025	1000.0
1 quart	57.75	946.35
1 pint	28.875	473.18

For each of the three objects, make a report formatted as follows.

Object: _____

Assumptions: _____

Sketches and measurements:

Approximate surface area: _____

Approximate volume: _____

Exact volume (if known): _____

acute angle	An angle whose measure is between 0° and 90°.
acute triangle	A triangle whose interior angles are all acute.
adjacent angles	Two angles that share a side and do not overlap.
algebra	The branch of mathematics in which symbols are used to represent numbers and relationships are explored that hold for all numbers.
alternate angles	Two angles that lie on opposite sides of a transversal.
angle	The space between two rays, lines, or line segments that intersect.
angle bisector	A line, ray, or line segment that divides an angle into two angles of equal measure.
arc	The curve between two points on a circle.
area	The amount of space (measured in square units) taken up by a two-dimensional object.
between point	A point that is collinear to two other points such that the sum of its distance from the two other points is equal to the distance between those points.
bisect	To divide into two equal parts.
center	The point from which all points on a given circle are equidistant.
central angle	The angle formed by two radii on a circle.
chord	A line segment whose endpoints are on the same circle.
circle	The set of all points in a plane that lie a given distance (called the radius) from a given point (called the center).
circumference	The distance (measured in linear units) around a circle.
collinear	Three or more points that lie on the same straight line.
complementary angles	Two angles whose measures add up to 90°.
concave polygon	A polygon for which at least one diagonal falls on the exterior.
congruent	Having the same shape and measure.

convex polygon	A polygon for which all diagonals lie on the interior.
coplanar	Four or more points that lie in the same plane. Also, two or more lines that lie in the same plane.
corresponding angles	Two angles that lie on the same side of a transversal and in the same position relative to the lines being cut by the transversal.
cosine	For a given angle in a right triangle, the ratio of the length of the side adjacent to the angle to the length of the hypotenuse of the triangle.
cubic unit	A measure used for volume.
decagon	A ten-sided polygon.
degree	$\frac{1}{360}$ of one complete revolution.
diagonal	The line segment that connects two nonadjacent vertices in a quadrilateral or polygon.
diameter	A line segment whose endpoints are points on a circle and that passes through the center of the circle. Also, the length of this line segment.
equilateral triangle	A triangle in which all three sides are congruent.
exterior angle	Two angles that lie on the exterior of two lines being cut by a transversal. Also, an angle formed by extending a side of any polygon that lies on the exterior of the polygon.
geometry	The study of the properties, measures, and relationships of points, lines, angles, surfaces, and solids.
heptagon	A seven-sided polygon.
hexagon	A six-sided polygon.
hypotenuse	In a right triangle, the side opposite the right angle.
interior angle	Two angles that lie on the interior of two lines being cut by a transversal. Also, an angle in a polygon whose vertex is a vertex of the polygon.
isosceles trapezoid	A trapezoid for which the legs are congruent.
isosceles triangle	A triangle for which two sides are congruent.

kite	A closed four-sided object with two pairs of adjacent congruent sides.
lateral height	The distance from the top of a cone to a point on its circular base. Also, the height of the triangular side of a pyramid.
leg	In a right triangle, a side that makes up the right angle.
line	In geometry, an undefined object whose existence and nature are understood intuitively.
line segment	The set of all points on a line that lie between two given points called endpoints.
linear unit	A unit of measure used for distance.
median	In a triangle, a line segment drawn from one vertex of a triangle to the opposite side that bisects the side.
midpoint	Given two points, the point that is collinear to them and is equidistant from each one.
n-gon	An *n*-sided polygon.
nonagon	A nine-sided polygon.
noncollinear	Three or more points that do not lie on the same straight line.
oblique solid	A solid whose side(s) make non-right angles with its base.
obtuse angle	An angle whose measure is between 90° and 180°.
obtuse triangle	A triangle that has an obtuse interior angle.
octagon	An eight-sided polygon.
parallel lines	Two lines that exist in the same plane but do not intersect.
parallelogram	A closed four-sided object for which the opposite sides are parallel.
pentagon	A five-sided polygon.
perimeter	The distance (measured in linear units) around an object.
perpendicular	Two rays, line segments, or lines that intersect to form one or more right angles.
pi (π)	The ratio of the circumference to the diameter in any circle; denoted by the Greek letter π.
plane	In geometry, an undefined object whose existence and nature are understood intuitively.
point	In geometry, an undefined object whose existence and nature are understood intuitively.

polygon	A closed figure made of line segments that do not cross.
Pythagorean Theorem	A theorem that states that the sum of the squares of the legs on a right triangle is equal to the square of the hypotenuse.
Pythagorean triple	A set of three natural numbers that satisfy the Pythagorean Theorem.
quadrilateral	A four-sided polygon.
radius (plural: *radii*)	The distance from the center of a circle or sphere to any point on the circle or sphere. Also, a line segment whose endpoints are the center of a circle (or sphere) and a point on the same circle (or sphere).
ratio	A comparison of two quantities written in the same form as a fraction.
ray	All the points on a line that start at one point and extend infinitely in one direction.
rectangle	A closed four-sided object for which all interior angles are right angles.
regular polygon	A polygon for which all sides are congruent.
rhombus	A closed four-sided object in which all sides are congruent.
right angle	An angle whose measure is exactly 90°.
right solid	A solid whose side(s) make right angles with its base.
right triangle	A triangle that has one interior right angle.
same-side angles	Two angles that lie on the same side of a transversal.
scalene triangle	A triangle whose sides all have different lengths.
scaling factor	A number that expresses the relationship between the sides of similar objects.
secant	A line, line segment, or ray that intersects a circle at two points.
sector	The area enclosed by two radii on a circle.
similar	Two or more objects that have the same shape.
sine	For a given angle in a right triangle, the ratio of the length of the side opposite the angle to the length of the hypotenuse of the triangle.
skew lines	Two lines that do not exist in the same plane.
solid	Any three-dimensional object.
sphere	The set of all points in space that lie a given distance (called the radius) from a given point (called the center).

square	A closed four-sided object for which all interior angles are right angles and all sides are congruent.	transversal	Any line that intersects two other lines.
square unit	A unit of measure used for area.	trapezoid	A closed four-sided object for which one pair of sides is parallel.
straight angle	An angle whose measure is exactly 180°.	triangle	A three-sided polygon.
supplementary angles	Two angles whose measures add up to 180°.	trigonometry	A branch of math founded on the study of the relationships between the sides of right triangles.
surface area	The amount of space (measured in square units) taken up by the surface of a three-dimensional object.	vertex (plural: *vertices*)	The endpoints of the line segments that make up a polygon.
tangent	For a given angle in a right triangle, the ratio of the length of the side opposite the angle to the length of the side adjacent to the angle.	vertical angles	Angles that lie on opposite sides of intersecting lines, rays, or line segments.
tangent line	A line that intersects a circle at one point.	volume	The amount of space (measured in cubic units) taken up by a three-dimensional object.
tangent segment or ray	A line segment or ray that intersects a circle at one point but, if extended into a line, would not intersect the circle again.		

SECTION 7 **Area and Perimeter**

1. square unit
3. area
5. F
7. F
9. about 13 cm^2
11. about 20 km^2
13. $P = 18$ ft, $A = 20.25$ ft^2
15. $P = 56$ ft, $A = 75$ ft^2
17. $P = 20\frac{1}{3}$ m, $A = 23\frac{1}{3}$ m^2
19. $P = 13.9$ in, $A = 6.46$ in^2
21. $P = 20$ cm, $A = 16$ cm^2
23. $P = 19$ cm, $A = 16.08$ cm^2
25. $P = 17\frac{8}{15}$ m, $A = 14\frac{14}{45}$ m^2
27. $P = 42$ ft, $A = 96$ ft^2
29. $A = 144$ cm^2
31. $P = 10$ in, $A = 4.2$ in
33. $A = 66$ in^2
35. 36 in^2
37. $P \approx 950$ mi, $A \approx 43{,}750$ mi^2
39. $P \approx 1100$ mi, $A \approx 67{,}500$ mi^2
41. $\ell = 9$ m, $w = 7$ m
43. 6 in, 18 in, 18 in
45. Drawings will vary.
47. Drawings will vary.
49. Drawings will vary.
51. $9800
53. $121
55. $285, 19 bags
57. $238
59. $3960
61. $35,496

SECTION 8 **Circles**

1. arc
3. radius
5. tangent
7. F
9. F
11. a. 12 ft; b. $6\frac{4}{5}$ ft; c. 11.6 mi; d. $(2b + 10)$ cm; e. $(14x)$ m
13. radius: $\overline{CB}$, $\overline{CD}$, $\overline{CA}$; diameter: $\overline{AD}$

15. There are 8 radii and 3 diameters.
17. Drawings will vary.
19. $m\angle TBK = 110°$, $m\angle HBT = 180°$, $m\angle HBK = 70°$
21. $C = 10\pi$ in, $A = 25\pi$ in^2
23. $C = 44$ in, $A = 154$ in^2
25. $C = 7.6\pi$ in, $A = 14.44\pi$ in^2
27. $r = 6$ m
29. $r = 15$ mi
31. $r = 5$ yd
33. $r = 2$
35. $A = 26.28$ ft^2. 20.28 ft of trim would be needed.
37. $A = 83.04$ ft^2
39. $A = 15.25$ in^2
41. one 13-inch pizza
43. Jasmine: 45°, Symphony: 22.5°
45. 1.83 ft
47. 90°
49. 120 cm
51. 72°
53. 18 cm
55. $x = 2$
57. $x = 2$
59. $P = 10.71$ ft, $A = 7.07$ ft^2
61. The width is 2 yd. The area is 138.16 yd^2
63. $P = 51.98$ in., $A = 184.93$ in^2
65. 113 hours
67. The circumference is doubled. The area is increased by a factor of four.

SECTION 9 **Volume and Surface Area**

1. surface area
3. cubic unit
5. T
7. T
9. Drawings will vary.
11. Drawings will vary.
13. Drawings will vary.
15. Drawings will vary.
17. Drawings will vary.
19. Drawings will vary.
21. $SA = 384$ ft^2, $V = 512$ ft^3
23. $SA = 348$ in^2, $V = 360$ in^3
25. $SA = 325.6$ mm^2, $V = 628$ mm^3

27. $SA = 98.7$ cm^2, $V = 28.5$ cm^3

29. $V = 14$ in^3

31. $V = 56$ in^3

33. $SA = 282.2$ m^2, $V = 314$ m^3

35. $SA = 1808.64$ m^2, $V = 7234.56$ m^3

37. $V = 80\pi$ m^3

39. $V = 480$ cm^3

41. $SA = 221.44$ cm^2

43. $V = 966\frac{2}{3}$ ft^3

45. $SA = 305.05$ cm^2, $V = 471$ cm^3

47. $B = 4.5$ cm^2

49. 24 bags

51. 140,672,000 mi^2

53. $SA = 254.34$ in^2, $V = 381.51$ in^3

55. 6.84 ft

57. 184.2 mm^3